LEARNING AND THE NATURE OF MATHEMATICS

edited by WILLIAM E. LAMON

University of California
Santa Barbara

SCIENCE RESEARCH ASSOCIATES, INC.
Chicago, Palo Alto, Toronto, Henley-on-Thames, Sydney

A Subsidiary of IBM

Library of Congress Catalog Card Number: 75-183335

Sponsoring Editor: Karl Schmidt
Project Editor: Lynn Peacock
Designer: Naomi Takigawa

Contributors

WILLIAM E. LAMON
University of California at Santa Barbara
HANS FREUDENTHAL
University of Utrecht
LLOYD SCOTT
University of California, Berkeley
RAYMOND L. WILDER
University of California at Santa Barbara
ZOLTAN P. DIENES
University of Sherbrooke
ROBERT DAVIS
Syracuse University
PAUL ROSENBLOOM
Columbia University
JEAN DIEUDONNÉ
University of Nice
JEAN PIAGET
University of Geneva
JOSEPH SCANDURA
University of Pennsylvania
ROBERT GAGNÉ
Florida State University
JOHN WILLIAMS
University of Sherbrooke
PAUL JOHNSON
University of California at Los Angeles
LEON HENKIN
University of California, Berkeley
MARSHALL STONE
University of Massachusetts

Dedication

All too often one finds that success and the consummation of a lifelong goal are accompanied in the shadows by tragedy and heartbreak. As if to balance an empyrean ledger, a great personal gain is accompanied by a great personal loss. Such a loss befell me on May 22, 1968, when a helicopter crash in Los Angeles County brought to a tragic close the life of Professor Arden K. Ruddell.

Born in Quincy, Illinois, on October 6, 1924, Arden Ruddell received an A.B. degree in 1948 and an M.A. degree a year later from the University of Colorado. After having been awarded an Ed.D. at Stanford University, he started to express more and more interest in the mathematical education of our young school-going population, a field in which he won a nation-wide reputation. Professor Ruddell was exceedingly popular among those students and scholars who were acquainted with his work. Several states called upon him to conduct workshops in mathematics education, to engage in lectureships or consultancies in their public school systems, or to observe and investigate innovations in their elementary or junior high school curricula. Being a man of sound judgment and integrity, he won professional admiration among many mathematics educators who, through their work and his advice, have made an enormous impact on current practices in modern mathematical pedagogy.

Because much of my work has been an extension of Dr. Ruddell's work, and my career a continuation of his principles and ideals, it is with profound and eternal gratitude that I dedicate this book to the cherished memory of this admirable man, dear friend, and revered colleague.

Contents

Preface

The writing of a book on mathematics education, whether it be a textbook or a reference book, is a very ambitious project. Teaching, or enhancing the learning process, is a fascinating but difficult task. To tell people how they might become better mathematics instructors or how they might better understand how our young school-attending population learns mathematics seems to me to be at the least ambitious and perhaps even presumptuous.

However, the task of communicating what mathematicians, educational psychologists, and educators have observed about how people learn mathematics is both a challenge and an opportunity for me. There is an urgent need for the understanding and insight that may be gained from the viewpoints that leading scholars in the disciplines of mathematics and psychology hold but may seldom convey to those people who have decided to dedicate their lives to the teaching profession.

This book should not be regarded as a collection of recipes for mathematical education. It does not provide solutions for teaching or learning problems that occur daily in classrooms. It is an attempt to help teachers and prospective teachers prevent such problems by acquainting them with the knowledge of eminent scholars in the fields of mathematics and psychology. Furthermore, it attempts to help the practitioner gain new perspectives toward learning and learning situations.

The authors hope that readers of this book will develop a greater appreciation for the structure of mathematics, a general understanding of human behavior in a mathematically structured environment, and a better understanding of the problems encountered in modern mathematics teaching-learning situations.

Classroom problems often cause exasperation and frustration for the learner as well as for the teacher, and current methods of teaching mathematics have produced their share of such problems. However, an improved understanding of human behavior in a mathematical learning situation and of the structure of mathematics can yield a better understanding of why people fail or succeed in mathematics. Therefore, a special effort has been made to convey not only the nature of modern mathematics, but also how people best learn it and how it is taught most effectively.

The contributing authors believe that the book should help reassure the prospective or practicing mathematical pedagogue that mathematics is a great field of knowledge, that it can be very rewarding to both the student and the teacher, and that an understanding of human behavior can yield a genuine appreciation of what failing or succeeding in mathematics means.

Furthermore, the authors hope that the book will serve both as a reference book and as a text. As a source book, it is addressed to those scholars in mathematics education and related fields who are concerned with the flow and role of learning mathematics, whether in an informal or formal mathematics learning setting. As a textbook, it is directed to those teachers or prospective teachers who want to study the hows and whys of modern mathematics education.

Because most aspects of learning are interrelated with most aspects of teaching, and because neither of these is totally separable from the knowledge of what mathematics is all about, it will be noted that "learning" and "mathematics" as single topics have not been allotted separate chapters.

Although the writing styles and the lengths of essays differ, the papers all display the range of theoretical positions concerning learning and teaching mathematics held by eminent leaders in the field of mathematics education.

It would be difficult to give appropriate credit to all the people whose help and ideas have made this book possible. There are mathematicians, educators, psychologists, and students who have described to me the factors that affected their successes or failures in learning mathematics. Furthermore, as we all know, preparing a manuscript demands the handling of many little but important details that only able and efficient assistants can handle well. Therefore, for such competent assistance with the manuscript, I thank Miss Diane Stowell for her enormous help in translating from French the articles presented by Professors Jean Piaget, Jean Dieudonné, and Hans Freudenthal. Without her contribution, I genuinely doubt if such translation would have been possible. Furthermore, I would like to extend my gratitude to Ingrid Duncan, Lloyd Connors and his wife Lois, Vernon Cotter, Diane Stowell, and the graduate students at the University of California at Santa Barbara for their tremendous help and suggestions with regard to the editing of this book. Finally, all of the contributing authors are indebted to Professors John Cotten, Martin Braine, Murray Thomas, and John Wilson, and to many other colleagues for their professional criticism and warm support.

William E. Lamon
University of California at Santa Barbara

Introduction

In this age of rapid communication, when Telstar hurtles through space and we learn of events half a hemisphere away as though they were a shout at our back door, there is a tendency toward a more and more organic view of man, human abilities, and human concerns. Interdepartmental disciplines have sprung up—biochemistry, astrophysics, philosophy of science, and many others. Innumerable elective courses in high schools and colleges indicate an almost Renaissance taste for experiencing many things simultaneously. Man's subjectivity is increasingly influencing the objectivity he seeks outside of himself, as in physics. We are seeing more and more the interrelationships of all things—something the ancients knew intuitively long ago, something we are learning today as the result of sophistication and self-consciousness.

Central to all human endeavors is learning, and central to learning is the manner of the first introduction of new material to the small child in school. Foremost among the earliest challenges is mathematics. Many children never learn to appreciate it, because it requires the harmonious interaction of so many factors. It is the rare child who can go off and discover algebraic formulas on his own, while many children secretly become poets without any external push or any aid other than the stuff of everyday life and speech. The language of mathematics must be learned; its practice must be evaluated constantly.

From their common vantage point as practicing teachers of mathematics, the contributors to this volume have an intimate awareness of the defects of current mathematics instruction and especially of its too thoughtless launching in the elementary school. There is a prevailing earnestness through-out the book, however restrained. Each author strives to articulate what he thinks mathematics instruction ought to be. Some of the articles are more theoretical than practical, while some are just the opposite. But all of them share the unifying tendency of the times: all emphasize that the language of mathematics is inseparable from its instruction; all see that the sequence of mental development is linked to that of increasing mathematical abstraction. As the title of the book implies, the learning of mathematics cannot be applied behavioristically upon the human mind, nor can the nature of mathematics be held separate from this apprehending mind. Mathematics is not a static body of knowledge; the student and the teacher are not passive agents, but active creators. The human mind endeavors to interpret. This organic view of mathematics and the human mind necessitates, however, a constant reeval-

uation of the two. Thus these articles approach the twin subjects of learning
and the nature of mathematics from many different angles with the common
aim of better understanding their interaction.

The book is divided into four distinct, though interdependent, parts. The
first deals primarily with the current state of modern mathematics instruction, a state that, as the three articles show, is a cause for real concern. The
flaws of modern mathematics education are glaring, though its aims are worthwhile. Concern for the actuality of mathematics instruction leads naturally to
the second section, which deals with the nature of mathematics and the specifics of its pedagogy. Some of the questions raised in this section deal with
what the learning of mathematics is all about and what constitutes effective or
ineffective teaching. It seems that by understanding what mathematics itself
does and what kinds of activities it requires (historically and conceptually),
the teacher will come to impart mathematical patterns in a more logical sequence and with the necessary concrete referents. The third section deals with
the psychology of mathematics—in other words, with those mental processes
that current mathematics instruction generates and attempts to understand,
and with what the learning of mathematics demands of the human mind. The
fourth section deals with the language of mathematics and its communication.
Understanding of the language and effective communication would obviate
much of the concern expressed in the first section; effective communication is
essential to effective pedagogy. It would bring out into the open many inconsistencies that cause so many of the psychological difficulties for the student
of mathematics.

In part I, the three scholars express a common concern: modern mathematics is not living up to its promise. The greater freedom of formulation, the
more comprehensive view of mathematics, and the incentive toward abstraction of concepts implicit in the revolutionized contents seem not to have
made any visible impact on improvement of students' learning or teachers'
instruction. Each of the authors offers different criticisms and a different set
of suggestions.

Lamon presents a theoretical alternative to the current conceptual approach.
He suggests that it is necessary to know what mathematical abilities are to be
taught before determining how to teach them. In other words, we need to
expand our understanding of the skills essential to doing mathematics. We also
need to recognize and reinforce those psychological traits that help develop
good mathematical habits, and to avoid categorization of students.

Freudenthal and Scott deal more with the specifics of current instruction.
On the one hand, Freudenthal lucidly points out discrediting deviations from
the ideal new mathematics. He recommends a Socratic method of discovery
of concepts, with the students participating as much as the teacher. The
article is primarily a critical one, although it affirms that the content and
goals of the new mathematics justify the improvement of methods of instruction. On the other hand, Scott scrutinizes the actual methods of instruction

by raising questions that provide a model for examining existing methods in detail. He submits a new plan for curriculum developers as a tentative remedy. In summary, Lamon, Freudenthal, and Scott all stress the urgency of examining the current situation critically, but they also imply that such an examination should encourage further efforts toward improvement.

Opening the second group of selections, Wilder affirms the paradoxical and ever-changing nature of mathematics: its purest abstractions may have consequences for the man on the street; its continuum of new concepts pushes out formerly accepted methods of proof and requires the mathematician to devise new ones; it even has a theorem—the Godel theorem—asserting its own inconsistency. He distinguishes the forces that influence the evolution of mathematics and shows how mathematics (a pure scientific instrument) is bound up with the cultural environment of those who study it. Thus the teaching of mathematics ought to be a continual process of discovery and creation; it should be free of dogmatism and center primarily on significant and comprehensive concepts.

In Dienes's article the emphasis is on pedagogy. He discusses the need for creative rather than rote learning, and he describes what truly creative learning entails, such as the ability to transfer what one knows to isomorphic cases. He distinguishes between different types of play—manipulative play, representational play, and rule-bound play. He offers specific recommendations for teaching techniques that both teacher and student must learn if a curriculum is to be established that corresponds appropriately to the structure of mathematics.

Davis's article is even more specific. His "basic paradigm" proposal is one possible answer to the mathematical learning situation that Dienes advocates so strongly. After discussing the importance of naïve source ideas to the "process of acquiring mathematics," he proceeds to demonstrate the value of a naïve source experience, such as the basic paradigm. Like a symbol or a parable, it would have emotional impact and manifold reference. Being more complex than the stimulus-response idea, it is better suited to the nature of the human mind and presents a greater challenge to the creative powers of man.

Manifesting a similar preoccupation with creativity and specific successful learning situations, Rosenbloom emphasizes the importance of insight to mathematics. Experience with students suggested to him that insight, despite its elusive nature, can be evoked at will by the right imaginative teaching methods. Both Davis's and Rosenbloom's approaches and theories supplement, and to some extent answer, Dienes's more general call for improvement in teaching methods.

Like Wilder, Dieudonné focuses on the nature of mathematics, though he looks specifically at its striking characteristic of abstraction. He carefully considers the history of mathematics and concludes that the rising level of abstraction throughout mathematical history is an indication of what is required in mathematics learning. The axiomatic method, emphasis on operational rules rather than impermanent objects, and abstraction of basic questions from a problem's contingencies are all essential disciplines to develop.

To implement all these directives toward more effective teaching we need a better understanding of the mental processes involved in learning mathematics. Hence part III investigates the psychology of mathematical learning.

Jean Piaget, who has done monumental work in the area of child psychology, raises the age-old question whether mathematical entities are the product of the intellect or external realities that the intellect discovers. The answer is not a simple one, as he shows. He does, however, affirm the creative power of the mind over any fixed, once-and-for-all, external objects. The gist of the article is that mathematical structures correspond to the operational stages of thought in human mental development.

Scandura's theory of mathematical knowledge centers on his definitions of rules, which form the backbone of mathematics. He tries to establish a sound basis for necessary reform of curricula, and proposes a technology (algorithmic analysis) for dealing with specific problems.

Both Gagné and Williams deal primarily with the psychology of learning. Gagné's article considers performance objectives and areas that need further research. He distinguishes between obstacles to learning and the conditions necessary for learning to take place. Perhaps the most important thing about this article is that the author lays the groundwork for the future research that he believes must be done.

Williams considers the source of learning problems. He affirms the necessity of identifying causes, rather than merely considering symptoms, before seeking solutions. He focuses on difficulties rather than remedies, but the understanding of such difficulties paves the way for later solutions.

The final section of the book is composed of three articles, all dealing with the language and communication of mathematics. Intrinsic to mathematics is its language—that unique, concise expression of vast underlying concepts and theories. This language is what confronts the learner and so often repels him forever. The three contributors to this part of the book are sensitive to the gap in communication that frequently closes the door to any further appreciation of the nature of mathematics.

Johnson analyzes four essential components of the communication process, and relates each specifically to mathematics. He suggests that the numerous factors of the four components have to be separated and evaluated. The responsibility for effective communication, however, can never be placed on only one of the components or on the factors of one component.

Henkin points out two particular areas of confusion—quantifiers and equations—where the symbolization process obscures the fundamental conceptual framework. He states that the equation should be presented as a tool for further investigation rather than as the object of investigation; that explanations should be given for rendering previous experience invalid; and that the expression of universal regularities (resembling Piaget's invariances) should be introduced as early as the first grade, rather than the arbitrary rules that are unverified by the child's own experience.

Both Henkin and Stone are confident that young children can learn more than they are now being taught in the areas of variables and logic. The theme of Stone's paper is that logic is second only to insight in the understanding of mathematics. He urges the introduction of logic at the earliest possible educational level, and he points out that the modern emphasis on the conceptual rather than the technical in mathematics makes this entirely relevant.

In conclusion, a dominant aspect of this book is the contributors' awareness that "teaching," as Carl Rogers discovered with horror, "can be harmful." For the teacher to become a better catalyst, it is essential that he consider the interaction of the many factors involved in the teaching process and that mathematics be viewed not as a stagnant collection of facts to be shelved away in the mind, but as a living, growing part of man's perception.

Mathematics: Viewpoints of Concern

PART ONE

1 Mathematical Literacy and Ability: A Matter of Grave Concern

WILLIAM E.
LAMON

*Born and raised in Belgium, Dr. Lamon completed an
Air Force career as a flyer and instructor in 1961, at
which time he immigrated to the United States. He
obtained his B.Sc. at the University of San Francisco
in 1964, his M.Sc. in mathematics at California State
College at Hayward in 1966, and his Ph.D. in mathematics education at the University of California,
Berkeley, in 1968. Having taught at both high school
and college levels, Dr. Lamon is now a professor
of mathematics education at the University of
California at Santa Barbara. He is the founder and the
research director of the Arden K. Ruddell Research
Laboratory for Mathematics Learning at UCSB and a
coordinator for the International Study Group for
Mathematics Learning (an organization presided over
by Professor Z. P. Dienes). Dr. Lamon has authored
several research papers in mathematics education and
is the editor of a collection of readings in this field.*

*Of the many aspects of mathematical education, the
author is particularly interested in the psychology of
learning mathematics, and more particularly the field
of abstraction and mathematical concept formation.
In his presentation, Professor Lamon conveys to the
reader his concern about the demands put upon the
educational machinery by a constantly changing
technological society, the attempts that are made to
meet those ever-changing expectations, and the effects
of such attempts on the teaching of mathematics.
How can one successfully convey mathematical skills,
concepts, or principles if one does not really know
the nature of mathematics and the mental operations
required in a mathematical environment? These are
some of the questions posed in this paper.*

Looking at the enormous changes produced by our society in the last twenty years, one has to conclude that the theory of mathematical ability and the concept of mathematical literacy have shared in both the virtues and the vices that such changes entail. Even the well-informed person sometimes finds it impossible to appreciate the revolutionary changes that have taken place in modern technology. Changes in the learning and the teaching of mathematics have been no exception to this phenomenon. On the one hand, this is due to the fact that changes of an abstract nature have ordinarily been appreciated or understood only by those who create or manipulate them, whereas on the other hand, present members of our society have not been educated or trained to comprehend the significance or the practical value of those changes.

If one were requested, for whatever reason, to compare the world of the mid-nineteenth century with the world of today, it would be obvious that the kind of mathematics education designed to serve the needs of the earlier world would not be appropriate to serve the needs of either today's world or the world of tomorrow. Furthermore, the kind of mathematical literacy needed in the early part of the twentieth century, to survive or satisfy the expectations of a society in the first stages of modern technology, was totally different from that expected in the 1960s. Hence the changes that took place between the mid-nineteenth century and the present have so dramatically affected the aims of contemporary mathematics education that it is not presumptuous to say that the aims of the earlier educational machinery are now considered obsolete. On the other hand, complete disregard of the content and methodology by which traditional mathematical pedagogy was communicated not only would be naïve, but would be a regrettable misunderstanding of what the learning and teaching of mathematics is really all about.

People so often ask, "What was really wrong with the way mathematics was taught when I went to school?" Of course, most of those people agree that in the old days too much time was spent on the various skills of calculation, and too little time perhaps on the development of the conceptual framework in which mathematical thinking must operate. However, it has become evident that the great emphasis put upon mathematical experiences that develop and enhance the process of abstraction or concept formation often leads to lower scores on standardized examinations, to teacher and parent complaints, and to more and more capable students leaving the study of mathematics during the high school years. Hence most mathematics teachers misinterpret the goals of the new mathematics . . . .

Modern thinking on the learning and teaching of mathematics has attempted to shed light on the fact that *less time* need be spent on the development of skills if there is more emphasis on the discovery and development of concepts. Not only can as much skill be gained with less drill, but the skill level can be raised significantly by teaching for understanding. More emphasis on structure, for example, leads to a greater appreciation of the need for skills useful in applying that structure to practical problems. A sudden discovery with a well-understood verbal generalization is better remembered and leads to a fruitful adaptation to all kinds of new conditions. Dynamic involvement in an environment founded on the humanistic values of education yields productive and creative patterns of behavior. Consequently, the need for students to discover concepts by exploring patterns used to find mathematical properties and relationships is advocated.

As the structure of mathematics is founded on three basic structures (the algebraic structures based on the concept of operation, the ordering structures based on relations, and the topological structures based on such concepts as continuity and proximity), structured learning experiences should receive predominant emphasis at all stages from the primary grades through the terminal years of secondary education. Furthermore, based on Gestalt psychology, appreciation and conceptual development of structure are enhanced in practice by a methodology that uses learning stiuations that encourage students to discover interrelationships of parts as well as wholes.

For a few years now, it has been widely accepted that *creative* mathematical learning situations have to be established at all grade levels (31). These learning situations develop the ability to understand commonly occurring relationships between concepts and ideas, which in turn develop proficiency and skill in the manipulation and calculation of mathematical ideas. As noted before, almost all current curricula in the first twelve years of school emphasize the concept of structure and those learning experiences that break down the artificial barriers erected for thousands of years between the different parts of mathematics. All this is done in order to yield unity, general patterns, and an appreciation of the *raison d' être* of many mathematical ideas to which the student of mathematics has to be exposed. But does this kind of psychological and pedagogical advocacy achieve the many worthwhile objectives set forth and conceived by the proponents of the New Mathematics?

Because one cannot conceptualize what structure is all about unless structural properties are abstracted, youngsters in the early phases of mathematical learning are presented with abstractions that can be closely connected with concrete referents as they learn to respond with verbal or written responses to specific verbal or written stimuli (30). But, because abstraction follows a hierarchy of cognitive operations, which cognitive operations should be activated? In other words, do we as mathematics educators take the time to identify those cognitive skills that should be developed in order to give the process of abstraction a chance to be efficiently generated? To go even further, what *can* people discover? What factors (time, amount of previously learned knowledge, and so on) actually do lead to insight in mathematics?

It is claimed that careful and logical development of questions and answers leads students to discover many facts in mathematics, and to feel thrilled that there is something they understand (16). I, for one, have never had the privilege of noticing any student "discover" a mathematical abstract without being prompted by an enormous number of clues. One reason for this is that in most instances the cognitive equipment or capacity for coping with the demands of a specified cognitive task is almost nonexistent in our students.

They cannot incorporate within their cognitive structure a relationship between two or more abstractions, because most of their learning tasks are not relatable and not anchorable to relevant and more inclusive concepts in their existing cognitive structure. As a matter of fact, if one accepts Ausubel's definition of cognitive structure as "the stability, clarity, and organization of a learner's subject-matter knowledge in a given discipline," one cannot avoid observing serious conflicts in the psychology of learning and teaching mathematics, as well as in the mathematics to which the learner is exposed. Let us not forget that the architecture of mathematics is founded on a hierarchy of abstractions. As abstraction is the extraction of what is common to a number of different situations and the discarding of what is irrelevant to the particular abstract, abstracting is an individual operational process. Furthermore, a mathematical abstraction is a classification of objects of thought requiring specific mental abilities and cognitive processes. Unless proper identification of those mental abilities and the prerequisite cognitive processes is made before presenting the learner with the abstraction, any methodology is futile. Because it is rather difficult to get the feel of these objects of thought through practice and at the same time judge correctly whether a certain simple or complex structure is like another structure from a particular viewpoint, abstraction has to be taught through multiple concrete representations. It is in this area that I feel mathematical pedagogy has been failing. Too little is known about the *number* and the *type* of concrete representations needed to generate and build the stability, clarity, and organizational structure of subject matter so that a retainable abstraction can take place (29) (33).

Abstractions are built upon previous abstractions through a process involving the movement from perception to symbolization and generalization. Hence one's ability to perceive, to discriminate, and to classify are only a few of the mental skills prerequisite to mathematical abstraction. But how much is known about these cognitive factors that probably have quite an impact on mathematical ability and therefore on one's potential for mathematical literacy? Before identifying how specific mathematical entities should be taught, wouldn't it be advisable to investigate the nature and the quality of those abilities that the student should have? I strongly believe in the existence of individual psychological traits that can determine the success of mathematics instruction. I do not deny, of course, that instructional or pedagogical skill has its significance, but I consider it absurd to blame either the pedagogy or the teacher for poor academic achievement and the fact that the majority of our population cannot rise above the most mediocre mastery of mathematics. On the other hand, assessing a student's aptitudes by looking at his previous grades in mathematics does not provide a sufficient basis for making a judgment about his ability to learn mathematics.

To constantly change methods of instruction or mathematical nomenclature in order to establish conditions for forming and developing mathematical competency is a waste of time unless we study those variables that both gifted and mediocre achievers display when put into a mathematics environment. It seems to me that looking at the individual psychological traits that help a student develop good habits and mental and cognitive skills and master subject-matter content should reveal to the mathematics community how to operate their educational machinery. Analyzing both complex and simple activities and then trying to clarify the psychological traits that a pupil should have to master them would have a profound impact on what to teach and how to communicate the ideas. Until we know what mathematical activities actually are, the prospect of a mathematically literate society is rather dim.

We very seldom hear anyone consider the question of whether failure or success in a mathematical task could be determined by a combination of those mental characteristics peculiar to the mathematician and those that are involved in more generalized skills. Nor has there been extensive work done on the process of mastering mathematics, which to me is the essence of finding out how the mechanics of abstract thinking operate. It should be apparent by now that I believe that in order to be successful in educating the mathematics student, one should study both the successful and the unsuccessful implementation of a mathematical activity from a psychological point of view. Until we have answers to the questions raised here, we will not be able to solve any of the problems discussed earlier in this paper. We have to accept the fact that the majority of our students have little or no interest in acquiring mathematics knowledge, and that this will often lead these students to believe that they do not understand mathematics and never will.

An examination of the current teaching practices would show that considerable modifications have been brought about in methodology due to the serious impact of current psychological theories. Motivational methods, for example, together with freedom of play and manipulation of concrete apparatus at the elementary level, have formed the basis for any innovative endeavor to teach mathematics. In addition, most contemporary mathematics contains many new topics such as sets, set theory, and set language. In this regard, it is interesting that almost everyone connected with curriculum or program design tries to build mathematical knowledge mainly on set theory and its language, so that one wonders whether it would still be possible to create a modern program in mathematics without appealing to the nomenclature of set theory.

Unfortunately, even with those changes, modern teaching approaches have not been very successful in meeting the expectations of the present world, and they probably will not even succeed in equipping the younger generation with the intellect to successfully evaluate and solve the problems of the world in which they will be adults. It is, of course, rather difficult to assess accurately what needs and expectations a future society will generate. But history has clearly shown that traditional mathematics teaching has produced and accomplished little with regard to people's ability to think and respond successfully in a mathematical environment. In other words, traditional approaches to mathematics have proven to be inappropriate, and modern approaches demonstrate distinct inadequacies in preserving the accomplishments past methodologies did produce and in improving upon past failures. Consequently, it should not be surprising that people are expressing dissatisfaction. Mathematics professors, education and psychology professors, as well as practicing teachers, question seriously the validity of current pedagogy and the wisdom of teaching youngsters the so-called New Math. A great deal of work has been done and is still being done in many educationally advanced countries in the world, through experimental investigations at both the elementary and secondary level, in order to evaluate the validity of these continuing expressions of discontent by teachers and students alike. Such work is being done by the International Study Group for Mathematics Learning, under the presidency of Professor Zoltan P. Dienes (34), by Professor Patrick Suppes at Stanford University (100), by the late Professor Max Beberman at the University of Illinois, by Robert Davis of the Madison Project (18), and by David Page of the University of Illinois, to mention only a few. Scholars in the field of psychology such as Jean Piaget, Jerome Bruner, Robert Gagné, William Hull, and Frederick Bartlett have spent much of their lives investigating the psychological problems generated by the learning of mathematics. This work has yielded some very important and challenging findings. All over the world, mathematicians, educationalists, and psychologists have been forced to re-evaluate their involvement in the educational process of their own nation as well as that of those nations whose survival depends on theirs. This has brought them closer together and has stimulated a closer collaboration. It has become quite apparent that if one wants to investigate the problems of teaching and learning mathematics, each process being ontologically distinct from the other, it should be done at the level at which a pupil is first acquainted with the teaching process—that is, in kindergarten. Unfortunately, many years will probably pass before any experimentation can be cited in support of the viewpoints this study group has put forward, since the final product of the processes it developed can be noted only in the adult who has completed his education.

However, it is one thing to state, through a variety of comments, observations, and thoughts, a critical appraisal of both the virtues and the vices of current mathematical pedagogy, and quite another to suggest remedies for the illnesses of present mathematics education. Consequently, what should the reader infer from my statements? What do I suggest or, even better, where do we go from here?

First, in order to curtail some of our current problems in mathematics education, the teaching of mathematics should be directly influenced by psychological research. In view of this, moral and financial support should be allocated to more *qualitative* rather than *quantitative* psychological research methodology, preserving however the current standards of design, analysis, and statistical reliability or validity. Work with small groups of subjects or even with one subject at a time, using qualitative methods, should be conducted for the purpose of penetrating the mental activity of the subjects and analyzing mental processes when working exclusively in mathematics. Like Bruner, Piaget, or Dienes, we should be concerned with the dynamics of mental activity when such activity is activated by a subject's interaction with a mathematical environment. We should operate in this manner for the purpose of arriving at the *principles* of the mathematical learning process itself. This will open up a variety of avenues for further investigation. I suggest that mathematics educators attempt to expand current methods of research and begin to focus on a careful technique for observing a subject's behavior under all kinds of instructional conditions over sustained periods of time. Such endeavor will yield hypotheses, which in turn can be tested for their validity and degree of possible generalization to an acceptable population sample. Thus I hope to see two kinds of researchers in mathematics education: the hypothesis builder, whose method may be more clinical in nature, and the hypothesis tester, who takes over after the clinical researcher has done his job. These types of researchers differ in their methods and objectives of research. Analysis and assessment of the findings produced by both will augment our understanding of mathematics learning and contribute to mathematics teaching methodology. It is my conviction that only then will we be able to say what, when, and how to teach mathematics to everyone who wants to or must study mathematics.

2 Recent Tendencies in the Teaching of Mathematics

HANS
FREUDENTHAL

*Professor Hans Freudenthal is a German-born mathe-
matician and mathematics educator. After graduating
from Berlin University in 1930, Professor Freudenthal
assumed academic duties at Amsterdam University
from 1930 until 1946, after which he joined the
mathematics faculty at Utrecht University, Holland,
in 1947. As visiting professor at Berkeley, Yale, and
the University of Pennsylvania, Dr. Freudenthal has
contributed an enormous amount of literature in the
areas of topology, lie groups, geometry, mathematical linguistics, history of mathematics, and mathematical education in general.*

*According to Professor Freudenthal, new mathe-
matics, a topic now familiar to nearly everyone, bears
a misleading name, for it is the instruction, not the
mathematics, that is new. In this article he is critical of
what passes for "new mathematics," and discusses
the abuses and the malpractices, as well as the modern
instructional design of our current mathematical
education. In his opinion, the abuse of new math—
particularily evidenced in the overemphasis on sets—
by imcompetent people and educational opportunists
has been the worst feature of our new programs and
has served only to discredit the new mathematics.
Examining the passion for set theory, the author
points out the vast misunderstanding of Piaget's work
and the introduction of an immense number of meaningless symbols in modern curricula. New mathematics has reinforced the unfortunate tendency to
teach mathematics as a system, relegating the method,*

This article was translated by the editor from the *Review
of Higher Education* (*Revue l'Enseignement Supèrieur*,
46-47, 1969, 23-29).

instruction, and even the subjects taught to a dogmatic, formal structure.

Instead of this systematic approach to new math wherein mathematics is presented as a ready-made subject, entirely structured and complete, Professor Freudenthal feels that it should be presented as a subject to be discovered and learned in the same order and manner it was created; axiomatization and formalization of mathematics should be performed by the students, not presented to them.

In concluding this rather critical assessment of our current practices in mathematics instruction, Professor Freudenthal warns that education must guard itself against a corrupt form of new mathematics and an undue stress on subject matter over and above pedagogy. Rather than merely criticizing new efforts, the mathematical community should reeducate and reorient those who are responsible for the dissemination of modern mathematical instruction. Only then will mathematics be appreciated as a worthwhile and meaningful subject of inquiry.

Who has not heard about the new mathematics? The parent of the child who has to learn it, the teacher whose colleague in mathematics has to teach it, the terrified, frightened engineer who asks himself what it is good for, the poor television watcher who identifies it with Venn diagrams—all know that such a thing exists, even as all have known for a long time that the other side of the moon exists.

In fact, it is difficult to construct a new mathematics that can be clearly distinguished from old mathematics. The history of mathematics has known marvelous and unexpected discoveries, but not abrupt gaps. Riemann's great discoveries in the middle of the nineteenth century have required half a century's slow development to be assimilated and integrated. Cantor's fundamental ideas (set theory) have infiltrated slowly but thoroughly the entire field of mathematics. Where then could this new mathematics be said to have begun? In 1870, with Cantor, Dedekind, and Jordan? In 1900, with Hilbert's axiomatics, or with Steinitz and Hausdorff, axiomaticians of algebra and topology? In 1930, when we learned the technique of amalgamating different structures? Did it begin with the electronic computers, or with the great codification of Bourbaki? All these dates are right, and all are wrong.

If one is looking for abrupt ruptures, these are rather to be found in the instruction of mathematics. Here, there is the phenomenon of the double time-lag: the time-lag involving the teacher who supposedly learned at twenty all that he would need until sixty, and the time-lag involving subject matter that was determined, fifty years or a century ago, by immutable official programs. It is true that in the universities where professors are researchers, and where one is freer to define and interpret programs, instruction has been able to follow the progress of research more closely. Even so, for personal reasons sometimes there have been considerable time-lags. The most dangerous one, which still exists and even seems on the increase, is that between the mathematics with which students are confronted in physics courses and the mathematics they learn from mathematicians.

School programs and methods of mathematics teaching were established in the middle of the nineteenth century. They have developed, but not along the line of mathematics proper. Mathematics in the schools has had an autonomous development that has led it to an impasse. The reform of the instruction of higher mathematics occurred in the period between 1935 and 1955, when only World War II could be said to indicate any rupture. At the end of this period, the gulf between current mathematics and that of the secondary educational establishments, which was noticed as early as the opening of the century, became unbearable. A radical reform became inevitable, and the clamor for it grew. It is natural that the subject matter to be taught was considered first; new programs were proposed, which, in general, did not differ much from one another, but whose details were discussed at length. Anyone who rereads the writings of this period must be struck by the underlying assumption that reform of instruction consists in decreeing new programs. One nonconformist document of this period is an article entitled "Instruction of Modern Mathematics or Modern Instruction of Mathematics?" The author of this article made a solitary effort to defend the priority of pedagogy and the art of teaching over programs. There have been many changes since then. Exorcised by a minority, pedagogy and didactics have gained more ground in the reform.

Another facet of the change that has taken place since that period is the growing participation of those who have to interpret the new programs at school. Though the old subject matter was out of date, it could not be denied that its content and the manner of its instruction were familiar to the instructors. To enforce instruction of new subject matter by old methods and by poorly prepared teachers would have been a nonsensical reform. It was noticed that the new subject matter required new methods of instruction, and that once the subject matter was well understood and accepted it would also make usage of renovated teaching methods easier. In many countries, preparation of instructors for the demands of new programs has become an important activity.

Reform continues, and it is too soon to evaluate the results. This is a period of transition and uncertainty. Without exaggerating the importance of some less acceptable tendencies, they nevertheless must be pointed out in order to be complete and perhaps to warn those who might otherwise be victimized by them.

If I were asked what the most widespread tendency is in the instruction of what is called new mathematics, my honest answer (of which, however, I am ashamed) would have to be "a hoax!" It is displayed in all its pureness in literature, movies, and television broadcasts produced by honest but incompetent people, or by those whom I would call the opportunists of new mathematics. If teachers regret not understanding this new mathematics that they have to teach, or if exasperated parents ask for explanations from university professors about this new mathematics that their children must learn, I admit that their complaints are often justified, although actually the complaints ought not to be aimed at new mathematics, but at the abuses of it.

I have seen a film called "Set Theory" in which, for a quarter of an hour, figures were surrounded by brackets in order to deliver the solemn statement after each procedure, "This is a set." In one book I saw a five-dollar bill between brackets with the explanation "a set of five dollars," and the "set" of the ten commandments illustrated by two stone tablets between brackets. I have seen brackets surrounding pictures of a boy standing up and a girl sitting down, separated by a comma, and this configuration was followed by an equal sign and more brackets within which appeared the same girl standing up with the same boy sitting down. I have seen notebooks with ten pages on which the student has to separate red and green spots, more and more numerous and blurred, each from the other by a closed line. I have seen books in which Jordan arcs were called closed lines and Jordan curves open lines. I have seen books in which for hundreds of pages it was suggested to the student that meaningless typographical symbols constitute sets as soon as they are surrounded by a graphic curve called a "Venn diagram." Good school teachers have traditionally insisted on the fact that, in mathematics, letters mean something—whether known, arbitrary, or unknown—and that a letter ought not to be introduced without explaining what it means. But then, this is granddaddy's mathematics, which they laugh at now. In modern literature, mathematics is a game with twenty-six letters that mean nothing.

All this is the consequence of a modernism that insists on sets no matter what. At school, sets are used for purposes alien to serious mathematics, which means that one cannot profit by previous experience. In just a few years, a kind of mathematics has developed in the schools that is a worthy counterpart to the mathematics of former times and is just as absurd. I have no fear that it will last (it is undoubtedly a transitory phenomenon), but it tends to discredit modern mathematics and consequently delay its true development in instruction. To sustain serious efforts, it is essential to criticize the idle production of manuals, films, and other methods of mathematics instruction.

Let us turn toward the serious work. It must be granted that here too the passion for sets has been only partially conquered. This passion has led to the exaggerated and sometimes ridiculous use of Venn diagrams and sets of letters, but in general these deviations are uncommon and unimportant. The passion for sets has left other traces, or rather other wounds. Such are the efforts, necessarily abortive, to introduce natural numbers by methods of pure set theory—that is, as classes of equipotent sets, otherwise called cardinals.

Here the influence of Piaget's work, superficially studied, becomes clear. In fact, it seems to be agreed that Piaget has demonstrated the priority of the cardinal number in the child's intellectual development. If one studies Piaget more closely, it appears that, impressed by what he considered a definition of the natural cardinal number, he undertook his famous tests, which are based on the assumption of the priority of the cardinal number, and that he drew from these tests more or less justifiable conclusions. That which was for Piaget a supposition, or rather a presumption, appears to his interpreters as a proven fact. But the basis of Piaget's research is not acceptable from either the psychological or the mathematical point of view. It is true that very young children and even animals know the first cardinal numbers, but it is a very primitive state. The child's first conscious mathematical activity is counting, and it seems that all the children with whom Piaget made his experiments on the evolution of the concept of number already knew how to count. For the child who has learned the names of numbers, counting is a game; classical instruction of arithmetic has greatly profited by this game's popularity, and good teachers still do. It is true that counting is primarily a rhythmical pleasure like jumping or dancing. The child has to learn little by little the invariance properties of counting, just as he has to learn all of the other invariances of this world—such as the fact that the number of his fingers is the same today as yesterday, that it will be the same tomorrow, that other people have the same number of fingers, and so forth. Compared with these invariances, the invariance of one-to-one mappings, studied by Piaget, is a facet of little importance, existing only in adult interpretation influenced by set theory.

The instruction of elementary arithmetic is seriously threatened by these poorly understood theories. Classical education began with the counted number in order to arrive at fundamental operations and apply them. To avoid needless counting, systematized and refined methods of counting by use of structured material were developed. Venn diagrams are the opposite of structured material; they allow only stupid counting.

It is not only the technique of mathematical calculation that can be harmed by this misunderstanding. Although "cardinal" is one of the aspects of the concept of number, it is one of the least important. It plays a very feeble part in mathematics, as well as in its practical application: for example, the number four in four minutes, four meters, four francs, and Henry IV, is not a cardinal. It is useless to emphasize this aspect at the expense of others.

One must admit that even today good teaching methods grant the cardinal aspect of the number a token of respect only. But it is quite different on the higher level, where the concept of number is used to lay the foundation for arithmetic. The majority of the manuals suggest a concept of the natural number based purely on set theory and ignore or obscure the mathematical fact that this is impossible. Natural numbers are introduced as the cardinals of finite sets; but to explain what a finite set is, the familiar sequence of natural numbers is used. This is simply going around in a circle. Even if the author is too prudent to declare explicitly that he aims at an autonomous definition of the natural numbers, the method remains circular from the didactic and psychological points of view. The circularity is again evident if one tries to introduce operations with the natural numbers and to demonstrate their properties. Whether explicitly or implicitly, use is made of the properties of the natural numbers, familiar since arithmetic. One assumes, without mentioning them, properties such as (1) finite sets are not equipotent to true subsets; (2) the union and the product of two finite sets is also finite. Or, if there are proofs, they are characterized by a succession of "et cetera." Well, the essence of the natural number is not its cardinal aspect, but this very "et cetera." The discovery that "that continues just like that" (counting, the operations, and their laws), the awareness of infinity—that is the psychological, historical, methodical, and systematic beginning of mathematics; and if there is a fundamental fact that needs to be explained, this is the one. It is a different matter to decide whether one should go up to formalizing complete induction. But there is no honest theory of the natural number in which this principle is kept quiet and applied furtively without explanation. I am not saying that a theory of the natural number should be offered at school and, if so, at what level. However, I am against the teaching of stork tales about natural numbers, and I consider it essential to point out this serious deviation.

No science is better fit for a deductive structure than mathematics. This structure is not only an important element of organization, it is also an esthetic experience for those who can appreciate it. If to the eyes of our ancestors this structure was marvelously represented by Euclid's *Elements*, and on a lower level by manuals adapting Euclid to the needs of schools, for a century now it has been recognized that Euclid was far removed from the ideal of rigorous deduction. Since that time we have been carried closer to this ideal by two waves: (1) that of the axiomatization of different areas of mathematics, and (2) that of formalization—that is, the conscious manipulation of mathematical language. The organization of mathematics, in which axiomatization and formalization are expressed, has made it possible for our contemporaries to grasp our enormously extended mathematics more easily than our predecessors could theirs, although theirs was of more modest extent.

If a science is systematic, it is tempting to teach it as a system, in such a way that the choice of matter, the method, and the instruction can be subordinated to this system. Mathematicians have often succumbed to this temptation, and the tendency toward systematism has been greatly reinforced by the reception of the new mathematics. The system now taught is constructed from the point of view of the author who masters mathematics and knows how the empty structure is filled. It does not mean much to the teacher who does not know the relation between this sytem and mathematics very well, and it means nothing to the student who does not know the mathematics that must be organized by the system. Systematism tends to be dogmatic; subjects, sometimes of no value, are chosen because they fit well into the sytem, while others of undeniable value are tossed out because they do not fit. Instead of following the path of progressive abstraction, one starts with the most abstract, which is the basis of the system, never to reach the most concrete, which appears in its final ramifications. Two examples: (1) the cult of relations at the expense of functions, which has brought about the most stupid chapters of an autonomous school mathematics; (2) the absence of computer mathematics, which does not fit into the system. Fortunately, the examples of the most rigorous systematism that now exist are at the same time the finest that exist in mathematical instruction. They can expose clearly the virtues and faults of systematism, untroubled by accidental disturbances.

If systematism has its historical origin in Euclid's *Elements*, the Socratic method can boast of just as ancient an ancestry. We know the dialogue of Meno, in which Socrates does not teach a ready-made mathematics, but a mathematics in *state nascendi*—the stylized discovery of a chapter of mathematics. With Socrates, the teacher talks and the student listens, although Socrates considered himself rather like a midwife of ideas. Since that time the student has become more and more a participator. In what is called the didactic of discovery, it is no longer the teacher who plays the game of discovering, but rather the student who must make his discoveries, directed by the teacher. In truly experimental schools, one does not make experiments with students; it is rather the students who proceed in an experimental manner.

The idea of the didactic of discovery (I prefer the term *reinvention*) is not peculiar to mathematics, but it adapts itself to no other discipline as well. For several tens of years it has been tried here and there, but with the progress of new mathematics in the schools it has gained a lot of ground. The increasing number of publications on this subject indicates great activity and a wealth of ideas. It is true that pilot classes are often led by exceptionally competent and active teachers, and that, in order to be widespread, this method of instruction ought to be organized for availability to any teacher, and perhaps integrated with the programing of instruction (another new tendency, but one not yet sufficiently developed).

Obviously, this new method of teaching requires a new general organization in the schools. Such teaching cannot take place in a classroom where benches face the blackboard and the teacher's seat. It requires subject matter that is less rigid and is analyzed with a different perspective. It also requires a revision of the purposes of mathematical teaching.

Many young people learn mathematics, but it is not betraying a secret to admit that the great majority never succeed in applying it (often even those who ought to make use of it). This is excused by the supposed benefits of formal mathematics training: the students will have learned to think better from it. However, it is improbable that traditional mathematics instruction fulfills this expectation. The subject of one of the latest conferences on the instruction of mathematics was "How to teach mathematics so as to be useful" (37). The general answer was not to teach some kind of mathematics applied a posteriori, but to start with situations to be mathematized in order to arrive at mathematical models.

Ten or fifteen years ago that would have been unheard of. The idea of programs ordained by a ready-made mathematics was predominant then. The focus of mathematics and its instruction was on pure forms that could be filled with content by those who applied them. Today we admit that a student learns mathematics in the same way that the researcher creates it. To mathematize reality and mathematics itself, to axiomatize (that is, to organize a mathematical area by axiomatical methods), and to formalize a mathematical area (that is, to analyze and restructure its language) are activities allowed the students, and are those that one wants to teach them. Instead of ready-made mathematics, these activities allow mathematics to be made.

I grant that this method of instruction, which is becoming more and more widespread, is still an exception. However, it is necessary to be on guard against a new mathematics that is more stupid, more sterile, more rigid, more alien to application, and more apt to corruption than the former mathematics itself. For this purpose, it is not enough to criticize new efforts, but above all one must devote oneself to the reorientation of the teachers. Of course, this is an enormous job. After courses for teachers of secondary education, there will remain the more numerous ones for teachers of primary education. We need new methods to reach them.

3 Increasing Mathematics Learning through Improving Instructional Organization

LLOYD F. SCOTT

Lloyd F. Scott, a native of Arizona, is currently a professor of education on the Berkeley campus of the University of California, specializing in mathematics education. Professor Scott completed his doctorate at the University of California in 1955, and has continued his interest in mathematics education through his research, his active involvement in teacher education, and his intimate association with schools and children. After considerable experience as a teacher and administrator in the public schools, he became the Coordinator of the Laboratory Schools of the University of California at Berkeley, along with his mathematics education responsibility. He was also one of the founding members of the University of California Elementary School Science Project and found in this activity an opportunity to study the integration of science and mathematics in the elementary school curriculum. Professor Scott's research and contributions to the literature on mathematics education have focused on elementary school mathematics. Currently, his interests continue to be child learning and curriculum strategies in elementary school mathematics.

This background and research eminently qualify him to discuss the need for a more humane and intuitive approach to the instruction of new math. Like Hans Freudenthal, the author of this article demonstrates his confidence in the ultimate value of the recent reform of mathematical curricula as well as his disapproval of prevailing methods by which they are expounded or enforced rather than taught. The entire impact of the paper lies in its implicit affirmation of the evolution to come in school mathematics; this

*makes his criticism of specific habits of current in-
struction and his suggestions for remediation both
constructive and informative.*

*Professor Scott begins with a brief analysis of the
origin of new math, stating that, paradoxically, it has
been a familiar program for at least fifteen years but
is still ripe for change and greater effectiveness. He
then poses some essential questions as to the results
of the new math. Do the new curriculum programs
raise the level of the students' achievement? Do they
inspire the students with a positive attitude toward
mathematics in general? Do they enable all students,
and not merely a capable few, to learn?*

*Answers to these questions lead to a deeper study
of some of the causes of the new programs' weaknesses. Professor Scott bases his observations on the
elementary levels of education, because these clearly
determine the outcome of later higher mathematics
learning. He shows how the insistence on imposing an
overall view of the structure of mathematics on an
unprepared child is too precipitous and insensitive. It
is antithetical both to natural growth in the understanding of concepts through concrete experiences
and to Piaget's hierarchy of cognitive developmental
stages, through which the child must pass in order to
develop an ability for true and creative abstraction.
Instructors' lack of perceptiveness, due to their difficulty in empathizing with the level-of-abstraction
adeptness of the child, their unrealistic expectations,
and their preference for easily prepared and prematurely abstract programs, is often responsible for
mechanical, nontransferable, and noninitiatory
learning on the part of the child. Abstraction, which
is so peculiarly appropriate to mathematics itself, is
not so appropriate to the elementary teaching of the
foundations of mathematics. This ought rather to
correspond to the stages of the child's mental development. Along with inappropriate haste to impose
the structure of math abstractly, the insufficient
application of mathematics to concrete instances
(which would aid in the learning of the related disciplines) and the excess application of drill routines*

result in a passive state of learning on the part of the child. He cannot form general mathematical principles on his own, because familiarity with them comes about only through their experiential application in a variety of situations.

Professor Scott concludes by offering a threefold remedy. He suggests that curriculum developers pass all their program plans through a three-phased screen. In order, the phases are (1) imagery, (2) symbolics, and (3) systematization. He stresses that it is neither the goal nor the content of the new methods that jeopardizes the child's creative understanding of mathematics, but rather the pitfalls in current instruction. Hence the correction of instructional weaknesses is not only worthwile but necessary in view of the potential strength of these new methods.

Since newness is a function of time, it is inevitable that the new is transformed into the old. Even the ill-named new math should not be immune to the aging process. Despite continuing signs of immaturity, this modern upstart is no longer in its infancy. Depending on the source of information, the origin of the current school mathematics revolution in the United States is marked at one of the following points: (1) in 1951, coincident with the founding of major curriculum projects that involved practicing mathematicians and federal funding; (2) in 1955, when the College Entrance Examination Board appointed its Commission on Mathematics to study and make recommendations concerning secondary school mathematics; (3) in 1957, when the space technology fire was ignited by the successful launch of the Russian Sputnik; or (4) in the early 1940s, when several empirical studies appeared that seemed to establish the efficacy of "meaningful" learning.

Regardless of the point and nature of its genesis, it must be acknowledged that this curriculum reform movement in the United States and many other countries is now at least fifteen to twenty years old. Whether or not its products are still modern is a subject for debate elsewhere. It is clear that the movement has already touched the lives of hundreds of thousands of children, teachers, and parents, and the promise for the future is more of the same. It is not logical that the influence of this modern creation should continue unabated if its defense is based principally on its newness or modernness. Max Eastwood once said, "Modernness is a poor thing to feel priggish about," and the message is particularly apropos to school mathematics today. It should be possible to consider the record of the modern program and to penetrate, if only slightly, the facade of novelty, virtuosity, and beauty, that has served as its shield. Some defensible speculations regarding its assets and liabilities can be offered with the intent of assuring its future viability.

Of course, certain assumptions and limitations must be recognized at the outset of this task. The modern mathematics program to be analyzed will involve a conglomeration of the features of many programs. It is not possible to deal with differences between various new programs even though some of these differences are quite pronounced. Neither is it possible to consider the extent to which the conglomerate program with which children are actually involved reflects the substratal principles underlying the entire movement. It must be assumed that modern curriculum materials include the mathematics of the reform movement and that, as a class, they represent the extent to which the forces in mathematics curriculum reform have been influential.

Now to the task itself. I could begin by referring to the apparently infinite amount of material written in defense of the goals of modern school mathematics. However, the program goals need no further eloquent defense. Those who doubt the virtues of the thrust of new mathematics need only to glance briefly at features of the similarly ill-named traditional program that it replaced. A change in the direction of school mathematics was imperative, and the change has been beneficial. The emphasis upon the structure of mathematics, the provision for continuity of significant topics, the refinement of nomenclature and symbolism, the greater emphasis on mathematical logic, the expansion of content, and the earlier introduction of foundation topics are distinctive qualities worthy of the highest praise. In the forward advance of the revolution, these features must be recognized as strengths and must be maintained.

However, it is revealing that these notable strengths fall mainly into the content dimension of the curriculum. It becomes quite apparent through continued analysis that the entire modern mathematics revolution has been a revolution in content, not in pedagogy. This revelation should not be surprising for two reasons. First, if one reviews the major changes of direction in school mathematics throughout history, it will be found that nearly all of them have been changes in content. Adjustment to such themes as mental discipline, transfer of training, utilitarianism, skills analysis, incidentalism, and stepped-up programs have been devoted chiefly to changes in choice or amount of content. Despite pronouncements to the contrary, the questionable pedagogy in each phase emerged almost unscathed. It seems quite apparent that content is more easily changed than manner of presentation, and it should not be surprising that the distinguishing features of the contemporary program are content features. Second, the innovators of the current reform movement were simply better prepared to modify content than they were to modify teaching approach. Notwithstanding extravagant claims, there was insufficient attention given to the manner of presentation, and this lack of attention was due principally to ignorance. Often changes of content were advertised as changes in approach, although teachers soon come to realize that the advertisements were false. In some cases, the architects of change overstepped the limits of their specializations, claiming expertise in the theory of teaching mathematics, when what they really knew was simply mathematics. More commonly, no such claims were made, but content and instructional theory were not distinguished as separate components of the program.

It will be argued here that the effectiveness of modern school mathematics has been impaired by this insufficient attention to instructional theory. The alteration of content has been beneficial, but the neglect of proper teaching presentation has been even more disadvantageous to the modern program than to the program it replaced. Of course, the argument will be wasted on those who do not accept the underlying contention that the contemporary school mathematics program is imperfect. Therefore, an examination of a part of the existing evidence supporting this contention is in order.

First, there is the matter of student achievement in mathematics. Has it been demonstrably enhanced under the modern program? Empirical studies, designed to compare student achievement under different programs, indicate that is has not. The best summary of the results of these studies is that achievement under modern and traditional mathematics programs does not differ materially. To be sure, some of the studies are assailable on the basis of methodology and/or analysis. Moreover, most of the studies draw their comparisons from performances on achievement tests that admittedly overemphasize algorithms, mechanics, and trivialities. In fact, steadfast advocates of the modern program hold that the equivalence of the traditional and the modern program when measured by these tests is evidence of the outstanding superiority of the modern program. They claim that some of the objectives of the modern program that surpass those of the traditional program are not measured by available mathematics achievement tests, and therefore they must be viewed as unmeasured fringe benefits. The position has some merit, but it seems grossly inadequate as a defense for what is billed as a bold new advance in school mathematics. It would seem that the modern program should surpass the traditional program in all aspects and by wide margins. To argue that it is the equal of the poor product it is designed to replace, if only in teaching computation, is to deny part of its *raison d' être*. The report of the International Project for the Evaluation of Educational Achievement gives further cause for concern. Students from the United States (the country that has purportedly led the way in school mathematics reform) were rated near the bottom in a comparison of mathematics achievement involving students from twelve industrialized countries.

Beyond this, there is the matter of student attitude toward mathematics. Most teachers would agree that when a program is properly graded and sequenced and properly taught, the majority of students will display positive attitudes toward learning. What is the record for modern mathematics? A representative study reported by Alpert, Stellwagon, and Becker is summarized as follows: "The overall results indicate that the [modern] program does not increase students' positive feeling toward mathematics, either absolutely or relative to the traditional mathematics program."[1] Surely the objectives of

1. Alpert, Stellwagon, and Becker, "Psychological Factors in Mathematics Education," *SMSG Newsletter* **15** (April 1963), p. 23.

the curriculum reform movement have not been realized when such indications abound.

One other observation merits attention at this point. Among teachers, it is the consensus that the modern program is best adapted to the more capable learner. This is not the same as observing that the more capable learner to a greater degree assimilates better that which is presented to him. Rather it is the view that somehow the prevailing modern program includes barriers to learning for students whose capabilities are average and below average. Of course, just the opposite should be true. All students should have the opportunity to enjoy considerable success with a program in general education. It is well known in teaching that some students will learn a great deal regardless of what teachers do—even despite what teachers do. Other students who do not share the same insights, competencies, and approaches are to a considerably greater extent at the mercy of the program as it is presented. With mathematics, when the presentation is not appropriate for these students, they are set adrift in a sea of nonsensical symbolism. When the program is effective, they find the means at hand for moving forward, even though the ultimate extent of their movement does not equal that of their more gifted peers. The apparent failures of the modern mathematics program in this regard are worthy of attention.

While argument in this vein could be greatly extended, the purpose of this paper would not be served by such extention. Summaries of the basic argument, including the essential documentation, appear elsewhere (95). My case is sufficiently complete if modern school mathematics is seen as (1) sufficiently mature that its successes and failures should be analyzed, (2) sufficiently beneficial that its strengths should not be reduced by attention to its weaknesses, and (3) sufficiently imperfect that the course of its future evolution should be recommended. Proceeding under the premise that such a case has already been presented elsewhere, consideration should be given to specific features of presentation, pacing, organization, and articulation that have an effect upon the success of a mathematics program. In this consideration, it will be necessary to refer frequently to early mathematics learning for two reasons: (1) later mathematics learning is crucially dependent upon the nature of the early foundation; and (2) the failures of improper treatment are more clearly revealed in, and debilitating for, younger children.

IMPOSING THE STRUCTURE OF MATHEMATICS

It is not likely that the goal of having the learner understand and appreciate the structure of mathematics will be vigorously attacked. This is probably the most defensible of all objectives of the modern mathematics program. Yet there is a characteristic approach toward the achievement of this goal that merits reevaluation. Consider for a moment the accumulation of knowledge in any field of endeavor. Simplistically, such accumulation proceeds from very primitive elements in an increasing melange, with rudimental relations between elements continually changing until the elements are very well known or, to use the vernacular of teaching, understood. More specifically, the assimilation-accommodation aspects of human learning find their germination in the trial-and-error puzzle solving of early experience. At some remote point in the learning process, the results of such activity and the inherent drive to bring order to a comprehensive field of such elements will culminate in a class construction designated as the structure of a discipline. Once such a structure has been conceived, it sheds new light on the meaning of the primitive elements and on the relationships between them. However, it is doubtful that such new light is a sufficient substitute for the conceptualization that is gained from the early experience. It is a summary ordering of knowledge, and offers little until those items included in the summary have a relatively seasoned meaning in their own right.

In arranging a mathematics teaching sequence it is very easy to lose sight of this pattern. The wish to display the beauty of the primordial structures of mathematics early in the sequence is seductively tantalizing. Yet, for the curriculum developer to yield to such temptation is usually disastrous for the learner. First, the student fails to see or appreciate the beauty in the structure because he cannot comprehend it. He has insufficient knowledge of its components and little awareness of the need for it. Therefore, he finds not only the easy route to success, but, in truth, the only route available to him: he memorizes, to the extent possible, the morass of nomenclature and symbolics on which the program is built and on which his teacher has placed such high value. He is cheated of the opportunity to extend his own field of concepts and relations to a penultimate orderly arrangement and, through this crucially important mode, to come to some appreciation of the beauty and value of the structure.

It is hypothesized that the goal of exposing structure has been too compulsive and untimely in modern school mathematics programs. There is no clear evidence that the attempts to bring the far reaches of symbolic logic or class theory into early mathematics learning have produced anything except an uneasy acquaintance with a primitive nomenclature of sets. Certainly, the formal presentation of symbolism and operations on sets has not enjoyed the expected transfer to operations on numbers. Moreover, when this popular early treatment is stripped of its formalism and unnecessary symbolics, one finds that the luster of innovation also has disappeared. To pretend that the introduction of collections of objects and the systematic treatment of cardinality are recent creations in the primary mathematics sequence belies their historical existence in arithmetic programs. To assume that there will be some clear connection between the early introduction of the nomenclature of set operations and later appreciation of the structure of mathematics belies experience.

In another vein, early introduction of the treatment of number systems would seem to be susceptible to the same criticism, and the evidence at hand indicates that it suffers the same fate. For the moment, formal axiomatics have not been introduced into the lower levels, but entities best appreciated through axiomatics are deemed proper topics. Probably, there is an insufficient regard for the difficulty of basic concepts of number, relations, and operations for young children. To expect a pupil in the early grades to gain much appreciation for the infinite set of natural numbers, much less the field of integers or rational numbers, is not realistic. He is involved for a considerable period of time in simply refining the meaning of number alone, particularly when he is presented with the simultaneous burden of deciphering the language and meaning of operations and relations. While there is something to be said for drawing attention to the need for defining the universe of discourse, there is serious question whether number systems will have much meaning for youngsters. For that matter, there is an equally serious question of whether the field axioms will be seen as anything other than neat little tricks for approaching symbol manipulations with some flexibility. Once again, the weakness in the modern program is not found in its goal or choice of content, but rather in the urgency with which it forces the encounter. Whatever real appreciation students finally gain for the structure of mathematics is most likely to come from a sequence that is paced to coincide with their development and their normal rate of experience accumulation. It is least likely to come from a sequence that has been designed to expose the elegance of the generalizations of mathematics at the earliest possible moment, regardless of the adequacy of the students' prior experience and the solidity of concepts upon which such generalizations depend. A sensitivity to the nature of human learning reveals that learners must have the opportunity to bring some order and structure to mathematics themselves before they are confronted with the more perfect orderliness developed by others.

PREMATURE ABSTRACTION

It would be heresy to consider the abstract quality of mathematics as disadvantageous. Without question, the refinement, power, and beauty of mathematics lie in its abstraction. Yet to the curriculum developer this particular virtue may become a vulnerability, sometimes almost an insuperable trap. Indeed, it is suggested here that the prime movers of modern school mathematics may be attacked on the basis that they are imprudently enamored of abstraction. However, again the assailable features are the pacing and the manner of presentation, not the goal. The substance of this point of view may be found in the nature of abstraction and the nature of the young learner.

It is irrefutable that the use of abstraction depends on having something to abstract. That is to say, the abstract representation of a concept must have a relatively unambiguous concept as its referent. This dependency is not reduced even at the higher reaches of abstraction when concept clusters are synthesized and abstracted. School programs for most disciplines follow this pattern rather straightforwardly. In prevailing school mathematics, the pattern often seems to be lost in confusion regarding the distinction between concepts and their abstract representations.

Of course, it is possible to ignore the dependence of abstraction upon concept formation, and reverse the pattern. In this mode, a special reverence is attached to abstract symbolics, and symbols are treated as preexisting building blocks for an edifice of knowledge. The symbol representing the abstraction of a concept simply continues in use until the concept and meaning are attached to it. Unfortunately, mathematics lends itself too readily to this latter pattern, while the preference in instructional theory clearly favors the former. As a result, the effectiveness of both elementary and secondary school programs is attenuated with the severity of the impairment, which increases as the age level decreases.

Whatever the contribution of the work of Jean Piaget to curriculum theory, too little has been said of his giving voice to the observations of experienced, competent teachers. Those who are best informed about the manifest characteristics of young learners find in Piaget's hierarchy of cognitive developmental stages the substance of their classroom observations. In particular, they are unreservedly loyal to the notion that children in the early school years (Piaget's preoperational and concrete operational stages) are very dependent upon presentations that appeal to the senses. Their view is that children learn best that which is concrete rather than abstract. Furthermore, they believe that later ability to manage increasing abstraction is a function of the early base built of concrete experiences. Yet, they are unable to fully implement this view because available curriculum materials are not sufficiently supportive. At the same time, many of them find mathematics to be such a special case of abstract study that they are reluctant to make departures from existing materials lest they be accused of neglecting some part that will later prove to be crucial. Their view of mathematics is circumscribed by the materials that are available to them, and at the moment these materials best present the image of laborious abstraction. So long as the materials emphasize the view that mathematics is an abstract morass of facts and computations, this will be the view promulgated by teachers.

At this time, children are repeatedly called upon to respond to abstract stimuli with abstract responses through paper-and-pencil methods. On the basis of intuition alone, this practice is fallible. On the basis of even superficial acquaintance with the best information on the nature of human learning, the continuation of this conspiracy against children is incredible. Yet the reform movement has done little to revolutionize this aspect of school mathematics. In fact, the modern program may well represent a retrogression.

In addition to the lack of sensitive attention given to the nature of abstraction and its relation to cognitive development stages, there are two other potential reasons for premature, unproductive abstraction. First, there is a reasonable speculation that those who have special competence in mathematics also have special difficulty in measuring the abstraction adeptness of others. They tend to use their own ability as a standard for others. In a curriculum-development enterprise, the divergence between such an expectation and the behavior of students is often considerable. Yet signs of failure in the program are commonly attributed to other causes. Revisions in the program maintain the same level of abstraction, with the inevitable similar result. Obviously, such an approach is particularly disadvantageous to most young learners. They have another language and have an abstraction ability that is not even on the same scale as that of the curriculum innovator. They simply cannot learn the abstract language in a short period of time, much less the abstract ideas that the language purports to communicate.

Second, it seems fair to say that modern mathematics programs are inordinately abstract in their early phases because such programs are easier to prepare. It is well known that creating an abstract mathematics lesson is infinitely simpler than creating a lesson with concrete referents. Those who have sought the correct situation or referent for a mathematical presentation know full well the difficulty facing those who attempt to minimize premature abstraction in the modern program. Yet the potential rewards would appear to be more than sufficient compensation for the extended effort. Felix Klein, one of history's great mathematics teachers, said, "It is my opinion that in teaching it is not only admissible, but absolutely necessary to be less abstract at the start, to have constant regard to applications, and to refer to refinements only gradually as the student becomes able to understand them." The modern program would profit from attention to this message.

DRILL INSTEAD OF EXPERIENCE

For some strange reason there is a continuing, almost fanatical, belief in the virtue of drill as a vehicle for mathematics learning. Based on the Law of Repetition, this view has a vacuous premise: If something is repeated sufficiently, it will become branded into the mind forever. The so-called traditional program was properly castigated for its extensive use of drill. The pages of algorithm forms to be completed were viewed as deadly, unproductive, and unimaginative. Yet in their stead today one often finds only modern versions. For example, in the past one found tasks headed "Find the sums," with many items such as this:

$$456$$
$$+879$$

One now may find a task headed "Find the standard names," followed by many items such as this:

$$456$$
$$+879$$

The apparent underlying rationale for these tasks is that through repetition some important mathematics is habituated. The challenge for this position is both intuitive and direct. Mathematics is a thoughtful, logical enterprise. Admittedly it includes some tasks that become relatively routine and are performed without conscious attention to underlying meanings until they are needed. But this is not to concede that there is value in either a failure to attend to meanings or in the substitution of habituation for what is otherwise an analytic procedure. In neither of these cases can transfer or generalization be expected. For example, with the exercises for addition computation to which I referred earlier, the curriculum developer may choose to habituate the skill through repetition, as is commonly done. In this light, the student gets a good deal of practice with the basic addition combinations, spends a lot of time with the task, and gains little else. He is unable to transfer his skill to algorithms for other operations that require somewhat different mechanical steps, and at the point of impasse with a particular computation he is unable to draw upon principles to aid in overcoming the difficulty. On the other hand, if the curriculum developer does not put such a high premium on repetition, he is likely to offer fewer examples, but include activities that call for analysis rather than mere mechanical performance. In the above case he would emphasize the positional characteristic of the notation system, the orderly pattern of right to left increases in the power of the base, and the nature of regrouping. His exercises would be designed to expose the principles upon which a large number of algorithmic forms rest and to offer the student the tools for thinking his way out of difficulty. In all of this, drill and repetition would not play a role. It is a different sort of task with different expectations. Even computation is not treated as a purely mechanical skill. Empirical investigations over the past thirty years have shown that competency is generated more through analytic procedures than through memorization and drill, regardless of the apparent perfunctoriness of the task. In light of this fact, the extent of sheer repetition in the modern program is oppressive, although some reduction from preexisting levels may be noted.

Of course, students are not going to master all mathematics concepts on the first encounter, regardless of the extent to which the underlying principles are clearly revealed and the language used is a language befitting their level of cognitive development (although given these conditions, many fewer encounters are needed). Instead of drill and practice, the concept of experience should be promoted, and this is not merely an exercise in semantics. Drill has as its methodology repetition of the same thing. Experience has as its vital component the nature of change. Under the existing drill worship, a concept is repeated as though it were a skill to be mastered. Under an experience orientation, the concept is introduced in a great variety of situations and its relation to many other concepts is exposed in a variety of ways. In fact, repetition is avoided. New embodiments are constantly provided, so that the students must repenetrate the concept with each encounter. Ultimately the concept is fixed in the mind—not because it is stamped there through repetition, but because it has become a part of a growing structure of interrelated concepts.

INSUFFICIENT REGARD FOR APPLIED MATHEMATICS

Regardless of any antagonism between pure and applied mathematics, there is little justification for their separation in early school mathematics. There is particularly little justification if the net result is much too little attention to the applied segment, as is the case at the moment. The bias favoring pure mathematics in the existing program is a natural consequence of the predisposition of the reform movement and the particular interests of its stewards. However, this movement cannot continue to be unresponsive to an important consideration in general education—that is, usefulness. Beyond this, the program has also been too insensitive to the need for integration of school subjects, particularly when the potential profit to the separate subjects is as great as it is for science and mathematics. There is little question of the value of mathematics in gaining knowledge about the natural world. There is also little question of the value of scientific applications in amplifying mathematics. Since the introduction of applied mathematics, with its practical situations and its inherent concreteness, also introduces features that have considerable consonance with the characteristic features of children's learning, the continuing neglect of applied mathematics seems indefensible. In March 1962 there appeared in the *American Mathematical Monthly* a statement endorsed by sixty-five mathematicians and mathematics educators condemning the overemphasis on theoretical mathematics and the underemphasis on applied mathematics in modern school programs. The statement was somewhat prophetic, given the results we have found. It included the following key paragraph:

> Therefore, to introduce new concepts without a sufficient background of concrete facts, to introduce unifying concepts where there is no experience to unify, or to harp on the introduced concepts without concrete applications which would challenge the students is worse than useless; premature formalization may lead to sterility; premature introduction of abstractions meets resistance especially from critical minds who, before accepting abstraction, wish to know why it is relevant and how it could be used.

Someone should have heard the message. To continue to avoid a coalescence of applied and theoretical mathematics in the program for the schools limits the advance of the reform movement.

The extent to which the foregoing assessment of school mathematics represents a consensus of opinion is not known. However, it is expected that even the most optimistic spokesman for the present course of school mathematics will find in this presentation some valid causes for concern. On this basis, new directions have been indicated and the means of their achievement should be proposed. Therefore, I will take this opportunity to present a modest proposal for the advancement and improvement of school mathematics.

The proposal is a simple one, and it will not be belabored in this article. It consists merely of a strategem for the curriculum developer to use in his preparation of programs in school mathematics. It is closely related to accepted descriptions of concept formation and has a direct association with the historical development of mathematics, but its function is more prosaic. Its use should help eliminate a good part of the existing programs' weakness. The strategem consists mainly of three phases, hierarchically ordered, through which the presentation of mathematical ideas must pass. The phases are (1) development of imagery, (2) employment of symbolism, and (3) generation of systems. Through the use of a curriculum-development model that includes these three phases, some safeguards are created against early imposition of mathematical structure, premature abstraction, abstract drill, and the neglect of applied mathematics.

In the first phase, it would be up to curriculum developers to find means other than those of pure abstraction for bringing mathematical ideas to the students. The material of the program would be that of the real world—that is, applied mathematics, science situations, and concrete embodiments. The activities would be designed to appeal to the senses, not merely the intellect, and they would be presented through the concrete language that children understand. The theoretical substance for such a program may be found in the emerging theory of imagery in children's learning and the work of Paivio, Reese, Palermo, and others, as well as in the cognitive developmental mappings of Piaget. It would be experiential, with variety as a key feature, and the experience would be replete in the use of measurement, tables, and graphs.

The second phase would be characterized by the extended use of conventional mathematical nomenclature. Developed concepts would be represented abstractly, and relations between concepts would be further extended through the symbolic mode. The program would include a significant amount of the material that is characteristically used today, with a much greater emphasis on mathematical logic. However, its organization would be changed. The introduction of the abstract material would carry with it the expectation that concepts would have prior form, and the tendency to reveal structure too early would be constrained by the expectation that students would be given an opportunity to build some order into their growing field of mathematical knowledge before the elegant structures are introduced.

Phase three would include all those mathematical ventures that serve to tie mathematical ideas together. Axiomatic systems would be evolved, and number systems and group theory would be advanced. Mathematical proof and symbolic logic would be the media of discourse. The goal throughout this phase would be the revelation of the most significant aspects of the structure of the discipline of mathematics.

This model would be useful in two ways. First, it would structure the instructional approach for all independent concepts or mathematical entities and provide a proper foundation for fruitful learning. Second, the relative proportion of materials characteristic of the separate phases would be distributed according to a pattern for grades K through 12. The form of the distribution would probably correspond to these rough guidelines:

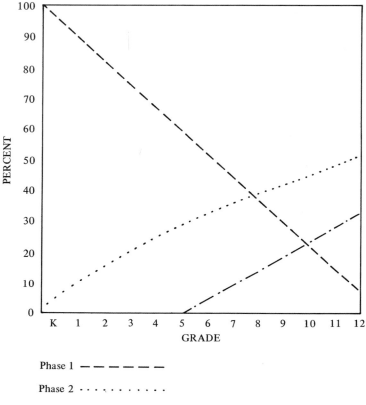

Phase 1 — — — — — —

Phase 2 · · · · ͺ · · · · · · ·

Phase 3 · — · — · — · —

Obviously, this strategem is not intended to direct the choice of program content, nor is it intended to prescribe particular teaching activities or embodiments at any level. Its sole function is to serve as a guideline for instructional planning, so that existing weaknesses in modern mathematics can be converted to strengths.

In summary, it has been hopefully presumed that the curriculum-reform movement has not yet run its course. It was suggested that further evaluation of school mathematics should be directed toward the remediation of existing weaknesses as well as toward the enlargement of existing strengths. Since the most pronounced weaknesses appear to be in the area of instructional approach, a guideline strategem for correcting weaknesses in instructional organization was proposed. It is expected that the use of this strategem would have a pronounced beneficial effect on students' mathematical learning and on their attitudes toward mathematics.

Mathematics: Its Nature
and Its Pedagogy

PART TWO

4 The Nature of Modern Mathematics

RAYMOND L.
WILDER

Born November 3, 1896, in Palmer, Massachusetts, Professor Wilder received his Ph.B. and Sc.M. degrees at Brown University in 1920 and 1921, respectively, following service in World War I, and his Ph.D. degree in 1923 at the University of Texas. Dr. Wilder started his teaching career of over half a century in 1920 as a junior instructor at Brown, and thereafter held an instructorship at the University of Texas (1921–23) and an assistant professorship at Ohio State University (1924–26). For the next forty-one years he was a member of the mathematics staff at the University of Michigan, becoming professor emeritus in 1967. He is currently a visiting professor at the University of California at Santa Barbara.

One of the original group responsible for conceiving and instituting the School Mathematics Study Group (SMSG), he has authored seventy-six articles for periodicals and books devoted to mathematical research and the betterment of teaching methods at all levels of our learning institutions. In addition, Professor Wilder is a member of the National Academy of Sciences and past president of both the American Mathematical Society (1955–56) and the Mathematical Association of America (1965–66).

In the article that follows, Professor Wilder affirms that though mathematics was bound in its beginnings by concepts furnished from the physical world and by its use as a description of an ideal world, it long ago became a creation of the human mind limited only by the cultural environment. Furthermore, far from being

This is a revision of an article published (under the same title) in *Michigan Alumnus Quarterly Review*, vol. 65 (1959), pp. 302–12. The ideas set forth have since been expanded and applied in *Evolution of Mathematical Concepts* (New York: John Wiley and Sons, Inc., 1968).

*the static body of revealed truths envisioned by many,
mathematics is an ever-changing evolving group of
distinct but interrelated concepts in various stages of
development. Viewing mathematics as being independent of Platonic ideals but still affected by external stresses, Dr. Wilder finds no clear distinction
between the theoretical and applied aspects of modern
mathematics. In fact, he states that with the onset of
greater abstraction, mathematics began to expand its
capacity for coping with reality.*

*Dr. Wilder feels that the rapid growth of mathe-
matics necessitates concise, efficient methods of instruction, employed by teachers who possess up-to-
date conceptual knowledge and who stress the receptive nature of mathematics to new concepts. His
observations in this regard, coupled with an interesting discussion of mathematical logic, comprise the
essence of his article.*

Any discussion of the nature of mathematics must emphasize its everchanging
character. This is probably the aspect of mathematics least known among
nonmathematicians, despite its basic influence on the formation of other
aspects of mathematics. For example, it seems likely that parents generally
have used a mistaken belief in the static character of mathematics to justify
their resentment of the introduction of the so-called new mathematics in the
elementary and secondary schools.

The extreme of this point of view is perhaps best exemplified by the words
of a famous orator, who in the opinion of many of his hearers easily eclipsed
Lincoln on the occasion of the latter's famous Gettysburg Address: "In the
pure mathematics we contemplate absolute truths, which existed in the di-
vine mind before the morning stars sang together, and which will continue to
exist there, when the last of their radiant host shall have fallen from heaven."[1]
These fine sounding phrases may be contrasted with the following, which
combine an element of truth with an insight into the popular conception of
mathematics: "Mathematics is a tool which ideally permits mediocre minds to
solve complicated problems expeditiously."[2] It must not be concluded that
because these opinions emanate from nonmathematicians they are not to be
taken seriously, for I am confident that they could be duplicated within the
ranks of those who make their living by mathematics.

1. Edward Everett, *Orations and Speeches*, vol. 3 (1870), p. 514.
2. F.A. Firestone, *Vibration and Sound*, 2nd ed., 1939, p. 8.

In certain of their aspects, as well as in the attitudes of their practitioners, there is a close analogy between religion and mathematics. To some of its practitioners, religion represents an ideal essentially superpersonal, existing independently of its devotees; to others, it affords rules by which to live, having no intellectual content whatsoever. Like religion, mathematics traces its beginnings back to prehistoric primitive cultures. As a result, the numbers with which we count, the so-called "natural numbers" $(1, 2, 3, \ldots)$, are frequently regarded in a mystical fashion not ordinarily associated with those numbers with whose historical origins we are familiar. Also like religion, mathematics furnishes a fascinating study from an anthropological viewpoint, only the meagre beginnings of which are to be found in anthropological literature.

We can gain a much better perspective regarding the nature of modern mathematics if we study the manner in which mathematics has evolved from primitive to modern forms. The average layman regards mathematics as a static body of truth, something that has come down through the ages uninfluenced by the varying fortunes of mankind, and, if he is at all aware that research goes on in mathematics, he probably thinks that its function is to discover the truths to be found in this Platonic realm. Now there is a sense in which discovery does form a part of mathematical research, for once a mathematical theory has been established, and its methods of deduction and proof agreed upon, the finding of the propositions to which it leads—called "theorems"—may properly be considered a discovery process. But the establishment of the basic concepts, the setting up of the theory itself, is more aptly called a creative process. And looking at twentieth century mathematics from a broad viewpoint, we see a sort of continuous creation process going on: modern theories, such as mathematical logic, game theory, and the like, appear on the mathematical scene, and fields such as topology, in a mature stage; still older fields, such as analysis, are continually invigorated by newer ones, such as topology and set theory; and finally, ancient fields, number theory and classical geometries, for example, are hoary with age but far from dead.

If we disregard the manner in which number words arise in primitive societies, and confine ourselves to the direct line of our own cultural development, Babylonian and Egyptian mathematics are of first importance to us. We have come to know in recent years, from new translations of tablets dating back to the second and third millenia B.C., that the Sumerian-Babylonian culture achieved a high level of mathematical development. The concept of number arrived at the first level of abstraction when it became a noun instead of an adjective—the number three, for example, instead of "three apples," "three men," and the like. Arithmetic became a real science of numbers in that it constituted a theory that could be applied in various areas—in architecture, finance, surveying, and so on. Moreover, it evolved into an algebra of respectable proportions for that day and age, embodying methods of solving quadratic equations (for real roots, of course) and even some cubics and higher degree equations.

But upon careful analysis we are struck by a curious fact—curious to us, that is: this Babylonian mathematics contained virtually no geometry as we know it. A historian might be shocked by this statement, particularly if he has heard that the Babylonians knew the Pythagorean theorem a thousand years before the time of Pythagoras. But let me explain. It may be true that the Babylonians knew how to find certain areas and volumes, and that they may even have known the relation between the sides and hypotenuse of a right triangle, but generally these things had no more *mathematical* status than any other rule, such as the rule for finding the interest on a sum of money for a given length of time. Since I find that the man who might be called the authority on this period, O. Neugebauer, agrees with this viewpoint, I will give no supporting argument. But it does seem to be the case that, for the Babylonian, there was no special branch of mathematics corresponding to geometry. Geometry was just a set of rules for applying the real body of mathematics, which consisted of arithmetic and algebra.

Two other comments regarding Babylonian mathematics: its algebra was *verbal*—it had no symbols such as we associate with algebra—and this was perhaps the chief reason why it did not develop further than it did. And *proof* for the Babylonian evidently consisted of empirical verification—the sort of proof that we associate with the natural sciences. The oft-heard statement that Babylonian mathematics contained no proofs is based on the fact, widely recognized but evidently difficult to realize in practice, that we are prone to interpret other cultures from the bias of our own. If we take the point of view of the Babylonian mathematician himself, mathematics is arithmetical and algebraic, and proof means empirical verification. The fact that some of their formulas were false is beside the fact.

I shall skip Egyptian mathematics, except to remark that the rules of a geometric nature that it contained were supposed to have been the chief source upon which the Greeks drew. For my purposes, the differences between Egyptian and Babylonian mathematics are too insignificant to justify recounting them.

The achievements of Greek culture were great, from the mathematical point of view. In the first place, it introduced geometry into mathematics. It would be interesting to reflect upon what mathematics would be like today if this had not happened. But I shall only state my opinion that, although undoubtedly modern mathematics would be quite different in many respects, the tremendous advantages to be gained by introducing geometric patterns into mathematics would probably have been recognized. What these patterns would have been like, without passing through the Greek culture, I cannot imagine (possibly topology would have been introduced earlier, for instance). In any case, to say, as some eminent mathematicians have said, that Greek mathematics was a "wrong turning" is, in my opinion, both unrealistic and unjustified.

In the first place, the Greeks brought mathematics to a higher level of abstraction; the geometric rule of the Babylonians and Egyptians became a mathematical theorem, and proof became a matter of logical deduction, not of empirical verification. As by-products, logic was brought into mathematics, and the axiomatic method was begun, to be brought to fruition in modern times as one of the most fruitful of research tools. Unfortunately post-Greek civilizations regarded Euclid's *Elements* as a textbook, which I am confident it was not intended to be. For the Greeks, geometry was as much a tool as a field of knowledge. They compensated for the Babylonian symbolic short-comings by setting up a "geometrical algebra." There is a remarkable amount of what we call number theory in Euclid, all done by using geometric figures instead of symbols as we know them. Using such geometric tools, the Greeks contributed an astonishing amount to mathematics, even to the extent of setting up some of the fundamental notions of analytic geometry and calcu-lus, as well as almost arriving at the modern concept of real number via the Eudoxian theory of proportion. Finally, because of the higher level of ab-straction upon which they placed it, mathematics achieved a dual character: on the one hand it was a science in that its theories furnished the means for handling problems in astronomy, physics, music, optics, and so forth; and on the other hand it was a description of an ideal universe, a Platonic world of ideals.

I must pass over the Indian and Arabic developments in arithmetic and algebra and come to modern times. With the invention of a symbolic appara-tus for algebra, Descartes and Fermat could achieve that fusion of algebra and geometry that we call analytic geometry. The roles now became reversed; while the Greeks used geometry as a tool to do arithmetic and algebra, arith-metic and algebra were now called into service to do geometry. But of greater significance was the new perspective and conceptual framework with which mathematicians could work. Any modern analyst who thinks Greek geometry was a "wrong turning" should reflect upon what thinking in geometric patterns did for the evolution of analytic notions, such as continuity, during these early times.

After analytic geometry, calculus matured. It was not invented entirely by Newton and Leibniz, but was the result of a long evolution that continued long after these gentlemen had placed it on a suitable symbolic and operational basis. And then early in the nineteenth century, the non-Euclidean geometries were conceived by Gauss, Bolyai, and Lobachevsky. And why were they in-vented? Purely as a means of attaining a final answer to the question of the necessity (that is, "independence") of the parallel axiom in the Euclidean system of geometry.

Why was this such an important event? What possible significance could it have for the so-called man in the street? For one thing, the man in the street has been quite concerned about the matter of nuclear bombs. But does he know that there is a direct line from such a seemingly impractical matter as the question of the independence of an axiom in an ancient Greek geometry to its answer in the non-Euclidean geometries of Bolyai, Lobachevsky, and Riemann, and thence to the theory of relativity and the development of nuclear fission? Of course physics was the ultimate medium of influence, but I am sure that every physicist would be gracious enough to recognize the part that mathematics played in this development.

Moreover, the effect of the non-Euclidean geometries on mathematics was tremendous. The dual character of mathematics still prevailed, but was profoundly changed in that, although its scientific function continued to be nearly the same, the Platonic conception of it was replaced by the recognition that, as I believe Einstein put it, mathematics is a free invention of the human intellect. No longer need mathematics be bound either by empirical considerations or by compliance with the ordinances of some imaginary ideal world of mathematics. It became just as free to create its concepts as any human activity can be—all freedom being limited by the level of cultural achievement. Moreover, the axiomatic method shared in this metamorphosis; no longer were axioms "necessary truths" or the like, but basic assumptions from which one derived a theory that might or might not have applications in this or that human affair. Without these developments, modern mathematics as we know it could hardly exist.

Finally, late in the nineteenth century, the theory of sets, or theory of the infinite, was created. Unfortunately, although it furnished a new and powerful tool for mathematics, it brought contradictions that required a long time to handle, and it necessitated the invention of new proof principles.

The above is an inadequate picture of the evolution of mathematics, but we must pass on to mathematics as it is today. Since they are still operative, and presumably will continue to be in the future, I shall name the forces which, I believe, influence and activate mathematical evolution: (1) cultural stress, both environmental and hereditary (by "hereditary" I mean those forces *internal* to mathematics which compel mathematical developments); (2) symbolization; (3) diffusion, in the anthropological sense; (4) abstraction; (5) generalization; (6) consolidation and diversification; (7) cultural lag and resistance; and (8) a process of selection.[3]

Now for my main topic: the nature of *modern* mathematics. First of all, I regard it as a *science*, an opinion which I will attempt to justify. In saying this, I am quite aware that many of my mathematical colleagues prefer to call mathematics an *art*. However, while I agree that mathematics has a great variety of artistic and humanistic aspects, I must still insist it is a science.

What is a science? However we define it, I think we would agree that it is a way of dealing with reality. But of course this is too broad a definition; primitive magic was a way of dealing with reality too, but we would not call it science. Science is a special way of explaining reality, and it has both a theoretical part and an applied part. In the theoretical part, concepts are formed that provide the guidance and direction for the applied part. But most important, science is characterized by an openmindedness that constantly

---

3. For an explanation of these and how they act, see Chapter 4 of my book, *Evolution of Mathematical Concepts* (102).

modifies the theoretical part whenever it is found lacking; in short, a theory that fails to work is amended or dropped.

It is a seemingly paradoxical feature of science that the farther its concepts seem to recede from external reality, the more successful they become in the control of man's environment. Consider physics, for example. Its concepts have become so abstract that years of training are necessary for an appreciation of them; and when one eventually comes to feel that he has an understanding of these concepts, he may have to adopt an attitude toward them very different from that which he holds toward the material objects of his environment. But modern physics works; no matter how abstract and seemingly unreal its concepts have become, they have enabled us to reach the threshold of what bids fair to be a new revolution—that of the atomic age. It is of course difficult, if not impossible, for the participant in great social changes to realize their significance. But one need not have much imagination to sense that, barring catastrophic wars, man has at his fingertips new sources of energy that can change his entire way of life.

Mathematics, in terms of which much of this seemingly unreal physical theory is phrased, shares this character. In its beginnings, it derived its concepts, such as number, directly from the external world, ultimately achieving in the Sumerian-Babylonian culture a first order of abstraction, in which these concepts were treated as things in themselves. And in this it first achieved the status of a science—a science of numbers, the concepts of which were directly applicable to the external world. But as mathematics evolved, a higher order of abstraction was achieved, in which concepts began to be applied to concepts. Mathematics gradually added concepts of its own to the world of reality, so that its domain of application included not only the physical environment, but the cultural (which includes the conceptual) environment. Concepts are just as real as guns or butter; merely ask the doubter how he could fight a war without them. The main difference between the so-called applied mathematician and the so-called pure mathematician is that each deals with different aspects of reality.

The pure mathematician, the one who supposedly does mathematics for its own sake, having no regard whatsoever as to whether what he creates will ever have any application in the real world, is continually being surprised by finding his concepts put to work in this so-called real world in a way that he, the pure mathematician, never dreamed. To put this another way, it appears that no matter how abstract and seemingly removed from physical reality mathematics may become, it works; it can be applied either directly or indirectly to the external world. Television, radio, air travel, and so many other things would not have been possible without mathematics. But this phenomenon simply bears witness to the cultural and scientific nature of mathematics. After all, a major function of culture, and especially of its scientific component, is to control man's environment. Even though the dual nature of mathematics may seem to split it into one part that can be applied and one part that seems to be just something for professional mathematicians to play with, there is actually no clear separation. Both aspects of mathematics serve a scientific function, and if the so-called pure part, which ordinarily functions in the conceptual area of the world of reality, often becomes instrumental in the physical environment, there should be no cause for wonder. Both it and the conceptual world in which it ordinarily abides trace their ancestry back to a world in which abstraction was only beginning to yield, under the play of cultural stress, the concepts that became mathematics.

And this brings me to the matter of freedom in mathematics. After the discovery of non-Euclidean geometry and the resultant feeling that one could create mathematical concepts without restrictions imposed either by an external world or an ideal world, it gradually became clear that the restrictions imposed by the external world still operated, but now once-removed.

Most mathematicians have certainly heard of their colleague who, disgusted by the uses to which a backward and laggard world was putting scientific concepts, exclaimed, "Thank God that there is no danger of my work ever being put to practical use." He was giving expression to that kind of freedom that the mathematical world came to feel during the past century. But I am afraid the gentleman in question was not well aware of the nature of modern mathematics, or he would not have been so confident. No one can escape his environment, and in particular no mathematician can escape his cultural environment. Specifically, he cannot cut himself off from his mathematical colleagues in order to indulge in mathematical fantasies that bear no relation whatsoever to the existing state of mathematics in his culture. He is a participant in the evolution of mathematics, whether he likes it or not. If he tries to exile himself and play mathematical games having no relation to the world of reality, he will not be heard. He too is an applied mathematician, but the applications, in his case, are to the conceptual mathematical part of his culture. We sometimes hear a mathematician say that his only criterion for the validity of a mathematical concept is that it harbors no inconsistencies. He is probably unaware that it is not only improbable that he will never run into contradiction, but that it is very likely that, if he isn't extremely careful about his methods of proof, he will run into some well-known inconsistencies.

This leads me to remark upon the methods that mathematics uses—a subject that is now called *metamathematics*. The Greeks brought into mathematics the notion of proof by logic. Another way of phrasing this is to say that the Greeks formed a merger of logic and mathematics; in fact, they merged these two items so closely that later some people began to assert that mathematics was nothing but a branch of logic. This thesis received great impetus from the work of Boole, Peano, Russell, Whitehead, and others, and, as one would expect from the history of Greek mathematics, it ties in closely with the axiomatic method. Now, as I remarked before, one of the contributions the Cantorian theory of sets made to mathematical thought at the beginning of the present century was a series of contradictions. This would seem to be a somewhat destructive kind of contribution, I am aware, but actually it led to productive soul-searching in the mathematical world. During the seventeenth and eighteenth centuries mathematics was too busy with its growing pains to worry much about rigor. The late E.H. Moore is often cited as saying, "Sufficient unto the day is the rigor thereof." This is not precisely what he said, but, like many quotations, it is an improvement on the original. This seems to have been the general attitude toward mathematics of the seventeenth and eighteenth centuries. Already in the nineteenth century, however, a great deal of work was done in laying more rigorous foundations for some of the mathematical edifices erected during the preceding two centuries. This type of work was greatly accelerated as a result of the discovery, around 1900, of the set-theoretic contradictions.

The work of Russell and Whitehead during the first decade of this century was both an attempt to show that by proper methods one can avoid such contradictions in mathematics, and also that mathematics can be derived from classical logic. They found that the latter could not be done, although at first they thought they had done it. Actually, they had to introduce new rules that were by no means recognizable in classical logic.

Against this idea that mathematics could be derived from logic was an assertion that the so-called classical logic was not and never had been a proper tool for the development of mathematics, that classical logic was a set of verbal rules invented for the purposes of argumentation, and that mathematics was too precise and fine a cultural tool to be guided by the rules of verbal discourse. It was much as if a watchmaker tried to work with the tools of a plumber. One school of thought, the intuitionist school, virtually threw out classical logic altogether, went back to the Babylonian science of numbers, and proceeded to rebuild upon it, using only methods that they termed constructive. Intuitionism is sometimes characterized as a mathematics of doing: you do not prove that something exists by showing that the assumption of its nonexistence leads to contradiction, as in high school geometry, but rather you show how to construct the thing you want to prove exists.

The intuitionists quite properly pointed out that classical logic evolved in a finite world and that mathematics is not confined to a finite world; it deals at the very least with the infinite collection of so-called natural numbers $(1, 2, 3, \ldots)$. And just as the seventeenth century analysts came to grief in trying to sum infinite series by the same methods that had been used in summing finite series, so did the intuitionist assert that the application of the law of the excluded middle to an infinite series of disjunctions could lead to trouble. (The law of the excluded middle is the either-or law of classical logic. For example, "Either it is raining or it is not raining.") If you are given, for instance, fifty natural numbers, it is quite proper if you say, without even looking at them, that either some one of them is odd or there is not an odd number in the lot. You can proceed to build an argument based on this assertion, without checking the numbers. But if you are given an infinite set of natural numbers, then you must realize that the statement "Either the first is odd, or the second is odd, or the third is odd, and so on" is an infinite disjunction, and to assert that it implies the existence of an odd number in the series is justified only if you can actually point out the number. But it may be that, in the case of such an infinite set of numbers, you cannot actually show an odd number in the collection, while at the same time you cannot show that the assumption that there is an odd number in the collection leads to contradiction. If you can show that the assumption that there is no odd number in the lot leads to contradiction, then nothing follows. You would then be saying that, by the law of the excluded middle, either there is an odd number in the lot or there isn't, and having shown the latter not to be tenable, you conclude the former (which is another way of resorting to the above infinite disjunction).

Now this approach to the difficulty engendered by the contradictions turned out to be quite radical. It necessitated an entire rebuilding of mathematics by constructive methods peculiar to mathematics and using only a part of classical logic. The result was that a great deal of what had been accomplished during the past three centuries turned out to be unattainable by the new methods. True, a decided virtue of the new methods was that no contradictions were encountered. But at what a cost!

It is not surprising that the majority of mathematicians turned to another way out. Instead of restricting the creation of mathematics to constructive methods (which almost amounts to making the method more important than the result), why not make a study of possible methods, including classical logic, in order to find out just how they have to be limited in order to avoid contradiction, and how they must be augmented for the purpose of expanding the reservoir of possible methods to attain the maximum amount of desirable mathematics? A new branch of mathematics called *mathematical logic* is now active in studying the possible new foundations. It has been found, for example, how to modify the Russell-Whitehead procedures so as to avoid the difficulties they ran into. It has also been found that it is impossible, within a system broad enough to encompass ordinary number theory, ever to prove the consistency of the system in question—the famous Godel theorem. Incidentally, just in case one is inclined to think that mathematical logic is pretty rarefied stuff, I might mention that we have here a kind of phenomenon mentioned above. It was during the first World War that the Germans discovered that mathematical logicians were most successful in decoding. Of late it is the computing machine industry that utilizes the logicians' services.

But to return to the methodology of modern mathematics, a method that is exceedingly important and relatively new centers on the notion of induction—not the kind of induction that we speak of in the natural sciences, however. Consider ordinary arithmetic, for instance. How does one prove theorems about an infinite collection of natural numbers? For example, how can one prove that for all natural numbers, $a + b = b + a$? This theorem asserts that regardless of what order one adds numbers in, one gets the same result. Everyone, or at least almost everyone, in our American culture knows this. But how to prove it? Merely observing that it holds for all values of a and b up to 100, or even to 1,000,000,000, would not constitute a proof; it might have satisfied the Babylonian, but not the modern mathematician. Arithmetic furnishes many instances of theorems that are valid for an amazingly large range of numbers, but are demonstrably invalid for certain numbers beyond this range. Since we are dealing here with an infinite totality, we need a new method of proof that is adaptable to infinite collections. Such a method is that which we call *mathematical induction*. With this method, one can prove the formula $a + b = b + a$ and all other such formulas of arithmetic.

The introduction of the theory of the infinite, and especially of the theory of transfinite numbers, has formed an extension of the usual numbers of arithmetic, and additional new methods of proof have had to be devised. I think one can see now what happens in mathematics. Certain *concepts* appear desirable, either for applications to physical problems or, at the other extreme, for the building up of mathematical theory itself. *Cultural stress* ultimately forces their acceptance, and we have to add them to the main body of mathematics. But then we find that in order to study their properties, which is quite necessary in order to improve their utility as mathematical tools, we have to augment the older methods of proof with new methods. At this point the old bugaboo of the mathematician rears its ugly head—that is, the fear that the new methods may introduce contradictions. Here is where the mathematical logician can help. He develops a suitable symbolism to represent the entire structure before he applies his methods of analysis. He has grown wary of the verbalisms and linguistic traps of ordinary language, and, although the average mathematician may find it convenient to continue using the natural language (the language of ordinary discourse) and to restrict the use of ideograms to a minimum, the logician cannot afford to do likewise.

I will not go into further detail; all I want to do is give the general picture. As I said before, we find that certain concepts are necessary to the further progress of mathematics, and if the methods that we already have in existing parts of mathematics do not suffice for the new concepts, we just invent new methods. And while this process is going on at what some choose to call the top of the mathematical tree, at the roots or foundations the acceptability and capabilities of the new methods are being studied. The analogy of a tree is not really so bad, since this growing process is going on both at the roots and in the branches, or fields, of mathematics, and new branches or fields are continually being added. But there is some question whether parts of the tree are not splintering off from the main trunk in order to grow independent roots and eventually trees of their own. I am not referring here to disagreements concerning the content and methods of mathematics such as we find in the example of the intuitionists, but to rifts that sometimes threaten division between pure and applied mathematicians. This kind of disagreement seems to be of a different nature, relating more to the functional than to the purely conceptual character of mathematics. One gets the impression that some feel that applied mathematics serves a useful function for the urgent affairs of life, whereas pure mathematics is a sort of ivory-tower endeavor having only an esthetic function to serve. There is little question that pure or any other kind of mathematics does give to its devotees an esthetic satisfaction; as a matter of fact, this may be, and probably is, the sole reason why most of them pursue it. But it does not follow that this is the only function that it serves, and from the viewpoint of the cultural nature of mathematics, it does have another function—that is, a scientific function. I believe that any attempt to separate mathematics into pure and applied is not scientifically sound. And, more generally, I think it not unlikely that any splinter from the parent mathematical tree is doomed to sterility unless it maintains contact with the pure mathematics (as most applied mathematicians actually do).

What is considered applied mathematics today may, by a curious reversal process, become pure mathematics tomorrow. And at any given moment of time, there is no clear distinction between what is pure and what is applied. I have even noticed how two groups of mathematicians, each of which considers itself applied, have each denied the propriety of the designation "applied" to the fellow group. And, as I remarked earlier in discussing freedom, even the mathematician who insists he is a pure mathematician is in reality an applied mathematician in that his interests are applications to the conceptual world of mathematics.

Every mathematician must recognize that whatever mathematical activity he may engage in, it is clearly and demonstrably connected with the mathematical culture of his time. If some of it is found to be what the layman calls practical, he should not be surprised. For while he may be working on a level of abstraction that seems so high on today's mathematical structure as to be virtually in the clouds, he should know that the relations between the various levels are such that even the concepts of the highest levels repeatedly find their counterparts not only in the lower levels, but also in the nonmathematical cultural environment.

We should also be aware that no matter how we feel about the relation of mathematics to logic, modern mathematics is modifying the bonds by which it was tied to classical logic by the Greeks. The practicing—and by this I mean the creative—mathematician is aware that content comes first and method later. Modern mathematics continually creates new concepts and seeks to justify them later by using logic or whatever other tools one has in addition to logic. If suitable tools are not available in modern logic, then they have to be invented. It is even conceivable that we shall never succeed in eliminating contradictions from mathematics, that they will continually recur in new forms. But perhaps this is an unavoidable feature of mathematics in its modern form. Of course, whenever we find that new concepts and methods engender inconsistency, we shall, if the concepts seem to aid in progress, try to patch up our methods before we reject the concepts. This has been the case in the theory of the infinite, in which the concepts have proved too useful to be thrust arbitrarily aside, and we have had to modify our methods to avoid the contradictions that ensue when they are unrestricted.

One can see, incidentally, how the old, much quoted definition of B. Pierce (1870) to the effect that "Mathematics is the science that draws necessary conclusions" is inept. Perhaps we should modify this quotation to read, "the science that draws unnecessary conclusions." Also, how inapplicable the old definition by Russell, that mathematics is "the science of p implies q," is unless we broaden and otherwise suitably modify what we mean by the word *implies*.

It appears, then, that in modern mathematics we have an ingenious scientific instrument for dealing with all aspects of reality, be this reality either the physical or the conceptual type. This instrument is not a static body of revealed truth, but a complex of concepts in various stages of evolution, each of which is related to and affects all the others and contributes to their growth. By a process of consolidation and generalization, these concepts frequently merge and are submerged in more all-embracing concepts that emphasize what the mathematician frequently refers to as "the unity of mathematics."

Although in its more primitive and elementary aspects its methods borrowed greatly from classical logic, mathematics has been forced, as it evolved into a more powerful instrument, to create new methods of its own. When the new concepts and methods seem to go too far, as in the engendering of contradictions, modifications have to be introduced. And although the body of mathematics grows ever larger and larger, these new concepts and methods enable us continually to introduce new simplifications and to unify further, so that the whole does not get out of hand.

Despite its size and continued rapid growth (the abstract journal *Mathematical Reviews* publishes thousands of abstracts of research articles every year), absolute splintering off from the main body has not, to date, proved feasible. In particular, to attempt to divide mathematics into applied and pure may be convenient for some purposes, but from the standpoint of the theory of knowledge it is quite unrealistic and unjustifiable. Just as unrealistic and unjustifiable is a separation into necessary and conventional parts. In the sense that mathematics is a creation by human beings, it gives an impression of conventionality; but in the sense that it evolves through the actions of cultural stresses, which themselves appear as inevitable concomitants of the evolution of culture, it is necessary. But necessity does not mean truth, and conventional does not mean free.

In its further development, mathematics seems destined, under the influence of environmental and internal hereditary stresses, to become ever more abstract and at the same time ever more powerful in its capacity for dealing with reality.

What do these conclusions signify for the teaching of mathematics? First, I think, is the necessity for arranging curricula so that only the necessary and most significant concepts are included and the methods chosen, both for derivation of and teaching of concepts, the most concise and efficient. As a consequence of natural growth as well as of the demands of the sister sciences for new and more sophisticated tools, the body of mathematics is growing so fast that great effort must be made to take up the slack in the elementary and secondary school courses in mathematics—an effort already evidenced in the various New Math programs.

There is little that is new about such a movement. However, the general public does not know that for some time now high schools have been offering most of the mathematics that a century ago constituted the entire mathematical curriculum of the colleges. The tendency to push college mathematics down into the high schools, and then from the high schools to the elementary schools, has been in existence for a long time. With the advent of Sputnik, however, American educators were startled into awareness that the new methods and concepts invented by modern mathematics had not been used to advantage in the primary and secondary schools. They also became aware that for some reason, possibly some little understood advance in general cultural awareness, youngsters today have a much greater capacity for abstraction, from preschool age to high school, than was realized.

A corollary of this is that secondary school teachers, and to a less extent perhaps elementary school teachers, find it continually necessary to bring their methods and conceptual knowledge up to date. This is presently being accomplished by such devices as in-service courses for teachers offered by colleges and universities, and the summer institutes for teachers conducted under such auspices as the National Science Foundation. Incidentally, the successful college instructor has had a similar compulsion for many years, this being one of the primary ways in which research in mathematics affects teaching. Teaching and research are by no means the mutually exclusive activities portrayed by many legislators and publicists.

In conclusion, I am convinced that in view of the continually changing character of mathematics, there is no justification for dogmatism in the teaching of mathematics. All teachers at all levels should make it clear to their students that mathematics is receptive to new ideas, be they new concepts or new methods. Thus a teacher who insists that a result (an answer to a problem) be obtained in a specific way (such as the way recommended by the text in use) is neither using sound pedagogy nor exemplifying the spirit of mathematical activity. Mathematics can always profit from new ideas. Recall the case of Gauss, an elementary school pupil, who astonished his teacher by summing an arithmetic progression in an unexpectedly short time, simply because a new and shorter method had occurred to him. Such originality should never be squelched!

5 Some Reflections on Learning Mathematics

ZOLTAN P.
DIENES

*A native of Budapest, Hungary, Professor Zoltan P.
Dienes was educated in Hungary, Paris, and England.
He obtained his B.A. degree with honors in 1937 and
his Ph.D. in 1939 from the University of London.*

*Since his childhood, Dr. Dienes has been fascinated
by the purely abstract. One of his long-lasting interests
has been the controversies surrounding the foundations of mathematics and the reasons why mathematicians have always been unevenly divided between
the formalists and the intuitionists in regard to these
controversies. His interest in the problem of why
mathematics is so difficult for most people arose
from his examination of the difficulties in establishing
the foundations of mathematics.*

*These considerations led him to examine the archi-
tecture of the formal foundations of mathematics in
relation to a supposedly open-closed psychological
dimension that he hypothesized would affect a
person's attitude toward the different parts of this
architecture. However, it is one thing to assume theoretically the existence of a psychological dimension;
it is quite another thing to verify the hypothesis experimentally. In seeking verification he turned his
attention to the psychological problems underlying
the understanding of mathematics at the elementary
school level.*

*Having accepted and built upon the theories of
Piaget, Dienes communicated through his work some
principles and methods that he believed should be
followed by all practicing teachers. Those principles,
forming the foundation of all his work, tell us that
children should learn by "doing" through their own
experience; they should learn with the aid of a variety*

of perceptual objects representing the concept to be learned, which they can handle at their own pace. In addition, they should be allowed to discuss freely with their peers the problems that they are required to solve, and they should occasionally be presented with mathematical ideas of a more difficult level, given that children think constructively—that is, they tend to build up their structures from separate components, all the while having an intuitive feel for the kind of end result they are aiming for.

After teaching mathematics from 1941 to 1959 in England, Professor Dienes joined his interests in psychology and education with his interest in mathematics by accepting a research fellowship at the Center for Cognitive Studies at Harvard University (1960-61), an associate professorship in psychology at Adelaide University (1962-63), and a current directorship of the Psycho-Mathematics Research Center of the University of Sherbrooke in Quebec, Canada. His contribution to the literature on mathematics education is enormous, and his international involvement extends from Canada to many developed and undeveloped countries around the globe.

In this article, Professor Dienes states that mathematics learning situations of an abstract nature are difficult to develop and that they must be utilized not so much to teach particular topics as to generate an ability in the child to meet and attack intelligently the unexpected problems of an increasingly complex world.

For Dienes, the science of mathematics is a means of categorizing the objects and events that comprise our complex environment and of establishing relationships between the categories and, finally, between the relationships themselves. Furthermore, the learning sequence used to teach a particular mathematical structure (set of relationships) consists of familiarizing the student with the concrete materials to be used (free play) and then presenting different concrete embodiments of the structure, with exercises to encourage the student's awareness of the correlations between the embodiments and the abstractions from

*the situations. A student's knowledge of a structure
is evidenced by his ability to transfer previous knowledge and rapidly cut through the irrelevant details of
a third isomorphic situation. In order to deal further
with a structure, it is represented spatially; a description of the image provides the beginnings of an axiomatization from which a formal system is derived
in which theorems can be proved.*

*Concerning the implementation of mathematics
learning, the author discusses a variety of problems,
starting with the fact that the present sequence for
teaching structure, whether by the modern or traditional approach, is backward. Secondly, he recognizes the differences in children and shows ways in
which relevant information might be gained from
sources other than the teacher.*

*Further problems are found in the area of teacher
preparation. Dienes suggests the mathematical re-
education of teachers, the learning of skillful questioning and motivating teaching techniques, and
further study in the psychology of learning. Finally,
in the area of generating the proper sequence of
learning situations, Dienes' hierarchy of mathematical
topics necessitates a radical, but not random, re-
structuring of curriculum.*

WHAT IS MATHEMATICS?

Since the dawn of history, man has been trying to make sense out of his environment. He has been trying to put events into relationships with each
other. Some of these were simply temporal relationships, as some events occurred before others. Some were causal relationships, as certain events appeared to have been caused by other events (sometimes, supposedly, by super-
natural powers). Other relationships were spatial—that is, certain events
happened in certain places rather than in certain other places, or far away
from each other, or close to each other, and so on.

Man has been doing this because he has been obliged to relate to his environment. We are not alone. We are part of a much bigger thing called the
universe. In order to act in ways satisfactory to ourselves within this universe,
we need to establish relationships with different aspects of this universe. This
desire is the basis of science and, in particular, the basis of mathematics. In
order to find his way around in the world, man has had to categorize objects

and events. A dangerous animal had to be distinguished from a harmless one, so the category of dangerous animals, accompanied by certain clues in the way of sounds and smells, became extremely important for man's survival.

In the early days, man's survival depended entirely on the accuracy with which he was able to forecast what was coming next. In order to do this accurately, he needed to establish certain categories that worked sufficiently well for him in his environment. Fundamentally, the situation has not changed. Today, in order to predict what is going to happen next in our complex world, we have to make even more complex predictions by making even more complex categories. This complex categorization and the establishment of relationships between the categories is what is known as the science of mathematics.

Not only objects, but also sets of objects, are put into categories. One of these categories is known as *number*. Relations are then established between numbers, and, subsequently, even these relations between numbers are categorized. These categories are further related to each other, and so the story goes on until we reach the extreme complexity of modern mathematics.

So mathematics relates. In order to relate, we need to have things to relate. These things, or elements, belong to a certain category or class of entities. This forms our universal set. We think in terms of relations between the elements of this universal set. A relation does what it says: it relates. So, if we take an element (X) and relate it to an element (Y) we have an ordered pair of elements of the universal set. Some of these ordered pairs will be allowed, so to speak, and others not. The set of all the allowed ordered pairs forms a representation of the relation we have in mind. For example, we may have a lot of objects of different colors, and our relation might be "to have the same color." If X has the same color as Y, then the ordered pair (X, Y) is allowed. If X does not have the same color as Y, then the ordered pair (X, Y) is not allowed. The set of all the possible ordered pairs by itself is known as the *Cartesian product* of the universal set. It must be understood that an element can also be paired with itself—that is, there are pairs such as (X, X). Any relation can, therefore, be represented as a subset of a Cartesian product.

Naturally, we can also relate elements of one universe to elements of another universe. This is the case every time we say that a certain object is an element of a set. Such a relation holds between an element and a set of elements. For example, we might take three objects and call them X, Y, and Z. It is possible to make eight different sets out of X, Y, and Z:

set $\{X, Y, Z\}$	set $\{X\}$
set $\{X, Y\}$	set $\{Y\}$
set $\{Y, Z\}$	set $\{Z\}$
set $\{X, Z\}$	set $\{\ \ \}$ (containing nothing at all, known as the *empty set*)

So our universal set is now this set of eight sets. The universe of elements is the set comprising X, Y, and Z. We now consider the relation "being an element of." We see that out of twenty-four possible element-set pairs, only twelve are allowed. X is an element of the set $\{X\}$, the set $\{X, Y\}$, the set $\{X, Z\}$ and the set $\{X, Y, Z\}$. The same applies to the element Y, which belongs to the sets, $\{Y\}$, $\{X, Y\}$, $\{Y, Z\}$ and $\{X, Y, Z\}$, and the element Z which belongs to the sets $\{Z\}$, $\{X, Z\}$, $\{Y, Z\}$ and $\{X, Y, Z\}$. So, out of the total Cartesian product set of twenty-four pairs, we pick out twelve ordered pairs that give us, in this case, the relation "is an element of." Here we are relating elements to sets of such elements, not elements to elements of the same universe.

The study of relations leads naturally to the study of operators, or functions. Here we also consider ordered pairs. In the case of a function, given the first member of an ordered pair, there is only one element of the Cartesian product that has that particular member as first member. In other words, if X is related to Y by a particular relation, then X cannot also be related to any other element but Y. If this is so, then this relation is called a *function* or an *operator*. In this case, the members of our universe provide the *states* on which we may operate by our *operator*. These initial states are the *inputs* for our operator. The members to which our relation uniquely leads will be the states that can be called the *outputs* of our operator. So, we have an input state and an output state. The input state leads to the output state through the application of the operator. Arithmetical operators such as "plus 2" and "minus 1" are simple examples. These are applied to arithmetical states. An arithmetical state is represented by a set. The state is determined by the class membership of the set. For example, a set of three elements belongs to the class of sets possessing the property "three." It belongs to a certain family of sets, known as "the threes." So, when in a classroom situation we use a set of three elements, we do not, of course, by magic create a number three, we represent the number three by a member of the family to which this set belongs. We may then use an operator that leads us to another family. If the operator is "one more," then from the three family we are led to the four family by the application of this operator.

Naturally, there are many other states and operators, as for example, geometric ones. We may be facing the wall and we may be told to take a quarter turn to our right. Then, we shall be facing another wall. There are four states in this game and four operators. These operators are:

Take a quarter turn to the right.
Take a quarter turn to the left.
Take a half turn.
Take no turn or a whole turn (both amount to the same thing).

Here, every state is related to one and only one state through the application of any single one of the above operators. For this reason, it is called an operator or function. If I am facing any particular wall, and I am told to take a half turn, I will be facing a certain definite wall—namely, the opposite one—when I have finished carrying out the operation required. On the other hand, if I have been told to take a quarter turn without being told whether it is to the right or to the left, then I have a choice of two walls. This relation, which is the one of rectangularity, cannot be considered to be an operator or a function, although "take a quarter turn to our right" is.

Of course, in mathematics we do not deal only with states and operators; we also relate operators to other operators. For example, in the turning situation, we might say that a quarter turn to the right followed by a half turn has the same effect as if we had taken a quarter turn to the left. So, we can establish equivalence classes of sequences of operators. We are now doing something to operators, saying things about operators, whereas before our operators were saying things or doing things about the states upon which they operated. This is one of the hard things a mathematics student has to learn how to do. Something that he was doing yesterday becomes a thing upon which he must now do something. A quarter turn one day is something you do in order to change your position from facing one wall to facing another wall. But tomorrow, a quarter turn may be something with which you combine something else in order to find a movement equivalent to this series of two movements. This is an example of passing from the preoperational to the operational way of thinking.

PROBLEMS OF LEARNING STRUCTURE

Having discussed what is meant by mathematics, we are now in a position to discuss what is meant by learning mathematics. Knowing what we are learning is a necessary condition for knowing what it is to be learning it. It is not, however, sufficient. Learning itself is a psychological set in which the input is the subject who does not know a particular piece of mathematics and the output is the subject who does know a particular piece of mathematics. In order to ascertain whether we, in fact, have isolated a psychological learning operator, we would need to have a criterion for judging in every case whether the piece of mathematics has or has not been learned. Now if mathematics consists of relationships between certain categories, relationships between these relationships, and so on, then we would need to devise some kind of a test for verifying whether a person does, in fact, know such structures (known as *sets of relationship*). But how could we possibly know if somebody knows these structures? We look at a person and wonder whether he does or whether he does not know them. How can we tell? Presumably, a mathematician, when he is speaking to another mathematician, will soon make up his own mind whether the other mathematician understands what he is talking about or not, because if he does not, the conversation will not make sense to him. On the other hand, if the two mathematicians are able to have a fruitful conversation about their mathematical topic, then each mathematician will assume that the other understands the mathematical structures about which the conversation is taking place. In other words, the criterion is of a practical nature. They speak to each other—that is, they communicate about certain mathematical structures in a certain language. If they do not understand, it does not necessarily mean that one knows more than another. They may simply be speaking different languages. Mathematicians, on the whole, are extremely conservative about the symbol systems they use. If they are brought up on one certain symbol system, they are reluctant to give way to another one.

But the languages they use do not necessarily differ from each other only in the symbols used. There are certain so-called modern ways of looking at mathematical structures and there are others that are less modern. The modern ways involve somewhat more generalized ways of thinking. To take a simple example, instead of talking about geometric relationships in terms of common Euclidean lines or planes, modern mathematicians very often will talk about the most general types of spaces in which such problems exist. Then they will simply put down the conditions necessary for them to be able to speak about their problem, and define a kind of space in which these conditions are satisfied. In the old days, there were no such sophistications necessary and an ordinary line and a plane with points in it were sufficient. So, it is possible that this tendency toward generality of thinking and, consequently, generality of expression may hinder some people from understanding one another, and yet the fundamental problems remain the same.

This has not brought us any nearer to defining what "knowing a structure" is. How do we know, for example, that a child in school has understood a certain equivalence relation? Take the positive and negative integers arising out of, and generated by, a certain equivalence relation between ordered pairs of natural numbers. We can ask him for a definition. Children can learn a definition; they can even learn to give some examples of the definition and solve some problems. But it is well known that when problems of a rather different kind are given to them, problems depending on exactly the same mathematical structures they are supposed to have learned, very few of them, if any, can tackle the new problems. It would seem that instead of having really learned any mathematical structure, they learned only some techniques whereby certain classes of problems can be solved. When this class is extended in some way, through some nonmathematical extensions whereby mathematical features remain unchanged, they are stumped.

What is there in these new problems that they are not able to do? How is it that they are able to solve certain types of problems and not others? In every problem involving a mathematical structure, there is a certain amount of *noise*. There is a certain amount of information contained within the problem that is irrelevant to the mathematical structure. This is inevitable in any application of mathematics. Some problems have more noise than others, or some noise may be more familiar through practice than other noise. So, it seems that one of the problems of applying a learned mathematical structure to a problem is to cut through a certain amount of noise. This is what is often meant by the psychological term *transfer of training*, in a mathematical context. Transfer of training means that we have trained somebody to solve a certain kind of problem and thereby made it easy for him to learn to solve another kind of problem. It is very likely that transfer takes place through the subject's realizing that the problem he has learned to solve forms a part of the much vaster class of problems and then noticing that the new problem he now has to solve forms part of this vaster class. Therefore, he can use familiar techniques when confronting the new problem. So cutting through noise simply means becoming aware that certain problems with more or less noise content do or do not belong to certain mathematical categories.

It seems that we may be able to arrive at some definition of "knowing a structure" by suggesting that a certain amount of noise-cutting has become possible. Before this idea can be applied, the problem of the measurement of the amount of noise cut through needs to be tackled. In other words, it involves the establishment of a space of concrete embodiments of mathematical structures in which a certain rough metric might be established so that "distances" between embodiments can be estimated. One concrete embodiment of a mathematical structure might be very much like another. For example, in multiplication, we might use matchboxes and put beans into them. If we put the same number of beans in each matchbox, all we have to do is count the matchboxes to find one factor, and count the number of beans in one box to find another factor of the total number of beans. Now, if instead of using matchboxes, we use old cans, clearly there is not a great deal of difference. However, if instead of using matchboxes we use rows in which we arrange objects (in other words, rectangles with rows and columns), then we are considerably changing the look of the situation and there is a certain amount of transfer to be made from one situation to another. We could go even further and use a balance beam with the same number of hooks on each side at the same distances from the fulcrum, and establish an addition and multiplication situation that could be entirely isomorphic to the matchbox and the row-and-column situations. We could also use the Cartesian product as another multiplication situation.

The problem is to discover some objective way of measuring the supposed distance between different embodiments. The matchbox-and-beans embodiment is not so far away from the rows-and-columns embodiment as it is from the balance-beam embodiment. Possibly the only way to settle this problem is by experimental and statistical means. While we must be satisfied with this type of solution (not yet in sight!), subject variables will always come into the application of such measures. A measure of embodiment-distance, calibrated over an area such as New York, will not necessarily work for a population in the Congo.

So the establishment of different embodiments whose purpose is the training of the subject to transfer from one embodiment to the other and discover the common features of these embodiments leads us to the problem of the establishment of learning sequences that would establish the learning of particular mathematical structures. The learning would presumably begin with the familiarization of each subject with the materials used in the abstraction process. If the subject is unfamiliar with the materials, he is not going to be able to manipulate them in any purposeful way. Such adaptation to a new situation is known as *free play* with the materials of this situation. Most inventors of so-called structured materials in mathematics suggest that the first thing a child should do with such materials is to play with them. Playing is adaptation. The subject adapts himself to the properties of the materials and learns the kinds of things that can and cannot be done with them.

After such free play, some structured exercises may be given in which the same mathematical structure is dressed up in different concrete embodiments. We may hope that eventually the subject will discover the common features incorporated in these exercises, although this is by no means certain to happen. In order to encourage its happening, we may set up end-point exercises in which the learning of the isomorphism between the different embodiments is encouraged. In other words, they will have to learn that, if in the first embodiment they put X together with Y to obtain Z, then in the second embodiment they put together whatever corresponds to X in the second embodiment with whatever corresponds to Y in the second embodiment, and they should obtain whatever corresponds to z in the second embodiment. If they are able to make the correspondence between the elements of the first situation and those of the second situation, so that whatever happens in the first has a correlation to whatever happens in the second, then they have seen the relationship between the two embodiments.

Here we are getting nearer to a behavioral definition of "knowing." We can test whether a certain activity in one situation can be translated into another isomorphic situation, and vice versa. To make sure that the subject has not merely learned to handle the two situations, we can test whether the abstraction achieved can quickly be related to a third isomorphic situation, both starting from the first and second concrete embodiments. If this is so, then something structural has been learned.

Here is a simple example of such structural learning. Situation 1 is as follows: Let us say that mother, father, son, and daughter are playing ball. There are four possible throws:

1. You throw it to yourself.

2. You throw it to your own age group but to the opposite sex.

3. You throw it to your own sex but to the other age group.

4. You throw it to the opposite sex and to the other age group.

A fifth person throws a die with the numbers 1, 2, 3, and 4 (indicating the possible throws) on it and the ball is thrown. Then the die is thrown again and you repeat the movement. The first player to shout the number of the move that will get the ball from the first to the third person in one go will start the next round. But before starting the round, his claim must be verified.

Situation 2 is as follows: Take a die with 1, 3, 5, 7 on it. Throw it twice and multiply the numbers obtained, but modulo 8.

Problem: How are these two four-games related?

It will be verified that:

Ball Game	1	2	3	4
Multiplication Game	1	7	3	5

makes an isomorphism between the games. Throw two followed by throw three can be replaced by throw four. But also:

$$7 \times 3 = 21 = 5 \ (\text{modulo } 8) \ \text{etc.}$$

Now if this structural knowledge is going to be of use, the subject is going to need a "peg" on which to hang it; he is going to need to talk about it in order to handle it effectively. So, he needs a representation. Such representation is usually a spatial representation. Functions can be represented by arrows, for example, and at the beginning of the arrow will be the input state. At the other end of the arrow, there will be the output state. Further arrows and further states will generate a visual map of at least part of the structure the subject has learned. If the structure consists only of a finite number of states, then a complete map can be drawn. Such, for example, is the graph of a mathematical group. If the structure has an infinite number of states and consequently an infinite number of possible operators, then only a part of the structure may actually be drawn and the generalization as to how the visual picture continues has to be reached by induction. In logic, for example, we can practice drawing logical networks in which the inputs are properties or statements that are joined by logical functions, and the outputs are correspondingly the resulting properties or statements. These outputs can be used for further inputs for further logical functions, and so forth. These networks can then be looked at and studied in relation to the concrete situations from which they have been abstracted. Equivalence relations between networks can be established and, consequently, reasoning patterns of the type "if, and only if" can be developed. Logical deduction patterns are developed through the use of the subset-to-set relationship. From the fact that a certain element is in a subset of a set, we can deduce that this element is also in the set of which the subset is a part. So, reasoning patterns in logic as well as in mathematics can emerge as a later part of the abstraction process. We start from the various concrete embodiments, we establish the isomorphisms between the embodiments, we draw networks corresponding to the composition of the various functions, and then we establish equivalence relations or deduction relations as a result of studying these networks.

Here is an example of a network that could be used at this stage:

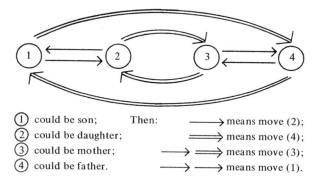

① could be son;   Then: ——→ means move (2);
② could be daughter;   ══⟹ means move (4);
③ could be mother;   ——→ ══⟹ means move (3);
④ could be father.   ——→ ——→ means move (1).

This would be a network that captures the modulo 8 multiplication game as well as the ball game, since we could put

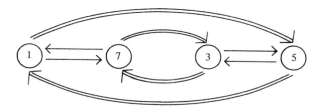

The networks or representations may be logical networks, function networks in arithmetic graphs of groups, or any other kind of representation that pictures the abstraction arrived at from the concrete embodiments. After they are established, we can start looking at this picture itself. If the picture really did arise as a representation of an abstraction and not of a particular activity, then when we describe the picture we are describing the properties of an *abstract structure* rather than a *particular game*. This is why it is important mathematically and psychologically that representations should not be given too freely until a certain amount of abstraction has taken place out of the concrete situations.

Looking at the picture may result in the *description* of the picture. Looking at parts of the network, we can see that certain networks are equivalent. We can establish a notation for this and thus establish some initial pieces of description. These, or part of these, will turn out to be the axioms in the axiomatic description of the structure. In the description of each structure there will be some general descriptions, such as the properties of the neutral element and properties of inverses, and there will be some particular properties relating to particular elements that were used in the structure. For example, we might be introducing the Klein group, which has four elements. We can begin with two elements: let us say X and Y. Then we could say that according to the schema, the product or combination of any two sequences of Xs and Ys with a third sequence of Xs and Ys can be replaced by the product of the first sequence and the product of the second and third. This is stating the associative principle for our system. On the other hand, we can say in particular that the product of X by X can be replaced by the neutral element or that the product of X by Y can be replaced by the product of Y by X, and so on. Here, for example, will be found an axiom system for the Klein group:

(Associative Principle) $P \square \triangle \, [\!] \equiv P \square P \triangle \, [\!]$, $P \, 1 \, \square \equiv \square$, (Neutral)

$$(1) \; P \, X \, X \equiv 1$$
$$(2) \; P \, Y \, Y \equiv 1$$
$$(3) \; P \, P \, X \, Y \, X \equiv Y$$

Where: P means "combine"
  $\square, \triangle, [\!]$ are "formulas"
  and $1, X, Y$, and PXY are the four elements
  and $\equiv$ means "is replaced by"

Now we may wonder whether everything we know about the Klein group is in fact included in this system. What do we mean by "included"? Perhaps we mean somehow hidden in it, but hidden so that we can still get it out one way or another. But how do we get something out that is hidden? We need to make up a new game in which we establish the rules for getting hidden things out. For example, we might say that we are able to replace any combination of Xs and Ys by the same combination preceded by the neutral element. This is expressed formally by $P1 \, \square \equiv \square$. Also, we should be able to say that we can replace any string of symbols by any other string of symbols to which the first is seen to be equivalent by virtue of an axiom. To replace means that we can start with any given combination of symbols, do an act of replacement, and then write the next member of the chain (another combination of symbols). Then we do another act of replacement and write the third member of the chain. When we have finished establishing our chain, we can say that every member of the chain is *equivalent* to every other member of the chain and write the $\equiv$ sign between any two members. In this way, from the initial information we can obtain other information that has, so to speak, been hidden. We have been able in some way to get it out. Here is an example of such a "getting out" procedure:

Start with this combination of symbols: $PPPYXYX$
In this combination we combine Y with X and write: PYX
Then we combine PYX with Y and write: $PPYXY$
Then we combine $PPYXY$ with X and write: $PPPYXYX$

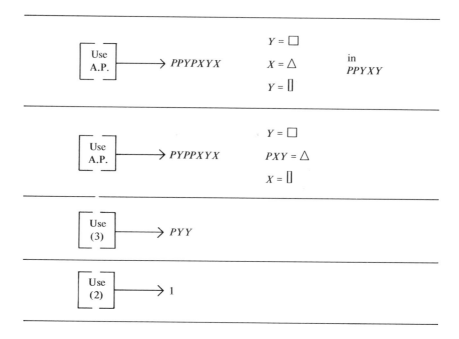

Hence $PPPYXYX \equiv 1$

So, by using associative law twice, then rules (3) and (2), we proved a theorem, namely that

$$PPPYXYX \equiv 1$$

The chain leading from the initial combination of X' and Y' to the final combination (1 our case) is known as our *proof.*

We have reached a formal system in mathematics. We started with the interaction of the child with the environment through concrete materials. We went on to identify a mathematical structure by likening one situation to another in a precise way. After that, we tried to represent structures spatially to enable us to handle them, look at them, and think about them. After that, we described this image, and the description gave us the germs of an axiom system. As soon as we established the rules of the "proof game," we reached a formal system in which we could prove theorems. Needless to say, it is very seldom that mathematics is learned in this rational manner.

PROBLEMS OF IMPLEMENTING MATHEMATICS LEARNING IN THE CLASSROOM

Upon looking at the present situation in the classroom, it becomes evident that the kind of learning described in the last section hardly ever takes place, whether the curriculum is of the so-called traditional or the modern type. The so-called modern mathematics is learned very largely on the supposition that a complex symbol system can be understood and quickly used by most children. We have seen that symbolizing our abstractions comes at the very end of the abstraction process. The actual abstracting comes long before. There is also an intermediate stage when a certain representational pattern is established, which can later lead to the establishment of the symbol system. The modern as well as the traditional way of teaching mathematics takes the opposite procedure. The symbol system is presented and explained through a few examples. Since few children are able to understand the symbol system well enough to solve problems, visual aids of various kinds are provided. This is now considered quite modern, and mathematics without visual aids is no longer considered good pedagogy. So, starting with the symbols, the traditional approach leads the student on to representation, and then, having to some extent broken through the difficulties of the symbol system through visual aids, it goes on to applications—in other words, to problems. The concrete situation is reached at the end of the road. It seems to me that this is the reverse of the more natural and possibly more effective process. It makes more sense to start with the world as it appears, abstract from it, represent the abstraction, and then symbolize it, than to start with the symbols, then represent the symbols in a visual way, and then relate to reality as an afterthought. If the cart has been pulling the horse most of the time, it is small wonder that so few people understand mathematics, whether it be traditional, modern, or any other kind.

The pedagogical problem is how to generate abstractive mathematics learning such as is described in the last section. As we have already seen, mathematics is extremely hierarchical; it is a network of all sorts of interwoven relationships, all built on top of and underneath each other. The learning of such an intricate set of patterns must naturally take into account the way in which the patterns fit together. This is one of the problems of getting any mathematical learning started. We must carefully take into account the subordinates and the superordinates of the subject. Another difficulty is the fact that children do develop at alarmingly different rates from each other in all sorts of ways. This is well known to psychologists, while lip service only is paid to it by educators, and not much is done about it. It is difficult to separate children into classes of slow ones, middle ones, and fast ones. Even if it might be possible to separate children into such classes, this would not get rid of the difficulties arising out of the different ways in which the children form concepts. Another problem is the fact that different rates of progress are evidenced in different areas of the same concept structure by different children. This means that collective instruction is highly impractical and inefficient. If thirty different children in the classroom were to be treated in exactly the same way, some would be wasting their time, others would receive presentations unsuitable to their ways of thinking, and others would not follow at all. This is directly due to the delicate nature of mathematics. If you have missed one part, it is impossible to understand the next, and for this reason most learning that is called mathematics learning degenerates pretty rapidly into rote learning of the responses required and approved by the teacher.

The problem here seems to be one of feeding mathematical information to each child when he is ready to accept it, so that he will be able to process it and then use it. In view of this, it is impracticable for the entire set of information to come from the teacher. He cannot provide different kinds and different amounts of information in several different ways, all at once. So some kind of arrangement is necessary whereby other sources of information besides the teacher are provided. One possible solution that is being widely tried out these days is programed learning. This is based on the assumption that by splitting learning into a very large number of minimal steps, it becomes possible for every subject to be able to put together whatever is necessary to arrive at the competencies required. The one great stumbling block to programed learning is that it is extremely boring. An adult who is motivated to learn something in order to improve himself in his job can discipline himself and say, "I must learn it," and go through a thousand-page text to pass an examination. But he does this to earn the privileges of higher pay. For children, on the whole, the reward has to be much more immediate than that.

Another objection to programed learning is that the actual learning we engage in, in relation to our normal environment, does not take place in minimal steps. We confront the total situation and respond to it totally. Some kind of nonlinear programing would seem necessary, which would combine learning small items with interaction with the environment and, consequently, with the added depth that such interaction can produce in the way of motivation. Computerized instruction may here provide a partial solution. Any program of mathematical activities should be one in which children can engage in exploratory activities in relation to their environment. The environment as we find it is not eminently mathematical, or, if it is, this mathematics is so hidden in a whole morass of prerequisite knowledge that for practical purposes it is not discoverable. So a certain amount of structuring of the mathematical environment would seem to be necessary in order that a series of programed activities might have some hope of success in establishing the learning of abstract mathematical structures. A large number of materials, especially mathematically structured materials, would be necessary. For example, some arithmetic materials should be provided in order to encourage children to cope with situations that are isomorphic to the mathematical structures they will need in their arithmetical work. This means that the idea of powers, bases, and exponents should be made clear to them through the provision of adequate materials. These materials could, for example, be the multibase arithmetic blocks that have the idea of powers of certain given base numbers built into them. Other materials for the learning of logical relationships in which categorizing is encouraged could be, for example, the attribute blocks, introduced first by William Hull and developed for logical work and for work on relations, functions, and geometry by the author.

Materials for playing various algebraic games that would lead to the establishment of the field axioms should also be envisaged.

These materials, of course, will be quite useless without instructions as to what to do with them, although the child's initial contact with such materials should be free play. A skilled teacher observing the free play of children will notice that such play eventually takes on a certain direction. Certain problems need to be tackled by children in order to express what they wish to express with the materials. They might not have enough of a certain kind of block, for example, in which case they would have to "make" that block out of other components. Or they might want to make a block in which there was a certain piece missing, such as a block with a hole through it, as they might want to make windows and doors for their buildings. This would entice them to look at the internal relationships of the pieces, which may, in the case of arithmetic blocks, prepare them for the ideas in powers of certain base numbers. A skilled teacher, when noticing such inquiries, can by a mere suggestion or remark generate a whole series of experiences for the children, who will then go on exploring along more and more fruitful avenues as they play with the materials.

Apart from such skilled questioning and suggestions, there would, of course, have to be a large number of standard games in the classroom that could be played with the materials. These games would be ordered in a certain way, because some games would be too difficult to play without some previous games having been played. Most mathematical structures can be learned by playing skillfully contrived and excitingly motivating games of a mathematical nature.

Another interesting possibility is the invention of mathematical stories. These can be invented by the teacher, and then others can be invented by the children themselves. The events in the stories would follow certain mathematical patterns. Some of these stories could also stimulate the imagination of the children through generalizations and other alterations on the one hand, and through artistic expression by means of painting or modeling of parts of the story on the other hand. In the Sherbrooke Mathematics Program (implemented by the Psycho-Mathematics Research Center at Sherbrooke University), we are developing such mathematical materials, games, stories, and instructions. These are put together in a nonlinear activity program such as suggested above.

From the foregoing it should be obvious that there are very few, if any, teachers who, without further training, implement, let alone develop, such mathematical environments in which children could grow into mathematical maturity through interaction with the environment. Every teacher who is going to be concerned with the generation of such mathematical environments and with the supervision of children within such environments, will have to be mathematically reeducated. Such persons will not only have to learn a great deal of mathematics, but also the corresponding classroom techniques used to create the mathematical learning situations. The mathematics taught today in universities or teachers' colleges is either inadequate for the job or too theoretical in nature or too symbolical in presentation for most practicing teachers to derive much benefit from it. So an extensive and thorough mathematical training program for teachers would have to be instituted before such a mathematics program as we have envisioned could be made into reality. Such a mathematics teacher-training program would have to involve workshops in which such games as those previously described could be played by the teachers themselves. They need to meet the same problems and the same difficulties as will be met by the children they will be supervising. Most teachers are not mathematically trained or mathematically oriented. They will not, on the whole, be able to understand a course of formal mathematics, regardless of whether it is given in a standard textbook or in a university mathematics classroom. These courses and textbooks are intended for specialists who will become future mathematicians or scientists. It is not a question of every teacher having to become a mathematician. Teachers will simply have to learn a certain amount of mathematics and learn it well, as part of the general culture and the general set of competencies required of tomorrow's citizen. Special techniques need to be developed to meet this need.

Another essential requirement is a certain amount of knowledge of the psychology of children. Teachers will have to know the salient facts about the development of the children under their care. They will need to learn about such development from the social, mental, affective, and intellectual points of view. The work of Piaget should be well known, as well as the work of other experimental psychologists such as Bruner, Bartlett, Suppes, and many others. Some of the work done by the author and his associates should also be learned, as it is relevant to the ways in which mathematical learning can be organized in a group learning situation in a classroom.

Last but not least, the future teacher responsible for creative mathematical interaction between child and environment must learn some new classroom techniques. Perhaps more important than anything else, she must learn to be less authoritarian. She must learn to replace her own authority by the authority of the truth. When a child is making an inquiry, it is not the teacher who should provide the answer but the situation, which should be so set up that the truth is discoverable. The objective facts will then become the arbiter of the truth rather than any one person who authoritatively states that this is so. It will also be necessary to concentrate on the techniques of getting children to work in small groups. Some children, of course, will want to work alone, some in pairs, others in groups of four or five. Work in groups needs a great deal of organizing. Each group needs to have its leader, if only in a temporary capacity, who is responsible for collecting the material for the work for each task, making sure that it is put back, and making sure that each member of the group gets a turn in thinking out some of the problems. Discussion between peers is a very important ingredient in learning. A great deal has been done, particularly in the United States, in discussion between teacher and child, but very little discussion takes place between child and child in matters of mathematical importance. This is probably because situations have not been contrived in which mathematics becomes important to children. If the games are motivating and the children want to play them, then they will want to discuss the difficulties that arise while playing them. Many teachers say in the beginning that coping with six or seven groups in the same class is beyond them. They are totally unable to look after all these groups at the same time. Of course, they do not have to if the work has been efficiently organized and the lesson prepared in terms of each group's needs. Three or four different games should be provided for each group so that when one is finished, the next game can be used. Teachers also find it difficult to accept that four or five different topics can be learned at the same time by different groups of children. They say they find it difficult to switch from geometry to algebra, from algebra to logic, and from logic to arithmetic within a space of five minutes. But this is surely because they are not sufficiently familiar with the subject matter. They would not find it difficult to switch from an addition problem to a subtraction problem because they know what addition and subtraction are.

Mathematics learning situations of an abstract nature, in which abstraction cycles follow one another in organic sequences, are extremely difficult to generate. This does not mean that it should not be done. Today's world is increasingly based on wielding more and more complex structures. We shall need large numbers of people who are able to face unusual and unforeseen situations in the extremely complex world we are constructing. It is probably quite useless to make up a fixed curriculum of what children should learn, because what they are learning now is probably of little relevance to the problems they will have to meet twenty years from now. We can see this by looking back twenty years and seeing all the competencies required today that were not even thought of twenty years ago, such as the computer sciences. On the other hand, the development of a curriculum should still receive serious attention, since we do have to teach children some mathematics even though it is not particularly important what mathematics we teach them. It is far more important to know how to teach what we wish to teach. This "how" should be determined by the need to train children to meet the unexpected. The technical problem of "what" seems to be to dovetail the development of the stages through which the child passes with the hierarchical data of mathematics itself. This problem probably has a number of possible solutions, and any solution naturally depends on the way in which we imagine hierarchies of mathematics to be built. Different solutions to the curriculum problem will correspond to different hierarchical conceptions. One solution to the problem is being provided by the Sherbrooke Mathematics Program in Canada. In this curriculum construction, we have tried to keep in mind the many connections that exist between the different topics introduced. We have tried to avoid the introduction of any topic that is not soon afterward made use of. If a certain mathematical topic is not going to be used at a certain stage, it is not introduced at that stage; it is introduced later or not at all. The hierarchy of abstractions has also been taken into account, with attempts being made to provide all the subordinates for the construction of superordinates. Having to fulfill this simple requirement has meant that certain topics have had to be displaced from their time-honored place. For example, during the first year of mathematics learning, between the ages of six and seven, very little, if any, numerical work is done. The work during the first year involves objects and their properties, objects belonging to sets, relations between objects, relations between sets, equivalence classes arising out of equivalence relations, as well as set operations connected with the logical ideas of conjunction, disjunction, and negation. Toward the end of the first year, or sometimes during the second year, children begin to work with the idea of cardinality. They do not get into natural numbers until the ordinality and cardinality ideas have been synthesized; this means putting off the usual arithmetical processes until much later.

Care has been taken to separate the preoperational and operational stages of learning in the construction of the curriculum in any area. For example, although children will readily learn that the "state of 2" operated on by the operator "3 more" gives rise to a "state of 5," they will not so easily learn that an operator "2 more" followed by a further operator "3 more" is replaceable (in virtue of a certain equivalence relation between chains of operators) by the operator "5 more." Whole learning sequences are introduced in terms of states and operators, followed later by more sophisticated sequences in terms of operating on operators. It is found that, in order to prepare in sufficient detail some of the complex arithmetical processes, it is necessary to leave multiple-digit multiplication and division to the fourth and sometimes to the fifth year of school, rather than introduce it in rote fashion much earlier, as is commonly done today. In spite of the hue and cry about the distributive law, the commutative law, and the like, children still have little understanding of the underlying mathematical structures. The distributive law is finally driven home in the Sherbrooke Program as a particular case of a homomorphism. The ideas involved are really quite difficult, involving some knowledge of mathematical groups, rings, and fields, if not of vector spaces.

Such a curriculum would, in all probability, not be practical without a radical overhaul of the methodology. Such an overhaul cannot be done in a haphazard way. Serious and relevant research into the learning of structures is a long overdue necessity. We are trying to make up for lost time at the Sherbrooke Psycho-Mathematics Center by starting several series of experiments of this nature. Inquiries are welcome, and long lists of unsolved problems are available on request.

6 Naïve Foundations for a Theory of Mathematics Learning

ROBERT B. DAVIS

Professor Robert B. Davis, founder and director of the Madison Project, entered M.I.T. as a freshman in June 1944 and received a bachelor's degree in mathematics in September 1964. Graduating with an M.A. (1948) and a Ph.D. (1951) from the same university, Davis started to express an interest in the psychology of learning and teaching mathematics. After a distinguished involvement in the teaching and applying of pure and applied mathematics, Professor Davis joined the mathematics and education faculty at Syracuse University in 1956 and became a full professor in 1965. On leave from Syracuse University, he went to Webster College, where he created an entirely new undergraduate mathematics program for prospective mathematics teachers at either the elementary or the secondary school level, after working for a year with the School Mathematics Study Group at Yale University.

His greatest contribution to mathematical education in the United States, however, is his creation and establishment of the Madison Project–a project named after his first experimental school in Syracuse. He assumed directorship of the Project in 1957. Professor Davis developed curriculum material by working directly with embryonic ideas in classrooms with children. He gave children an opportunity for the first time to help develop a project's materials. This led him to produce a vast number of films on both what to do in a mathematical environment and how to do it. Involved in a variety of innovative endeavors all directed toward the question of how mathematical content is related to activities that can be used with elementary school children, he has helped improve mathematics programs from New York to California.

Currently, one of Professor Davis's wishes is that his own college teaching will give him an opportunity to develop some college undergraduate courses in mathematics for prospective teachers. These courses would combine mathematical content with those curricular innovations essential to effective pedagogy at the elementary school level.

In the following paper, Dr. Davis gives his views on how several naïve notions, each corresponding to a possible use of human mental data processing, could be selected as the starting point for the study of mathematics learning. He proposes a basic paradigm that, with subsequent use of analogy and extension, more closely corresponds to thought typical of mathematics.

From the diversity of naïve views in mathematics learning, Davis proposes the idea of a "basic paradigmatic experience" as the foundation for an alternate theory. He concentrates on a description of this overlooked concept of "learning through doing," and discusses its initial and subsequent uses as well as its implications for curriculum, classroom teaching, testing, and learning theory itself.

While the basic paradigm offers a more complex starting point in mathematics learning than that of the stimulus-response bond, Davis feels that allowing the learner active involvement creates a more meaningful educational experience. He states that a good deal of meaning is transmitted through the experience (or activity) itself.

In presenting examples of paradigmatic experiences, Davis illustrates the difficulties involved in designing experiences that strictly parallel mathematical concepts, fit the level of sophistication of the students, and still retain the qualities of being active and dramatic.

This paper does not attempt to build the learning theory based on paradigmatic experience, but it provides a rationale for its foundation. That rationale is best summarized in this Chinese motto: "I hear, and I forget; I see, and I remember; I do, and I understand!"

The process of acquiring mathematical ideas is coming to receive more extensive and more penetrating study than ever before. It is this process rather than mathematics itself that will be discussed here, and when we search for "concepts" we shall mean concepts that will help us understand how the human mind thinks about mathematics. In that sense we are not talking about mathematics, but about human mental data processing.

To pursue this study we shall need certain basic ideas. By way of illustration, the study of physics became fruitful only as certain ideas were developed—ideas such as energy, velocity, acceleration, and so on.

Where can we get the corresponding ideas for the study of mathematics learning? Most of the refined ideas of any science have similar histories: they begin as intuitive, naïve, or primitive ideas, and are gradually refined. This already appears to be the case in the study of mathematics learning. That suggests that considerable importance should be attached to the collection of "naïve" ideas from which mathematics starts.

In particular, I wish here to suggest a new candidate that has been largely overlooked in the past—what shall be called "the basic paradigm," with subsequent use of analogy and extension.

I. WHY ARE NAÏVE SOURCE-IDEAS IMPORTANT?

To a great extent, this question answers itself. When we start from different naïve ideas, we proceed to develop different sophisticated (or "scientific") theories. Thomas Kuhn shows this clearly in the case of early notions of electricity. Those investigators who thought of electricity as "something that flows" developed appropriate experiments, and refined their ideas of current, potential, and so on (55). At the same time, other investigators thought of electricity as a force that repelled or attracted, and developed quite a different set of experiments as they refined their own different "naïve" ideas into the more sophisticated notions that we usually call science. (Indeed, the larger importance of Benjamin Franklin's famous kite experiment is usually overlooked in the drama of crashing thunder and flashing lightning. The deeper importance of this experiment was that it served to establish a crucial relation between the view of electricity as "something that flows" and the alternative views in terms of attraction and repulsion.)

In the case of mathematics learning, we have, as we would expect, a diversity of naïve views from which we can start out. We can start with stimulus-response notions, as in the use of flash cards to teach addition facts (such as $3 + 2 = 5$). In this case, it is clear that such an approach—essentially a rote approach—will fail to develop the kind of understanding necessary for the learner to handle problems in the form $3 + \Box = 5$ or $\Box + 4 = 7$, and empirical evidence supports this theoretically clear conclusion. We can start with the idea that the child develops abstract symbols that he can manipulate mentally in ways that parallel possible physical acts. For example, can you look at this flat paper figure and "fold" it mentally into a three-dimensional closed solid?

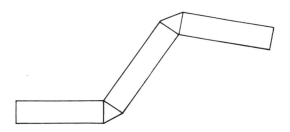

What solid shape do you get? Which edge joins onto which other edge? As a second example, if ⠇ is an odd number of dots, and if .⠇⠇ is also an odd number of dots, can you see by a kind of mental visualization that the sum will be an even number of dots. Does your "proof by visualization" seem to generalize, so as to apply to the sum of any two odd numbers?[1]

We can start with naïve notions of learning to follow verbal directions. We might say, "If a vector is represented by an ordered pair of numbers, we can find the sum of two vectors by adding the first number in each pair to get the first number in the answer, and adding the last number from each pair to get the last number in the answer." Such explicit verbal instructions would probably be followed by practice in applying this rule to several specific examples. We could call this the "verbal rule followed by examples and drill" approach.

Each of these naïve notions certainly does correspond to a possible use of human mental data-processing capabilities. But are we getting reasonably close to the kind of thought that is most typical of mathematics?

Without proposing anything approaching a complete catalogue of naïve ideas—a wildly ambitious undertaking at this point—I want to call attention to one specific point of departure that is usually overlooked.

II. THE IDEA OF "BASIC PARADIGMS" AS A STARTING POINT IN LEARNING MATHEMATICS

Suppose we want a child (in grade 2, 3, or 4, for example) to develop the necessary ideas to solve the problem $3 - 5$ by writing $3 - 5 = {}^-2$, or by saying "three minus five is negative two." A method for accomplishing this has been developed and shown to be reliable. It goes like this:

A. We arrange our "apparatus"—a bag, containing 30 or 40 pebbles ("infinitely many," as far as anticipated demands are concerned), together with an additional 30 or 40 pebbles lying loose on the table.

B. We establish a clearly defined starting point in time, for example by having Laura clap her hands and say "Go!"

---

1. Primarily, this applies to children learning mathematics at the precollege level, but the discussion applies to mathematical thought at any level. Notions strikingly similar to these can be seen (in action, as it were) at the level of professional mathematicians in the following article: H.L. Alder, "Partition Identities—from Edler to the Present," *The American Mathematical Monthly*, 76, 7 (August-September 1969) pp. 733–45.

C. We take 3 loose pebbles from the table and put them into the bag, writing 3 on the blackboard. We agree that there are now three more pebbles in the bag than there were when Laura said "Go!"

D. We remove 5 pebbles from the bag, put them out loose on the table, and write 3 − 5 on the blackboard.

E. We ask "Are there more pebbles in the bag now than there were when Laura said 'Go,' or less?"

F. The children almost invariably will agree that there are fewer.

G. We ask, "How many less?"

H. Children will again almost invariably respond that there are 2 less.

I. We express this last fact by writing $3 - 5 = {}^-2$. This experience might be repeated two or three times, using different numbers. It constitutes what we mean by a "basic paradigm"—that is to say, whenever in the near future a child encounters a problem such as, say, $8 - 12 = \square$, we hope he will think about this as "putting 8 pebbles into the bag . . ." and so forth.[2]

How does a basic paradigm or paradigmatic experience differ from other approaches? How does it resemble them?

Well, first, from a more abstract mathematical point of view, we analyze the abstract foundation underlying the preceding paradigmatic experience as defining an integer by an equivalence class of ordered pairs of counting numbers:

$$^-2 = \ (0, 2), (1, 3), (2, 4), (3, 5), \ldots \ .$$

This analysis is quite different from the actual classroom experience. We have not, indeed, attempted to communicate the idea to a second-grade child by a concatenation of abstract notions such as "equivalence class" or "ordered pair," and so on. Instead, we have provided an active and reasonably tangible *experience* for the child. We have led him into doing something. Thereafter, we can refer back to this shared experience, much as one might say, "Remember that big animal with the huge snoutlike thing on his face that we saw when we went to the zoo?"

Clearly, arranging for the child to participate in a paradigmatic experience is quite forcefully made in the British film *I Do . . . and I Understand*,[3] which takes its title from an ancient Chinese motto: "I hear, and I forget; I see, and I remember; I do, and I understand!"

Something akin to paradigmatic experience has been well known for a long time, but has been little discussed in education. Elsewhere the idea seems much less novel. Frank McGee of NBC News recently commented that in creative writing "your reader will never believe what you *tell* him, but he will always believe what you *show* him." There is a vast collection of illustrative

---

2. This method, in actual use with second-grade children, can be observed in the film *A Lesson with Second Graders* (available from the Madison Project, 915 Irving Avenue, Syracuse, N.Y. 13210.) Cf. also Robert B. Davis, *Explorations in Mathematics: A Text for Teachers*, chapter 4 (Addison-Wesley, 1967).

3. Available from Radim Films, 211 E. 43rd St., New York, N.Y. 10017.

examples testifying to the power of giving the learner the most active possible involvement, in as dramatically clear a form as one can arrange. Karl Menninger's book, *The Crime of Punishment* (Viking Press, 1968), might be cited as one very compelling example: Menninger shows us things that would leave us unmoved if he merely told them more abstractly. (An abundance of other examples are available, including television coverage of the war in Vietnam and the Democratic convention in Chicago.) If this active, direct, deep involvement in something dramatically clear is actually as important as it seems, then the fact that educational practice in the United States has been allowed to drift away from experience and toward abstract "telling" must reflect some failure somewhere, very possibly in our methods of studying education. Are our testing procedures unable to detect the deeper emotional impact of experience over telling? Are we unable to recognize the "understanding" to which the ancient Chinese referred, despite the fact that perceptive teachers today who themselves possess this understanding usually do believe that they can recognize it in their students when it is present? If the force of showing has been lost on educators, it has not been lost on those who write, make movies, or produce television programing—and certainly not on those who make television commercials. From the point of view of a science of thought, it may be especially relevant to observe that, if we build a concept in a child's mind by causing him to participate in a paradigmatic experience, the meaning of what has happened is drawn from the experience itself, modulated by the child's preexisting cognitive awareness.

This is probably true of meaning much more generally. For example, the very young child waving goodbye to a departing parent is probably behaving by imitation of the adults who wave, but this experience provides its own small increment to what it means to wave goodbye, or to what it means to say farewell to someone. Obviously, meaning does not come exclusively from experience (in any sense of outwardly observable behavior), for the adult mathematician can "experience" the discovery of a new meaning as a result of mental activity that is totally unaccompanied by outwardly observable behavior. Nonetheless, the importance of behavior—that is to say, of actually "doing something actively"—may partly explain why telling something to an attentive listener is often so much more effective than merely thinking of it when one is alone (a mystery that is sharply apparent in, for example, psychoanalytic therapy).

A paradigmatic experience, as we are using the term, will often be active, dramatic, and memorable, but we mistake the nature of paradigmatic experiences if we think they are merely this. They must also be carefully designed to be an accurate paradigm (in the usual sense of the word *paradigm*) for the notion they are intended to establish in the learner's mind. Many teaching attempts in schools fail, by our criterion, precisely because they are not accurate exemplars of the central underlying notion. Accuracy and relevance are as important as experience and dramatic emphasis. Although we have in mind a procedure for helping a child learn mathematical ideas, there are striking parallels with other forms of human thought. For example, both in accuracy and in dramatic impact, a paradigmatic experience seems to be very much like the vignettes, or parables, by which the Bible seeks to teach specific points. Indeed, the Greeks appear to have had several words for the very idea we have in mind. (See *Webster's Third New International Dictionary*, for the definition of *parable*, which refers to its origin in the ideas of "juxta-position," "comparison," "superposition," and "setting alongside.")

III. THE FLEXIBLE SUBSEQUENT USE OF BASIC PARADIGMS

From a classroom point of view, the precision of a paradigmatic experience is of central importance. The interest shifts somewhat when we consider para-digmatic experiences from a theoretical point of view.

Giving the child a vivid experience is not particularly mysterious. Thus we can relatively easily accept the theoretical idea of establishing or learning a paradigm. What is considerably more complex, it would seem, is the flexible subsequent use of a paradigm.

In the case of the "pebbles-in-the-bag" model for introducing signed numbers, we do not require the same numbers—3, 5, ⁻2—on subsequent use. Paradigms are used metaphorically, by analogy, and by extension. Even quite drastic modifications of paradigms are possible, in fact commonplace, as Michael Polanyi demonstrates in *Personal Knowledge* (71). If we see

$$13 - 14 = \square,$$

we can interpret this readily, even if we have never seen this particular pat-tern of numbers before.[4] One could argue rather convincingly that the mathematical concept of "variable" is an inherent part of human mental data processing, and makes possible the adaptive metaphoric use of a paradigm. In different lines of work, variables are indicated variously, but the meaning is essentially the same, whether the variable is designated "John Doe," "Richard Roe," "line 21" (as in "Subtract line 21 from line 12 and record the differ-ence here"), "NAMEREQUEST," or even "Judas" or "Quisling." In fact, the mind even accepts the number 3 as a variable. A Los Angeles teacher, dis-cussing $\square + 3 = 3 + \square$, commented "That 3 doesn't have to be a 3," and ulti-mately wrote $\square + \triangle = \triangle + \square$. The phrase "That 3 doesn't have to be a 3," which is quoted here verbatim, is surely one of the most provocative instances of an implicit use of the concept of variable that one is likely to encounter. In somewhat the same fashion, primes work quite nicely as variables for many multiplicative arithmetic problems, and provide an effective means of com-municating generality to young children without the need for special nota-tional conventions.

---

4. This is, of course, mainly a different conceptualization of at least part of what is ordinarily called "transfer of training." See Stephen S. Willoughby, *Contemporary Teaching of Secondary School Mathematics* (106).

IV. THE CONCEPT OF "FUNCTION" PRESENTED VIA A PARADIGMATIC EXPERIENCE

Consider this teacher-class discussion:

Teacher:	All right. Now, Bill and John will make up a rule—like, whatever number we tell them they'll double it and add one and tell us the answer. They won't tell us their rule; it's our job to guess what their rule is. What number do you want to tell them?
Class:	5
Teacher:	(*To Bill and John*) O.K. Use your rule on 5 and tell us the answer.
Bill/John:	24
Teacher:	(*Starts recording the results on the blackboard, as a table*) If we tell them 5, . . .

Teacher writes:

□	△
5	

they tell us 24.

□	△
5	24

I'll use □ for the number we tell them, and △ for the number they say back to us. What number do you want to tell them next?

Class:	6
Teacher:	(*To Bill and John*) Use your rule on 6, and tell us the answer.
Bill/John:	35
Teacher:	If we tell them 6, . . .

Teacher writes:

□	△
5	24
6	

they respond by telling us 35.

□	△
5	24
6	35

Does anyone know their rule?

Class: Try 0.
Teacher: (*To Bill and John*) Use your rule on zero, please, and tell us the answer.
Bill/John: Negative one.
Nancy: Oh! I know! Whatever number we tell them, they square it, subtract one, and tell us the answer.
Teacher: (*To Bill and John*) Is that right?
Bill/John: Yes.
Teacher: (*To Nancy*) Can you write that rule, in the □ and △ notation?
Nancy writes: $(\square \times \square) - 1 = \triangle$ [5]

Much could be said about this example from the point of view of a classroom teacher, or by consideration of the mathematical ideas involved. We do not do that here, since our present interest is in looking at the *experience* the class has just shared—a paradigmatic experience in the sense of our present remarks (16).

Again, once this paradigm has been experienced, it can be used flexibly in the future. A child who has been through this sort of game a few times can understand other functions, tables, and formulas by referring back to this original paradigm. Extensive trials have demonstrated that paradigmatic experiences allow quite young children to get a firm hold on such mathematical notions as negative numbers, variables, functions, graphs, implication, contradiction, uniqueness, matrix multiplication, logical proofs (in various forms), the extension of mathematical systems, and so on (17) (25).

Evidence is in (more than 120 hours of actual classroom lessons have been recorded on film and can be viewed in detail) that shows unequivocally that children in grades two through six (ages seven to eleven) can learn mathematics usually associated with high school and college (ages fourteen to twenty), provided that certain school (and community) conditions can be maintained. A central condition is probably the use of paradigmatic experiences to establish new mathematical ideas.

V. HAVE WE SAID ANYTHING OF VALUE?

Does the notion of paradigmatic experiences add anything to our understanding of how children learn mathematical ideas? Obviously, if this method of establishing concepts can be found in the Bible and in writings of the ancient Greeks, it cannot be called new, even though we may have lost sight of it somewhat in recent years. The notion that human thought is made up

---

5. This game of "What's My Rule" can be observed in an actual classroom lesson with (alledgedly) culturally-deprived children (grades 6 and 7) in the film *Guessing Functions* (available from the Madison Project, 918 Irving Ave., Syracuse, N.Y. 13210).

of some sort of "elementary-particle" things as small as a single stimulus-response bond has a certain simplistic appeal that is lacking in a complex notion like the paradigmatic experience. Can paradigmatic experiences, nonetheless, serve as valuable naïve ideas from which we can build a more sophisticated description of human thought? I believe that they can, and that examples can be found in mathematics and elsewhere. (Notice, for example, how family life, seen through the eyes of a child, seems to become the paradigmatic foundation for the metaphoric rhetoric of most adult religions: "Our Father . . . .")

Implications for Curriculum

A large amount of mathematics can be taught pleasantly, interestingly, and effectively to quite young children through an appropriate use of paradigmatic experiences to establish new mathematical ideas. By contrast, the present curriculum seems almost incredibly slow and inefficient, primarily because it is wedded to less powerful interpretations of the nature of learning and consequently relies upon less powerful kinds of learning experiences.

Implications for Classroom Teaching

There is a world of difference at the practical classroom level between a paradigmatic presentation and, say, teaching addition facts under the direction of a stimulus-response theory, such as the rote use of flash cards. The stimulus "3 + 4 =" is intended to evoke, as quickly as possible, the response "7"—which the teacher may emphasize by showing, on the reverse side of the flash card, the complete equation "3 + 4 = 7."

In contrast to the preceding classroom procedure, probably based on S-R theory, a paradigmatic presentation of addition might be something like this. First, the teacher seeks some dramatic activity that offers a precise parallel with the concept of addition. We suggest here two possible candidates, and will be grateful for better ideas if anyone has any.

A Discrete Model: An empty bag is held by Mary. John picks up three pebbles. Alice picks up four pebbles. John dumps his three pebbles into the bag, while the class counts "one, two, three." The teacher might record this by writing 3 on the blackboard.

Now Alice drops her four pebbles into the bag, while the class counts "one, two, three, four." The teacher may record this on the blackboard by writing

3 + 4.

The question (which the teacher might emphasize by writing 3 + 4 =) is, obviously: How many pebbles are there now in the bag? This can be settled by having some child count the pebbles in the bag. The teacher might then write on the blackboard: 3 + 4 = 7.

If this model were used, it would give dramatic emphasis. It could also be modified to cope with □ + 2 = 7, as follows: The teacher would pick up five pebbles and show them privately to one or two children. The children would secretly record the 5 for future reference (perhaps by writing 5 on a piece of paper and hiding it away in a special drawer).

A child would now add two pebbles to the bag. The teacher would record, say,

$$\underline{\hspace{2cm}} + 2 =$$
$$\uparrow$$
Secret Number

and the number of pebbles in the bag would be determined by counting. The teacher would record this result by writing

$$\underline{\hspace{2cm}} + 2 = 7.$$
$$\uparrow$$
Secret Number

The other members of the class would try to decide how many pebbles the teacher had originally put into the bag. When the children were ready to test their conclusions, this would be done in either (or, preferably, both) of two ways: (1) by referring to the hidden paper on which 5 had been written, or (2) by repeating the entire process, but this time beginning with the number the class has decided on, to see if you do in fact end up with seven pebbles in the bag.

A Continuous Model. A fairly obvious adaptation of this can be made, so as to get to continuous representations of numbers instead of discrete representations. The idea is to "add lengths" by placing wooden sticks end to end. One could use Cuisenaire rods, Stern rods, or rods made by the teacher. Here, too, one would deal almost simultaneously with the three problem types:

$$3 + 5 = \square$$
$$3 + \square = 6$$
$$\square + 3 = 9$$

Implications for Testing

If a paradigm strategy is used, the testing program should determine whether the child is familiar with the simple basic paradigm example, and then whether he can adapt it to the demands of analogous situations.

Implications for the Study of Human Mental Data Processing

The implications here may require more thought, but they almost certainly include the role of variables as they are used, metaphorically, in human thought. One is, in effect, concerned with the phenomenology of analogy. When we read the novel *Fail-Safe*, do we recognize a fictional portrait of John Kennedy? What specific data-processing procedures allow this? Deletion of some attributes in determining equivalence? (That is, if object A has attributes

A_i for $i = 1, \ldots, N$, and if object B has attributes B_i for $i = 1, \ldots, M$, then we might consider "deletion equivalence" as: A is equivalent to B, mod K, if $A_i = B_i$ for $i = 1, \ldots, K$, where $K \leqq N$, $K \leqq M$, the real relevance lying in cases where $K < N$ and $K < M$.) Association by opposites? (With the same notation, allow $A_i = \sim B_i$ for some values of i—that is, a tall man is pictured as short, and so forth.)

VI. SOME CONCLUDING EXAMPLES.

Quite aside from theories of human data processing or from curricular matters, there is a wealth of important pedagogical detail involved in selecting or creating really appropriate paradigms. An example would be the paradigm for binary operations on signed numbers (that is, technically, on integers—positive, negative, and zero). Many curriculum-revision projects have struggled with this and come up with different models or paradigms. Max Beberman's UICSM group developed the well-known device of a motion-picture projector showing a tank of water filling or emptying. In this model, a product of negative numbers corresponds to emptying the tank in reality, but running the projector backward when showing this. Objections to this model include the fact that it relies upon what is essentially the usual calculus notion of related rates, thereby injecting complications that need not be inherent in work with signed numbers.

Another model has made use of a magician who does certain "magical" things. We consider this model unacceptable because it is so essentially arbitrary. The structure of the "story line" does not induce a corresponding reasonable structure for the mathematical ideas. After all, why can't the magician make any response whatsoever? His actual responses in the story show no clear rationale.

Our own choice is the "postman story" model. This is not original; it has been used by teachers in upstate New York (and probably elsewhere) for decades. The postman handles "bills" and "checks," and he can deliver these or take them away. This model, also, has been criticized by adults, but works very well indeed with children. It has been considerably improved by Miss Katie Reynolds, an elementary school mathematics specialist in the Banneker District in St. Louis (17).

The major complications in the postman model are avoiding double-counting—that is to say, getting a paradigm that is strictly isomorphic to the actual mathematical ideas—and accommodating the level of sophistication of the children. Double-counting is avoided by introducing the postman's act of "taking away" as a matter of error correction: he rectifies an earlier error. For the rest, the precise isomorphism is obtained by using the recipient's (the "housewife's") *estimate* of her available reserve funds as the amount of money to be considered, and by focusing attention on a specific visit by the postman (that is, on what change in the housewife's estimate must be made because of the postman's visit this morning). All of these matters are fully described in Davis's *Explorations* (17).

The Madison Project made extensive trials with children on the question of developing the arithmetical operations for integers (positive, negative, and zero). Generally, three approaches were tried: first, extension of patterns, extension of definitions, or extension of systems (much the kind of idea that is involved in *analytic continuation* or in Abelian summation of divergent infinite series); second, an axiomatic approach; and, finally, an approach via models, or paradigms. Classes from grades four through ten (and some college classes) have been involved. Every class has shown an overwhelming preference for the model, or paradigm, approach (79).

A film, available from the Madison Project, shows the same class of children considering the product $^-1 \times {}^-1$ in three different ways. (The title of this film is *Three Approaches to Signed Numbers.*)

The axiomatic approach is the usual one taken. After sums and differences have been established, and after products where at least one factor is nonnegative have been established, we are left with the traditional "hard" case: the product of two negative numbers. However, we have the *distributive law*:

$$\square \times (\triangle + \triangledown) = (\square \times \triangle) + (\square \times \triangledown)$$

and suitable replacement of variables settles this one remaining case. If we make replacements as follows,

$$^-1 \to \square$$
$$^-1 \to \triangle$$
$$^+1 \to \triangledown$$

the result is $^-1 \times (^-1 + {}^+1) = (^-1 \times {}^-1) + (^-1 \times {}^+1)$, which, because of cases settled earlier, gives us

$$^-1 \times 0 = (^-1 \times {}^-1) + {}^-1$$
$$0 = (^-1 \times {}^-1) + {}^-1,$$

but we know that the open sentence

$$0 = \square + {}^-1$$

has the truth set $\{{}^+1\}$, so that we must have

$$^-1 \times {}^-1 = {}^+1.$$

(This impresses me as both elegant and conclusive; in our trials it has not really impressed most ninth-graders, or, for that matter, most other children, though it probably works best at around the fifth-grade level. Time and again in our experimentation we have been impressed by the fact that fifth-graders are natural mathematicians.)

There are many "extension-of-patterns" or "extension-of-systems" approaches. In our trials we have used one suggested by Paul Rosenbloom. By inductive inference from repeated trials, we decide that the graph of the function $(\square \times n) = \triangle$ has a slope pattern of "over one to the right, and up n," where n is a positive integer and we use positive integer values for $\square$ and $\triangle$. In particular, then, if we call this f_n $(\square)$, we have f_n (m) located as "over n to the right, and up $n \times m$"—that is, it is the point $(n, n \times m)$.

Now we have a method for locating the point f_n (m) on a graph that does not necessarily depend on multiplication; in fact, we can locate the point by the counting method just indicated. Consequently, we do use this method, and proclaim it as our definition of multiplication.

As in the axiomatic approach, we now proceed to consider first the easier cases. We make graphs of f_n (m) for $n > 0$, $m < 0$, and also for the case where $n < 0$, $m > 0$. We notice that all graphs of this type consist of a linear pattern of points. We proclaim the extension of this linear pattern. This now defines f_n (m) for $n < 0$, $m < 0$, and thereby defines f_{-1} $(^-1)$ as $^+1$. (Personally, I think this is elegant, but ninth graders can either take it or leave it and seem generally to prefer the second alternative.)

The third approach shown on the film *Three Approaches to Signed Numbers* is, of course, the "postman stories" method. As usual, this method wins with the children.

Matrices for Young Children

Finally, we present a paradigmatic experience suggested by Gerald Thompson, coauthor (with Kemeny and Snell) of the well-known *Introduction to Finite Mathematics*. Our goal is to introduce matrix multiplication to, say, ten- or eleven-year-old children, or, for that matter, to older children as well.

We have a candy store that sells chocolate almond bars for 10 cents each, peppermints for 2 cents each, and chocolate-covered ants for 50 cents a box. We summarize this data by a price vector, which we write as a column vector:

$$\begin{pmatrix} 10 \\ 2 \\ 50 \end{pmatrix}$$

John goes into the store, and buys three chocolate almond bars, seven peppermints, and zero boxes of chocolate-covered ants. We summarize this by a demand vector, which we write as a row vector:

$$(3 \quad 7 \quad 0)$$

Together, we have

$$(3 \quad 7 \quad 0) \quad \begin{pmatrix} 10 \\ 2 \\ 50 \end{pmatrix}$$

which we have written in the traditional form for the product of a covariant vector and a contravariant vector, as the reader has undoubtedly observed.

The teacher now asks the students how much money John spends: "Work the problem out, don't just show me the answer." The result (almost always) is

$$(3 \quad 7 \quad 0) \begin{pmatrix} 10 \\ 2 \\ 50 \end{pmatrix} = (3 \times 10) + (7 \times 2) + (0 \times 50)$$

$$= 30 + 14 + 0$$

$$= 44$$

What is needed here, of course, is dramatic emphasis. Crashing cymbals and blaring trumpets would be dandy, but it is quicker if the teacher just shouts: "Congratulations! You have just correctly computed the inner product of a covariant and a contravariant vector!"

It may not sound credible on paper, but with children it works. One can proceed from here to develop a considerable amount of matrix algebra, if one wishes, with fifth- or sixth-grade children, as shown in several films available from the Madison Project.[6]

VII. FINALE

There is nowadays a new interest in the more serious study of how children learn mathematics. This can be valuable and can go far beyond the demands of mathematics alone. School can become more fun for children, as the British have shown, at the same time that it becomes more profitable.

In the past decade a considerable amount of interesting and even profound work has been done in school mathematics, but this work has generally been badly misunderstood. The diversity of approaches has passed unnoticed, so that quite dissimilar and even irreconcilable innovations have been lumped together and known as "the new math." Considerable attention has been focused on discovery, although the large amount of attention has not been matched by equally great penetration and subtlety. Other pedagogical aspects of the innovative work have passed largely unnoticed, or at least unremarked upon.

Hopefully, this new seriousness of purpose may carry us into deeper matters than "new math" and "discovery." Probably the notion of the paradigmatic experience as a powerful learning experience—and as an alternative to other kinds of learning experiences—is at best only one small step forward. But one small step can be very important.

---

6. See, for example, the films *Matrices, Solving Equations With Matrices,* and *Complex Numbers Via Matrices.*

7 Some Aspects of Learning and Teaching Modern Mathematics

*A native of Portsmouth, Virginia, Professor Paul C.
Rosenbloom obtained his undergraduate education at
the University of Pennsylvania and his doctorate in
mathematics at Stanford University in 1944. He has
been a member of the faculties of Stanford, Brown,
Syracuse, and Minnesota. He is the recipient of many
honors, of which a Guggenheim fellowship (1947) and
the Frechet prize by the Mathematical Society of
France (1950) are notable examples. Professor Rosenbloom founded the Minnesota Mathematics and
Science Teaching Project (Minnemast) in 1961 and
acted as its director until 1965. The project, the goals
of which were to produce coordinated mathematics
and science curricula for kindergarten through sixth
grade and to organize materials for in-service education of teachers, was one of his most distinguished
contributions toward improving the mathematics and
science education of both students and teachers at
the elementary school level.*

*Concerned with the identification of the most mean-
ingful and efficient objectives of mathematics education, Professor Rosenbloom presents some interesting and significant thoughts on how to generate
those mathematical learning experiences that present
mathematics as a science, as a language, and as an art.*

*This paper is concerned with mathematics as an art—
that is, with* doing *mathematics. For him the essence
of doing and learning mathematics involves insight.
Because insightful behavior has seemed unpredictable,
unreproducible, and accidental, little scientific investigation has been made of this phenomenon. However,
Rosenbloom has accumulated a repertoire of insightful performances that can be evoked at will with*

PAUL C. ROSENBLOOM

*large classes of subjects. These paradigms can be used
for scientific investigation of insight in terms of defined overt behavior. Hence, the intent of the paper is
to stimulate further study in order to discover the
conditions and the individual factors necessary for
insightful learning. More specifically the author encourages studies of the assimilation of scientific
method and the ability of the student to pose problems and investigate them on his own.*

Although the sixties offered a variety of innovative projects and sometimes
unusual and exciting experimental programs for mathematics teaching and
learning, the seventies seem still to be faced with the dilemma of defining the
most meaningful and efficient objectives of mathematics education. With the
creation and the development of several new branches of mathematics as well
as new applications of mathematics, the functions of a mathematics curriculum
seem to be dependent, more than ever before, on how we organize mathematical learning experiences and on how we perceive the nature of mathematics
and its related pedagogy.

I. THE FUNCTIONS OF THE MATHEMATICS CURRICULUM

The development of the objectives of mathematics education is a complicated
and complex process. The identification of those objectives that give tribute
to the recognition of the importance and the relevance of mathematics to the
individual and to society is a difficult task for several reasons. On the one
hand, certain objectives are based on the nature of mathematics. It is a science, an art, and a language. A curriculum that does not attempt to present
this threefold nature of mathematics is unsound. The balance among these
aspects in any course within the curriculum is, to a large extent, a matter of
taste. On the other hand, some of the objectives are cognitive. We want a
child to be able to compute, and an adult to be able to translate simple problems into mathematical language. Some of the aims are affective. We want a
child to learn that mathematics can be fun, and that it can be beautiful. We
want a citizen to feel that he benefits by a social investment in mathematics.
However, some objectives are individual. A person should learn the mathematics he needs for the vocation he chooses. Some objectives are social. We
need to produce a supply of people with the distribution of mathematical
competencies and interests required in the various trades and professions.

In the school mathematics curriculum we aim to teach certain organized
bodies of knowledge about numbers and space, and a certain way of organizing any body of knowledge. The sciences organized in this way are called
deductive sciences. These are the finished products of mathematics.

We also aim to teach mathematics in the making—the art of creating and applying mathematics. We aim to teach the language of mathematics, and the process of reading, writing, and translating from and into English.

In the conventional curriculum, arithmetic and algebra are presented as practical arts. Some attempt is made to present geometry as a science. Until about 1920–1930, some attempt was made, in the presentation of "originals" in geometry, to teach the art of mathematics. A reasonable attempt is made to teach mathematical language.

These are objectives based on *what mathematics is.* They can be analyzed systematically in the ways suggested in *Bloom's Taxonomy* (6).

Other objectives are based on *why mathematics is taught.* In our rapidly changing society, mathematics is the primary vehicle for teaching one of the two principal methods of obtaining new knowledge first-hand—the method of deductive reasoning. (The other is the method of inductive reasoning.) Mathematics also plays an important role in the main second-hand way of acquiring new knowledge—reading and listening—since it is the language in which the literature of most fields of knowledge is now written.

While deductive reasoning is taught in the curriculum primarily in mathematical contexts, it is probably not important for most students to be able to deduce new mathematical knowledge from what they know. It is important for most students to be able to carry out simple reasoning processes in non-mathematical contexts. Brownell's classical experiment (7) on the teaching of subtraction illustrates the value of teaching simple reasoning processes in mathematics.

Mathematics is also taught because it is now essential to all sorts of people: bakers, electricians, farmers, linguists, engineers, economists, and even psychologists. To find out whether we have achieved the objective of preparing the population for its diverse vocations, we must test not only achievement but also perception of the relation between mathematics and career choices and motivation to acquire the necessary knowledge.

We teach the other arts in order to help people fulfill themselves by perceiving beauty in various forms and media. The steady popularity of mathematical recreations indicates that the art of mathematics can contribute to self-fulfillment for a much higher proportion of the population than is usually realized.

Another objective is education for citizenship in a society where 80 percent of the bills before Congress involve science and mathematics. This involves the perception of the relation between public policies, scientific research, and education, the understanding of the difference between science and technology, and an understanding of the nature of evidence. It involves also a perception of the citizen's role in social decision making.

The most controversial issue, from the point of view of the mathematician, is the balance between logic and intuition in the mathematics curriculum. Essentially, it is a question of the relative emphasis on mathematics as a science and mathematics as an art. A mathematical truth is established by logical reasoning. A deductive science is built up as a chain of theorems and definitions starting with assumptions and undefined terms. The content of mathematics consists of bodies of knowledge organized in this way. This gives mathematics a coherent intellectual structure, in contrast to a mass of isolated propositions and skills. Certainly an ultimate objective is to impart this structure to students.

While this is the final product of mathematical work, it is not the way one does mathematics. Mathematical work consists largely of observation and experiment, guessing at what might be true, feeling what ought to be true, testing hypotheses, looking for analogies, building mental pictures, and trying out ideas without any certainty of success. At an elementary level one would want a child to feel that $1/67823.5$ is a small number, even if he cannot calculate it to seven decimal places, or that the error in calculating the area of a rectangle is small if the errors in measuring the sides are small, even if he cannot estimate the error rigorously. The most complete analysis of the cognitive processes involved is given in the writings of Polya (72). The few references to his work in the psychological literature show a deplorable lack of understanding.

The question of the proper relative emphasis on these different objectives is to a large extent a matter of taste. *However, we are only giving lip service to objectives unless we try to find out whether we can achieve them.* Let me illustrate what I conceive to be the essence of mathematical learning and how one can successfully attain this goal.

II. INSIGHTFUL LEARNING IN MATHEMATICS

I shall not attempt here to define *insight*. In some respects the concept of insight is similar to that of revelation in religion. No amount of verbal explanation will convey the concept to someone who has not experienced it. We have heard descriptions of how it feels to attain insight. People remark on the suddenness, the "moment of illumination." After this moment of insight, the world doesn't look the same. We may have seen something all our lives, but now, and forever after, we *notice* it.

Poincaré, Hadamard, and Wallas, among others, have described some of the conditions under which insight occurs and is established. They all have analyzed the process into stages such as preparation, incubation, illumination, and verification or application. Polya has written extensively on the strategies for evoking or acquiring insights efficiently. There is still some confusion in the literature between the description of how people think insightfully and the recommendations concerning how people ought to think.

The scientific investigation of insight has suffered, by comparison with that of reflex behavior, because insightful behavior has seemed less predictable, less reproducible, and indeed often accidental. Since the acquisition of insight is an irreversible process and affects the subject's entire future behavior in relevant situations, its dynamical laws are not accessible to the same sort of investigation as lever pressing, maze running, and so forth. It may, however, be defined in concrete situations in terms of definite actions. The functional dependence of the behavior on the subject's characteristics and history can be determined, as well as the effects of the acquisition of insight on the subject's subsequent responses to certain stimuli.

In many cases the technique may be a modification of Piaget's clinical procedures, with more attention being given to measurement of the subject's traits before the experiment, to random selection of subjects from a well defined population, and to the presentation of a specific program of stimuli. Also, Piaget presents his subjects' responses at various stages of development with no data on the intervening experiences. He seems rarely, if ever, to have captured the moment of transition from one stage to another, or to have investigated the conditions that bring about the necessary insight.

In other cases, a group of human beings may be, for our purposes, regarded as a composite organism. We may sometimes be virtually certain that, say, a randomly selected class of thirty-five American thirteen-year-olds will have such a distribution of abilities that we shall obtain a certain response within an hour on presentation of certain stimuli. A problem in group communication and presentation of stimuli is allowing for differentiated responses to insure the spreading of the insight from a few to the rest.

It may be useful to build up a repertoire of insightful performances, with various degrees of complexity and kinds of logical structure, which may be evoked at will with large classes of subjects under conditions subject to experimental control. These may also supply samples of cognitive behavior in which the relation between stimulus and response is more natural and less *ad hoc* than that between pressing a lever and obtaining food. These paradigms of behavior thus provide materials for scientific investigation of insight in terms of clearly defined overt behavior.

The performances that I shall now describe are part of such a repertoire built up over a period of about four years. During the past year I have visited forty-six school systems. On each visit I have taught three or four classes ranging from sixth grade up, taking the children as they come in the school. Thus the subjects have only rarely been specially selected. In addition I have taught gifted youngsters from fifth grade up during the past four years, and have recently taught demonstration classes with second and third graders. Besides these experiences with groups, I have also experimented with the children of my friends on many social occasions. I have gradually developed for each item of this repertoire a sequence of stimuli, consisting primarily of questions and tasks with variations corresponding to alternative responses, and an associated pattern including digressions, jokes, and so forth. On the basis of my experiences, I can time and pace these lessons so that I know what responses I will evoke within an hour. My timing is rarely off by more than a few minutes.

The structure of mathematics that is considered in most studies on the psychology of mathematics is that of mathematics as a science—that is, as an organized body of knowledge. In this paper we are concerned with mathematics as an art—with mathematics in the making rather than mathematics as a finished product. Thus insightful behavior is related to *doing* mathematics. Other kinds of behavior are relevant to knowing mathematics.

III. PARADIGMS OF BEHAVIOR

1. My first example was conducted in a half-hour session with a class of bright second graders this summer and with about ten individuals ranging from grades one to five on social occasions. In this lesson I begin by telling about a country called Lower Slobbovia where the people are called Slobs. Instead of nickels, dimes, and quarters, the Slobs have only pennies and two-cent pieces. How many ways can a Slob make 5 cents into change?

The response of 5 pennies is usually almost immediate. If there is any hesitation, I then ask, "Can you think of any other way?" The response is always 2 two-cent pieces and 1 penny. I ask, "Is there still another way?" If after a little while there is no response, I ask, "Could you change a two-cent piece into pennies?" Then I get the response of 1 two-cent piece and 3 pennies. I then ask whether there are any other ways. We then list the ways like this:

5¢

Pennies	Two-cent Pieces
5	0
1	2
3	1

I ask whether it is easy to see from this arrangement whether there are any other ways or whether these are all of the possible ways. I point to the two-cent column and ask whether 2 is more or less than 0, and whether 1 is more or less than 2. We discuss whether a more systematic arrangement wouldn't be better. The child soon decides to arrange the observations with either increasing or decreasing numbers of two-cent pieces.

I next pose the question of how a Slob could make 6 cents into change. It is sometimes necessary to repeat the same questions as were used in the previous case. Sometimes it is sufficient to remind the child of the results and methods used before. Now I ask the child to make a table of the amounts of money, the ways, and the numbers of ways:

Amount	Ways				Number of Ways
5	(5, 0)	(3, 1)	(1, 2)		3
6	(6, 0)	(4, 1)	(2, 2)	(0, 3)	4
7					
8					
9					
10					

When the child is finished, I ask him to predict and verify the result for 11 cents. Then I direct his attention to the largest number of two-cent pieces used for each given amount of money. I ask him to tabulate these numbers in a fourth column. I ask for the reason for the relation he notices.

Then I ask for the number of ways of representing 20 cents and, with older children, 101 cents. So far I have always gotten the right answer.

I am still in the process of learning how to communicate with younger children, especially in the matter of giving directions. I should also like to experiment with concrete materials.

At my first opportunity for a follow-up study, I shall present the children with the problem of Upper Slobbovia, where the Snobs live. In this country there are one-, two-, and three-cent pieces. I should like to know whether there is any transfer of training in method, and whether the children are able to discover the more subtle pattern.

2. In visiting classes from fifth grade up, I often write on the board the numbers

$$3 \quad 5 \quad 7 \quad 11 \quad 13 \quad 17 \quad 19 \quad 23 \quad 29$$

and ask, "Why did I choose these numbers, and omit 9, 15, 21, 25, and 27? What is special about the numbers I chose?" Within a minute I obtain a response that these are prime numbers, whether the children are familiar with the concept or not. The answer may be phrased, "These numbers have no divisors." If so, then I ask, "Are you sure? Is 7 divisible by 1? Is 7 divisible by any other number?" It is interesting to note that the children usually do not mention the exceptions (1 and the number itself) unless I question them further. A frequent intermediate response is "5 goes into 25." I then ask, "Well, what about 21 and 27?"

I have performed this experiment with about fifty classes, and have never had to wait more than a minute for the correct response. I have not tried varying the length of the given sequence of primes. I usually check the attainment of the concept by asking, "What is the next number in the list?" I continue up to 41. The children often make mistakes on 33 and 39, but they correct themselves after the question "Are you sure? Why?"

3. In about a dozen classes ranging from fifth to seventh grade, I have begun by asking for the divisors of 12. I then arrange them in a diagram:

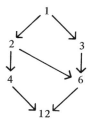

I explain that I connect *a* to *b* if *a* divides *b* but there is no other divisor *c* of 12 such that *a* divides *c* and *c* divides *b*. I then divide the class into groups and tell them to draw the "factor lattices" of different subsets of numbers from 2 to 30. During this time I walk about the room correcting mistakes like

Then I ask, "For which numbers does the factor lattice look like this?"

The children may give particular cases, but within 30 seconds someone identifies these numbers as primes, as in the previous example. If necessary, I give them the term *prime* and check their understanding of the concept.

Now I continue, "Which numbers have factor lattices like this?"

The children reply, "4, 9, and 25."

I ask, "What is special about these numbers?"

They answer, "They are squares," or "You get them by multiplying a number by itself."

I ask, "What about 16?"

They respond, "Oh, these numbers are squares of primes."

Then I ask, "What is the next one? Draw its factor lattice and check."

Now I introduce the abbreviations *p* for prime and p^2 for the square of a prime, and label these lattices:

I then ask, "Which numbers have factor lattices like this?"

We usually repeat the same pattern of questions and answers as before. Within a minute the children tell me that these numbers have the form p^3.

Now it is easy for the youngsters to discover the classes p^4 and p^5 for

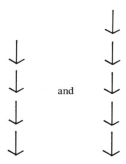

They also finally make the generalization, "The factor lattice is a straight chain only if the number is a power of a prime."

We then discuss the diagram

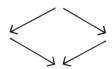

It is usually necessary to suggest that they factor the particular cases they find. They tell me that these numbers are the products of two primes.

I ask, "What about 4? Isn't $4 = 2 \cdot 2$ a product of two primes?"

They answer, "Oh, the primes have to be different."

Then I suggest the abbreviation $p.q.$ for the product of two distinct primes.

We then discuss 12, 18, and 20. By the end of the hour the pupils tell me that these have the form $p^2 .q$.

4. This lesson takes about half an hour with children from fifth to eighth grades. I have done this in about twenty-five classes.

I explain what a polygon is, and define a polygonal map as one in which the countries are polygons. Then I say that each pupil should draw five polygonal maps with no islands, and count the number of vertices, edges, and countries. The surrounding ocean is counted as a country. I work an example at the blackboard.

We then tabulate the results on the blackboard in three columns:

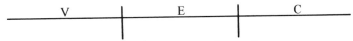

It is often necessary to correct the youngsters' counting.

In every case but one, by the time we came to the seventh map, someone announced Euler's revelation

$$V + C = 2 + E$$

in this or some equivalent form. On the way to this response they may also say that

$V + E + C$ is always even, or
$E \geqq V$, and $E \geqq C$

I answer, "That's pretty good, but there is still something more for you to discover."

In one case I found it necessary to have the children tabulate $V + C$ in a fourth column.

I have already described at the St. Louis conference my procedures for leading children to discover Fermat's theorem. I have used the technique involving only arithmetic in about eighty cases, and failed only twice to obtain the desired response within an hour. I have also used the technique involving algebra in about fifty ninth-grade classes with no failures within an hour.

IV. THE LOGICAL STRUCTURE

1. In those cases in which the children are led to discover something empirically, we are concerned with a certain propositional function—$F(x)$. My questions and tasks lead the children to find that

$$F(x), \text{ for } x = x_1, x_2, x_3, \text{ etc.}$$

where $x_1, x_2, x_3, \ldots$ are particular cases. The inference is from a certain number of special cases to this generalization: For all $x, F(x)$.

The psychological problem is to find the preparatory conditions and the factors of individual differences that affect the outcome. How do we put the subject in an "exploratory set"? How do we direct the gathering and arrangement of evidence so as to be most suggestive? How much time should be allowed for examination of evidence and mediation? How many special cases does a child of given intelligence, personality, and mathematical knowledge need before leaping to the generalization? How much verification and application is needed in order to establish confidence in the conclusion, and how should this activity be scheduled in order to fix the insight permanently? How much practice with simpler problems and how much explicit discussion of method is needed before the child learns how to investigate such problems independently, without the steps being laid out in advance by the program of questions and tasks? Are there measurable electrical or visceral phenomena associated with the moment of illumination?

With younger children (even up to sixth or seventh grade) a general abstract proof does not seem convincing or meaningful. The children do follow, and often enjoy, reasoning in terms of a particular case by methods that they recognize as perfectly general. Thus, when I ask why the number of ways that a Slob can make a given amount of money into change is one more than the largest number of two-cent pieces he can use for that amount, the child may reply, "For 6 cents the largest number of two-cent pieces is 3. There is one way of using 3 twos, another with 2 twos, another with 1 two, and another with no twos. There is one way for each number from 3 down to zero. The number of numbers from 1 to 3 is 3, and zero makes one more." The reasoning can be drawn from the children by breaking up the argument into steps and asking further questions. Children vary in their ability to give the reasoning, or part of it, spontaneously without this more detailed questioning.

In some cases the reasoning can be reduced to a scheme such as this: If p, then q; if q, then r; if r, then s; therefore, if p, then s. It is effective to record the first three steps at a particular place, separated from the rest of the work, as the children discover these propositions. Then one asks, "Suppose you know p. What conclusion can you draw?"

2. The same procedure works with mathematical induction. For example, with ninth-graders we have noticed that

$$(0^7 - 0 = 7 \cdot 0).$$
$$0^7 - 0 \text{ is divisible by 7.}$$

We have also proved that if $x^7 - x$ is divisible by 7, then $(1 + x)^7 - (1 + x)$ is divisible by 7.

I record these two propositions at a conspicuous place on the blackboard. Then I call on some student with an obviously blank face and ask him to read the second sentence, substituting zero every time he comes to an x. I write as he dictates. When he comes to $(1 + x)^7$, I interrupt as he says "One plus zero," and ask "How much is one plus zero?" When he replies "One," I compliment him: "Very good!" (Positive reinforcement.) When he comes to $(1 + x)$, I remind him, "What did you say that one plus zero is?"

After we have this written on the blackboard, I point to the first and third propositions and ask the class, "What conclusion do you draw?"

We repeat the procedure, substituting 1, 2, 3, and so on for x. I have never had to go beyond 5 before someone interjects, "It works for all numbers!"

"What works for all numbers?" I ask.

"If you raise a number to the seventh power and subtract the original number, the answer is divisible by 7."

Then I ask, "Any number? What about 6.2 or π ?"

"Oh, I mean a whole number."

"Let us express it in symbols." I write

$$\text{If } x \text{ is any whole number, then} \dots$$

and ask the class to complete the sentence.

I then stabilize the insight by telling the class to imagine a row of tin soldiers placed in such a way that if you knock any one of them down, the next one falls down. "What happens if you tip the first one over?" Chorus: "They all fall down." Then we draw out the analogy with the induction argument.

I then check the understanding of the class by asking, "Suppose we supplied the same reasoning starting with the fact (discovered earlier) that in the equation

$$(1 + x)^5 = 1 + 5x + 10x^2 + 10x^3 + 5x^4 + x^5$$

all the coefficients on the right, except for the two 1's, are divisible by 5." I always obtain the correct response: "If x is any whole number, then $(x^5 - x)$ is divisible by 5."

It is not possible to formulate all the arguments in the examples given in simple schemes. Some may still be amenable to the kind of investigation carried out by Bruner and his associates.

V. OPEN PROBLEMS

The first task, of course, is to investigate the properties of insightful behavior. We want to know in what way the response depends upon the amount and arrangement of the evidence, the cues supplied by the tasks and questions, the timing of questions and meditation periods, the intelligence of the subject, the external conditions, and so forth.

More important, and involving research of longer range, are questions concerning the assimilation of scientific method. How many and what sort of experiences of the kind in which the program is laid out explicitly are needed before one can gradually put the subject more on his own? What is the effect on his independent performance, first on similar problems and then on quite different problems? Clearly, many of these questions are also relevant to learning in other fields.

Finally, can a course of these experiences be programed in such a way that the student will be led to pose problems himself and investigate them in a similar fashion? Perhaps one could measure the fluency with which the youngster raises questions about a given topic or devises methods of attack on given problems. For example, one could suggest to a student that he investigate products of any number of consecutive integers, such as 11, 12, 13, 14, 23, 24, 25, and so on. What conjectures could he come up with after a week of examination of such products? How would he approach the problem of explaining why the product of 4 consecutive integers is always divisible by 24?

Many of these problems will require the collaboration of creative scholars in several fields. I hope that this paper will stimulate fundamental research of this kind.

8 Abstraction in Mathematics and the Evolution of Algebra

JEAN
DIEUDONNÉ

*Professor Jean A. Dieudonné, ancien élève of the
Ecole Normale Supérieure, graduated with a Dr.Sc.
(Doctorat d'Etat) in mathematics from the University
of Paris in 1931. After several appointments at French
universities, he visited the United States for the first
time in 1946 in order to teach mathematics at the
University of St. Paul, the University of Michigan,
and the Liberal Arts and Technological Institute at
Northwestern University. He is currently a faculty
member at the University of Nice, France.*

*In the following article, Dieudonné defends the ab-
stract nature of mathematics and discusses the evolution of algebra. He believes that the essence of mathematics lies in the power to create abstractions and
then reason with them. For him, this is the mathematical method and is what ought to be taught as
mathematics. If the ordering of thoughts according to
the mathematical method is the goal for teaching, the
author feels that the student will develop "a clear
mind and a rigorous judgment."*

*In light of this point of view, Jean Dieudonné
demonstrates the abstract nature of mathematics by
surveying the progressive steps of abstraction involved
in the development of algebraic structures. In his
opinion, this development resulted, historically, from
rigorous simplification of problems down to their
structural essence. This involved at once a divorce
from a problem's concrete particulars, a recognition
of the indeterminant nature of a problem's objects as
opposed to the significance of its operational rules,
and an acceptance of seemingly senseless computation
that is verified abstractly. Professor Dieudonné
strongly believes that the power and the versatility of*

*mathematical structures are directly proportional to
the degree of abstraction involved. Furthermore, the
ability to reason abstractly (as opposed to the acquisition of mathematical particulars) is the goal of
mathematics education.*

Mathematics has always shared with metaphysics the characterization of being
a realm in which one worked only with abstractions, rather than the concrete
reality of sense experience. From this characterization derives the grim aspect
both fields assume in the public's eyes, and the fact that so many minds,
which appear first-rate in other directions but remain obstinately rebellious to
all abstract thought, give up in the face of mathematical reasoning. We are inclined nowadays, and especially in the teaching world, to deplore this state of
affairs and to contrive to mask or attenuate as long as possible the abstract
nature of mathematics. This is, in my opinion, a serious mistake. Not that one
should have young students immediately confront concepts too abstract for
their brains to assimilate, but, while the structures of thought little by little
become more clear to the adolescent, it is necessary that mathematics unveil
itself in its true light. For indeed, what goal do we seek, in our modern civilizations? Certainly it is not to introduce to them a collection of more or less
ingenious theorems about the bisectors of a triangle or the sequence of prime
numbers (which they will not use in the least later on unless they become
professional mathematicians), but rather to teach them to order and link their
thoughts according to the method mathematicians use, because we recognize
in this exercise an excellent way to develop a clear mind and a rigorous judgment. It is then the essence of the mathematical method that ought to be the
object of this teaching, the subject matter being only well-chosen illustrations
of it.

But then what is the essence of mathematics if not the power to abstract
notions? One would hesitate to state such a truism if its truth did not sometimes tend to disappear from sight. This is why I believe that it is useful to
remember that the greatest steps forward in mathematics have always been
linked to progress in the capacity to raise oneself a little higher in the realm
of abstraction. In the pages that follow, the history of algebra, from its first
stammerings to our modern algebra, will illustrate this thesis.

I. ALGEBRAIC NOTATION

We will not linger over the fairly obscure origins of the first mathematical
ideas, such as number, space, or time; however, it should be pointed out in
passing that, although deriving from the needs of their application, these
notions are already quite abstract. If modern civilization (of which they form
the frame) should tend to make us forget this fact, it would be enough to
convince oneself to look at the difficulties the child has in acquiring a clear

conception of these ideas, or even to look at certain primitive civilizations where counting does not go beyond a few units and where sometimes even the numbers' names change according to the nature of the objects numbered.

The notion of number goes hand in hand with the usual operations of arithmetic. The desire to do these operations as rapidly and as accurately as possible, as we know, leads certain civilizations to represent numbers by special signs, arranged in such a way that arithmetical operations could act directly on the symbols representing the numbers under consideration by means of suitable rules (and not by returning to the definition itself of these operations, or by helping oneself when necessary by the use of methods of rapid enumeration such as the abacus). Moreover, there were many attempts of this kind, more or less fortunate, and it took many centuries before a system as satisfying as our present "numeration of position" could be conceived. We only mention it here as an example of a tendency that is the fundamental tendency of algebra: to write down operations one has to perform and their results in an abbreviated fashion, by a kind of stenography that is supple and perfected enough to make the manipulation of these operations at once clearer, faster, and easier.[1]

The usefulness of such abridged notation appears as soon as one combines arithmetical operations in a slightly complicated way. For example, the identities that we write

(1) $1 + 2 + 3 + \ldots + (n-1) + n = n\,(n+1)/2$
(2) $(a+b)^3 = a^3 + b^3 + 3ab\,(a+b)$

can undoubtably be stated in ordinary language, but in a manner much less suggestive than the written-out formula.[2] We will observe in passing that the very conception of such identities requires a level of abstraction already higher than that required by the mere notion of number. In fact, one must imagine that the operations that we transcribe in the two members of the operations (1) and (2) are performed in a general fashion—that is to say, without taking account of the particular values of the numbers in them. It is remarkable that such laws were already recognized (at the very first empirically, no doubt) by the most advanced civilizations of antiquity, such as the Babylonians and the Greeks. But they are invariably expressed in ordinary language, and in spite of the obvious simplification that their algebraic transcription appears to offer, it does not seem that the need for such a "stenography" made itself felt very soon.

Undoubtedly it is in regard to the solving of equations that this need first manifested itself. We know that such a problem consists of determining one or

---

1. Notice, in reference to "numeration of position," the appearance of 0, which constitutes an essential part of, and bears witness to an effort of, abstraction of which even the Greeks never showed themselves capable.

2. For example, the identity (2) can be stated: The cube of a sum of two numbers is the sum of the cubes of these numbers added to the triple of the product of the sum of the numbers multiplied by their product.

several numbers satisfying given conditions, which can be translated by algebraic equalities. Let us take, for example, the following problem: Find a rectangle of which the difference between the sides is 2 and whose area is 8. We
immediately translate it into the equation

(3) $x(x+2) = 8$

where x is the smallest side. As long as it is a matter of simple problems, the
solution can be described in ordinary language without too much difficulty.
Nowadays we still proceed this way with problems of so-called arithmetic in
our elementary classes: it is a matter of problems which all come down to the
solving of an equation of the first degree, $ax = b$, but which, depending upon
the way the question is asked (mixtures, messengers, and so on) one solves in
each case by ad hoc reasoning. Such recipes go back, it seems, to the Babylonians,[3] where we find them, moreover, without explanations (at least in the
manuals of computations that we know of); we also find there the classical
rule of solving the second-degree equation, without knowing anything further
of the procedure by which they obtained it. The Greeks of the classical period
solved the second-degree equation by turning it into a problem of geometric
construction, and thus stayed outside the flow of what is called algebraic
thought; and if the existence of a theoretical algebra for the Babylonians appears likely enough, it is only, however, with Diophantes (fourth century
A.D.) that we find the first written evidence that has come down to us.

Direct analysis of an equation, strictly by algebraic methods, consists, as we
know, of performing a series of operations on the unknown (or unknowns) *as
if it were a known quantity*: for example, for the equation (3) we write successively

$$x(x+2) + 1 = 9,$$

noticing that the first member is equal to

$$(x+1)^2,$$

which yields

$$(x+1)^2 = 9,$$

from which we derive

$$x + 1 = 3, x = 2.$$

We find numerous examples and variants of this method with Diophantes,
who manipulated it with rare virtuosity. A modern mathematician is so used
to this kind of reasoning that his boldness is now barely perceptible to him.

---

3. It is probably their venerable antiquity that is the reason why these rules are still
taught as they are today, in spite of mathematicians' repeated protests. If indeed it is
proven that a ten-year-old child is not ready to understand the mechanics of equations to
the first degree with one unknown, one should at least wait the few years necessary and
in the meanwhile stop cramming his head with quantities of recipes that have no bearing.

In fact, however, it requires a capacity for abstraction of which many of our contemporaries, even those with a scientific education, reveal themselves incapable as soon as they leave the beaten track.[4]

It is certainly no accident that we also encounter for the first time with Diophantes a special sign to express the unknown of a problem. It is easy to understand the necessity that led him to it, when one tries to explain in ordinary language the operations performed for the solving of the equation. In our example (3), one would have to say: "If one unit is added to the area of the rectangle, the area of a square is obtained whose side is the smallest side of the rectangle increased by one unit; the area of this square being 9, the side of the square is 3 and the smallest side of the rectangle is thus 2." One can manage easily enough in this example, thanks to the geometric interpretation. However, if one tries to do the same in problems of pure algebra, and especially when there are several unknowns, one falls very quickly into inextricable nonsense, of which jurists' jargon ("the aforesaid, speaking to the third person . . . ") gives only a slight idea.[5] At any rate, Diophantes indicates the unknown and its six first powers by the symbols ς, $δ^{\widetilde{ν}}$, $κ^{\widetilde{ν}}$, $δδ^{\widetilde{ν}}$, $δκ^{\widetilde{ν}}$, $κκ^{\widetilde{ν}}$, but he has no notation for representing several unknowns at once. This prevents him from giving complete solutions to problems with more than one unknown.

In the course of the Middle Ages, Diophantes' methods and notations were perfected very slowly. Symbols were introduced, which enabled several unknowns and their powers to small exponents to be designated, and also special signs for the current algebraic operations (for example, many algebraists of this period indicate + and – by p. and m., and the square root by R; but the sign = is only introduced in the middle of the sixteenth century, and not universally adopted before the end of the seventeenth century). Not until Chuquet (fifteenth century) do we see the notation of exponents appear, and this enters definitely into use only after Stevin (1600). But here again, the

---

4. All the student officers in courses of anti-aircraft antillery around the year 1930 in France remember the famous inaugural lesson on shooting down airplanes: it is a matter of shooting a mobile target, with a direction supposedly known. The instructor officer presented the problem in the following way. If at a given moment one knows the position (M_O) of the plane, one knows the time (t_o) that the shell would take to reach M_O; at the end of this time (t_O), the plane will have reached a known point M, and it is then tempting to aim (at the initial moment) at point M; but the duration of the shell's trajectory, from the cannon to point M, is no longer equal on the average to t_o. Therefore the instructor concluded, "One ends up in a vicious circle, which one gets out of," he added, "by successive approximations!" In reality, if t is the time it takes the airplane to go from M_O to any point P on its way, the time T that the shell would take to reach P is a function $F(t)$, already known from tables of shooting; the point on the future path of the airplane at which one must aim is then reached at the end of time t_1, which is the root of the equation $t = F(t)$. This is all there is to the "vicious circle" of the problem.

5. A delicious example of this kind of statement can be found in the rule (in verse!) by which Tartaglia divulges to Cardan his method of solution of the equation to the third degree. See M. Cantor, *Vorlesunoan über die Geschichte der Mathematik*, t. II, p. 448, Leipzig (B.G. Teubner), 1892.

most important advance is linked to a more abstract concept of algebra. Aware of the fact that procedures for the solution of equations known in his day (that is, formulas for the solution of algebraic equations up to the fourth degree) depended only on the degree of the equation and not on the values of the numerical coefficients of the powers of the unknown, Vietus (1540-1603) had the idea of indicating not only unknowns but also the "given" coefficients of the equations by letters, and his notation, notably improved on by Descartes and Newton, was already very close to our own. When, after Newton and Leibniz, one indicated by a letter the degree of the equation itself, and by the indexed letter a_k the coefficient of x^k in the equation, a point was reached at which one could consider in a general way the problem of the solution of any algebraic equation:

$$a_o + a_1 x + \ldots + a_n x^n = 0.$$

The study of this problem occupied the entire eighteenth century, culminating with Galois' theory (1830). Here we are putting our finger on an entirely general phenomenon: such vast problems could not even be correctly formulated, much less approached with some chance of success, before the ideas present had become sufficiently abstract to lend themselves to reasoning free of all the contingencies clouding over particular cases known before.

II. THE IMPOSSIBLE EQUATIONS

Very soon algebraists had to encounter insolvable problems. We will not discuss at length here how "insoluble" problems of the first degree led Hindu algebraists (fifth through eighth centuries A. D.) to introduce negative numbers. Even though at the beginning it was, no doubt, a matter of a formal extension of ordinary computation (of the kind which we are going to examine below), these new "numbers" took on quite quickly concrete interpretations that led in a natural way to rules governing their calculation. The formal point of view was not to reappear in regard to them until a much more evolved stage of algebra (even though negative numbers have been for many centuries an object of suspicion for many mathematicians: Vietus, right in the middle of the sixteenth century, refused to hear anything about them!). A much more typical example is furnished to us by the arithmetic of imaginary numbers.

As soon as the computation of square roots was established, it was noticed that a square is necessarily positive, and it seems never to have occurred to the rare algebraists of the Middle Ages, who manipulated negative numbers without hesitation, to calculate square roots of these numbers (which would certainly have seemed as gratuitous as paradoxical). It is the discovery of the solution by radicals of the equation of the third degree that was to show the need for expanding the usual computation of square roots. At the beginning of the sixteenth century, the Italian mathematician Scipio del Ferro discovered the formula (usually attributed to Cardan) that gave a root of the equation $x^3 = ax + b$:

$$(4) \quad x = \sqrt[3]{\frac{b}{2} + \sqrt{\left(\frac{b}{2}\right)^2 - \left(\frac{a}{3}\right)^3}} + \sqrt[3]{\frac{b}{2} + \sqrt{\left(\frac{b}{2}\right)^2 - \left(\frac{a}{3}\right)^3}}$$

When, in the given equation, we have

$$\left(\frac{b}{2}\right)^2 - \left(\frac{a}{3}\right)^3 < 0,$$

the formula (4) makes no sense. However, Cardan and his students soon saw that even in this case the equation can very well have roots. Let us take, for example, the equation $x^3 = 15x + 4$, considered by Bombelli at the end of the sixteenth century; it allows for the root $x = 4$, even though

$$\left(\frac{4}{2}\right)^2 - \left(\frac{15}{3}\right)^3 = -121.$$

But, just as Bombelli did, let us calculate *as though square roots of negative numbers were real numbers* to which the usual rules of algebraic computation would apply; we then have, according to the formula (2),

$$(2 + \sqrt{-1})^3 = 8 + 12\sqrt{-1} - 6 - \sqrt{-1} = 2 + \sqrt{-121},$$

which then allows us to write

$$\sqrt[3]{2 + \sqrt{-121}} = 2 + \sqrt{-1}$$

and similarly,

$$\sqrt[3]{2 - \sqrt{-121}} = 2 - \sqrt{-1},$$

and the formula (4) then yields, by addition, the root $x = 4$. In other terms, *we come to an accurate result by the intermediary of a senseless computation!*

Before this apparent paradox could be explained, two centuries of thinking and groping were to go by, during which mathematicians grew little by little more used to "imaginary" quantities and learned to make more and more fruitful use of them. But it was only at the beginning of the nineteenth century that it was finally realized that one could calculate with certain "things" that are not numbers, *as though they were numbers*. As this is perhaps the most difficult step to overcome in the escalation towards abstraction, we are going to try to analyze in more detail the mechanics of computation with imaginary numbers.

1. Let us start with calculations—initially devoid of meaning—that are performed on the "imaginary" quantities $a + b\sqrt{-1}$ when $\sqrt{-1}$ is manipulated

as though it were an ordinary number with the square -1. Algebraic operations all being derived from addition and multiplication, it is enough for us to consider the latter, with the following results:

(5) $(a + b \sqrt{-1}) + (a' + b' \sqrt{-1}) = (a + a') + (b + b') \sqrt{-1}$

(6) $(a + b \sqrt{-1})(a' + b' \sqrt{-1}) = (aa' - bb') + (ab' + ba') \sqrt{-1}.$

Let us insist on the fact that, as such, these equations mean nothing, since $\sqrt{-1}$ does not exist as a customary number. But if it is observed that introducing an "imaginary quantity" $a + b \sqrt{-1}$ is equivalent to introducing a couple of ordinary numbers (a, b), we see immediately that the equations (5) and (6) can be interpreted as *defining* the operations of addition and multiplication on the pairs of ordinary numbers (a, b) by the conditions

(7) $(a, b) + (a', b') = (a + a', b + b')$

(8) $(a, b)(a', b') = (aa' - bb', ab' + ba').$

Furthermore, we will observe that in the "meaningless" calculation on the imaginary numbers $a + b \sqrt{-1}, a + 0 \sqrt{-1}$ is replaced by the ordinary number a. This is what allows us eventually (as we have seen above) to end up, after calculation on the imaginary numbers, at a final result that is a common number. In our interpretation, this means that a couple $(a, 0)$ is assimilated to the number a; this "identification" is justified by the fact that the number a and the couple $(a, 0)$ correspond to each other in a one-to-one fashion, and, what is more, that this correspondence *respects the operations of addition and multiplication*, for, according to (7) and (8), we have

(9) $(a, 0) + (a', 0) = (a + a', 0)$

(10) $(a, 0)(a', 0) = (aa', 0)$

One can say, therefore, there is isomorphism between customary computation and calculation with pairs $(a, 0)$.

2. This first step has led us to define two operations on the pairs $(a, 0)$ of ordinary numbers. However, it can be easily conceived that we could define many other operations on these pairs: for example, at first sight it would seem more natural to take for a rule of multiplication the rule

$$(a, b) \cdot (a', b') = (aa', bb')$$

instead of (8); besides, this rule also satisfies the condition (10). This does not explain to us at all the fact (empirically proven) that the algebra of imaginary quantities obeys the same laws as ordinary algebra. This last assertion is rather vague, but we can make it more accurate in the following fashion: it is easy to verify that all the rules of ordinary algebra, with the exception of those where inequalities intervene, are logical consequences of the following rules:

$$(R) \begin{cases} x + (y + z) = (x + y) + z, \ x + y = y + x \\ 0 + x = x, \ x + (-x) = 0 \\ x(y + z) = xy + xz \\ x(yz) = (xy)z, \ xy = yx \\ 1 \cdot x = x, \ x \cdot (1/x) = 1 \text{ if } x \neq 0. \end{cases}$$

For example, it follows from these rules that

$$x \cdot x = (0 + x) \cdot x = 0 \cdot x + x \cdot x,$$

hence,

$$0 = (x \cdot x) + (-x \cdot x)$$
$$= (0 \cdot x + x \cdot x) + (-x \cdot x)$$
$$= 0 \cdot x + [x \cdot x + (-x \cdot x)]$$
$$= 0 \cdot x + 0 = 0 \cdot x.$$

In the same way, if $x \neq 0$ and $y \neq 0$, we have $xy \neq 0$; if fact, in the opposite case, we would draw from the relation $xy = 0$ successively

$$(1/x)(xy) = 0,$$

then

$$[(1/x)x]y = 0, \ 1 \cdot y = 0,$$

and finally

$$y = 0,$$

which is absurd.

This being the case, when the numbers x, y, z are replaced by the pairs (a, b) with the rules of arithmetic (7) and (8), the rules (R) *are again verified,* as long as 0 is replaced by the pair $(0, 0)$, 1 by the pair $(1, 0)$, $-(a, b)$ by $(-a, -b)$, and $1/(a, b)$ (where a and b are not both at once equal to 0) by

$$\left(\frac{a}{a^2 + b^2}, - \frac{b}{a^2 + b^2} \right).$$

This is what explains the possibility of performing all the calculations of ordinary algebra on our pairs (a, b). Besides, in this new system of "complex quantities," the pair $i = (0, 1)$ is such that $i^2 = (-1, 0)$, according to (8). Calculation on imaginary quantities is thus entirely justified.

3. However, this is only a verification and one can naturally ask oneself if other rules of calculation for the pairs (a, b) might be imagined that would also satisfy the conditions (R). In reality, it can be shown that every other definition fulfilling these conditions essentially results in the same calculation,

as long as the definition (7) of addition is kept and there is the relation

(11) $(a, 0) (c, d) = (ac, ad)$

otherwise said, the particular case of relation (8) where the first factor is of the type $(a, 0)$. We then allow ourselves to "identify" $(a, 0)$ with the number a [the relations (9) and (10) being verified], in particular the pair $(1, 0)$ with the number 1. If we present $e = (0, 1)$, every pair (a, b) can then be written $a + be$, the first four rules (R) are verified with the same substitutions as above, and the relation $a + be = 0$ is then equivalent to $a = b = 0$. This being the case, we must have in particular

$$e^2 = \beta + ae$$

for two appropriate numbers α, β; but this condition is written

$$(e - \frac{\alpha}{2})^2 = \beta + \frac{\alpha^2}{4} \text{ or}$$

(12) $e'^2 = \gamma$, with $e' = e - \frac{\alpha}{2}$ and $\gamma = \beta + \frac{\alpha^2}{4}$.

We are going to show that the number γ is necessarily negative. In fact, in the opposite case, one could write $\gamma = \lambda^2$, and immediately there would result from the rules (R), supposed as verified, and from (11), that one could also have

$$(e' - \lambda) (e' + \lambda) = 0.$$

But we have seen above that the rules (R), in this case, necessarily yield that there be $e' - \lambda = 0$ or $e' + \lambda = 0$, and neither of these two conditions is possible, because in the first member of each, the coefficient of $e \neq 0$. One must then suppose $\gamma < 0$, or $\gamma = -\mu^2$, with $\mu > 0$. Putting

$$e'' = \frac{1}{\mu} e',$$

we then have $e''^2 = -1$; but notice that

$$a + be = a' + b' e''$$

can be written, with

$$a' = a + b\frac{\alpha}{2} \text{ and } b' = b\mu.$$

From these formulas we can derive inversely a and b linearly a function of a' and b', and we see that a one-to-one correspondence is thus established between the pairs (a, b) and the pairs (a', b'), in such a way that the addition and multiplication given for the pairs (a, b) correspond, for the pairs (a', b'), to the addition and multiplication defined by (7) and (8). In other terms, there is isomorphism between the two calculations, and this is the property of uniqueness that we had in view.

4. Another natural idea, expressed since the beginning of the nineteenth century, consists of seeking to determine whether such similar results could be obtained by calculating, no longer on pairs (a, b) of ordinary numbers, but on triplets (a, b, c), or more generally, on systems

$$(a_1, a_2, \ldots, a_n)$$

of such numbers. It is remarkable that then one can no longer verify the rules (R)—at least if the definition analogous to (7) is kept for addition and the only condition analogous to (11) is kept for multiplication.

Let us show it, for example, in the case of $n = 3$; the conditions imposed are thus

(13) $(a, b, c) + (a', b', c') = (a + a', b + b', c + c')$

(14) $(a, 0, 0) (a', b', c') = (aa', ab', ac')$,

from which it follows in particular that

(15) $(a, 0, 0) + (a', 0, 0) = (a + a', 0, 0)$

(16) $(a, 0, 0) (a', 0, 0) = (aa', 0, 0)$,

which enables one to write a instead of $(a, 0, 0)$, from which it follows that

$$(a, b, c) = a + be_1 + ce_2,$$

with $e_1 = (0, 1, 0)$ and $e_2 = (0, 0, 1)$. The first four rules (R) are still verified for $0 = (0, 0, 0)$ and

$$-(a, b, c) = (-a, -b, -c);$$

the relation

$$a + be_1 + ce_2 = 0$$

is thus equivalent to

$$a = b = c = 0.$$

Such being the case, the theory of linear equations shows that, since one must have

$$e_1{}^2 = (\alpha, \beta, \gamma)$$

and

$$e_1{}^3 = (\alpha', \beta', \gamma')$$

for suitable triplets, there must then be a linear relation between the four triplets $1, e_1, e_1{}^2, e_1{}^3$, all with coefficients not equal to 0, that is

$$a_0 + a_1 e_1 + a_2 e_1{}^2 + a_3 e_1{}^3 = 0.$$

It is obviously impossible to have at once

$$a_2 = a_3 = 0;$$

if $a_3 \neq 0$, the polynomial of the third degree

$$a_3 x^3 + a_2 x^2 + a_1 x + a_0$$

admits at least one real root b, and can be written identically in the form

$$a_3(x - b)(x^2 + b_1 x + b_0).$$

We conclude easily from the rules (R) that we then have

$$a_3(e_1 - b)(e_1{}^2 + b_1 e_1 + b_0) = 0$$

and, as we have already observed, given that

$$a_3 \neq 0 \text{ and } a_1 - b \neq 0,$$

this must result in

$$e_1{}^2 + b_1 e_1 + b_0 = 0.$$

In every case, then, there is a relation of this kind; and in reasoning as above for the pairs, it is seen that by replacing a_1 by a proper combination of the form $\lambda e_1 + \mu$, with $\lambda \neq 0$, it can be supposed that $e_1{}^2 = -1$. In the same way, we can assume $a_2{}^2 = -1$, but from the relation

$$e_1{}^2 - e_2{}^2 = 0,$$

it follows, by the rules (R), that

$$(e_1 - e_2)(e_1 + e_2) = 0,$$

which is absurd, because none of the elements

$$e_1 - e_2, e_1 + e_2$$

can be equal to 0. An analogous method leads to the result pointed out above for the systems

$$(a_1, a_2, \ldots, a_n)$$

to any number of elements.

III. FORMAL ARITHMETIC AND MODERN ALGEBRA

The presentation of the theory of complex numbers, which we have just sketched, is due to Hamilton (around 1840), but substantially it goes back to the fundamental works of Wessel, Gauss, and Argand on the geometrical representation of imaginary numbers, at the beginning of the nineteenth century. These works, like others dating from the same period, in which the theory of groups takes form, make a decisive first step towards abstract algebra: here the risk is taken of *defining* operations, which were not given "naturally," on certain types of objects. To put it differently, the mathematician becomes aware of his power *to create* new calculations on new objects, instead of passively limiting himself to those seemingly imposed on him by the concrete origins of mathematics.

Besides, the nature of revolutions is never to stop halfway. Hardly had this first step towards emancipation been accomplished, when new attacks succeeded in destroying the ancient prison in which classical mathematics was enclosed. With the arithmetic of complex numbers, one sought, no doubt, to expand the *domain* of numbers on which operations of ordinary algebra remained possible, but one did not think to modify the fundamental *rules* (R) of algebraic calculation; from hence in particular derive the fruitless attempts we have pointed out above. A second act of liberation was to crumble this taboo.

Here, it was the "arithmetic of transformations" that showed the way. The geometric interpretation of complex numbers, where the point of the plane of rectangular coordinates (α, β) is associated with the number $\alpha + \beta i$, supplied among other things simple geometric interpretations of certain algebraic operations. For example, we know that the function that makes $z + a$ correspond to every complex number z, with $a = \alpha + \beta i$, corresponds to the vector translation (α, β); similarly the function that makes ζz correspond to every z, where $\zeta = \cos \theta + i \sin \theta$, corresponds to the rotation of the angle θ around the origin. To perform two successive rotations of angles θ, θ' then is the same as multiplying z in succession by the two fixed numbers ζ and $\zeta' = \cos \theta' + i \sin \theta'$, which is the same thing as multiplying z by $\zeta'\zeta$. From there we pass naturally to a symbolic notation, where the rotations themselves (and no longer the associated complex numbers) are designated by the letters S, S', and where $S'S$ designates the rotation obtained by performing in succession rotation S, then rotation S' (besides, we have here $SS' = S'S$). This notation is evidently very close in meaning and in form to the notation $f[g(x)]$ used since Leibniz for the superposition of functions, and it is natural to extend it to arbitrary geometric transformations. For example, denoting with a letter any positional change of the plane, we will write TS for the displacement obtained by first performing the displacement S and then the displacement T. We then find ourselves in a situation having some analogy with our arithmetic of pairs: this time we have defined a "multiplication" between displacements, and therefore a single operation instead of two. Can we also compute further on these new objects?

At first sight, this hardly seems possible, for the first five rules (R) no longer make any sense. Furthermore, it is no longer correct that in general $TS = ST$: we see this, for example, by taking for T a translation and for S a rotation of $180°$ around a point. Nevertheless, we still have $(ST)U = S(TU)$ for any three displacements S, T, U; and by properly interpreting the symbols that occur there, the two final rules of (R) are also satisfied by our new "arithmetic." In fact, it is enough to consider as a displacement the "identical displacement"

I, the operation that consists of transforming each point on the plane into itself, and, on the other hand, to assign to every displacement S an "inverse" displacement S^{-1}, whose effect, at every point, is to return to the position it occupied before the displacement S took place. With these conventions, the rules in question are

$$IS = SI = S$$

and

$$SS^{-1} = S^{-1}S = I.$$

Thus, in this way we arrive at a "partial arithmetic" in which not only are the objects of calculation no longer numbers (and even have only rather distant relationships to ordinary numbers), but also the very rules of this arithmetic are no longer the usual rules. We then see that the latter are in no way intangible; and, from the middle of the nineteenth century, one could conceive of a vaster algebra in which would be contained, with the old classical algebra, all the "arithmetics" that were appearing little by little in the manifold realms of mathematics along with their advances.

It is towards this program that, more or less consciously, the majority of algebraists have worked for more than a century, and of this program a constantly increasing portion is being actualized in our modern algebra. In the course of this long effort, we have become more and more clearly aware of the fact that of the two fundamental constituents of every arithmetic—that is to say, on the one hand the objects on which one operates and on the other hand the operational rules—only the latter are really essential. At this final stage of abstraction (toward which the innumerable examples of isomorphism noticed everywhere naturally lead), the objects of calculation are of a nature that remains almost completely indeterminate; more accurately, in his calculations the algebraist wants to know only one thing about these objects— namely, whether they obey the laws he studies. This is called the *axiomatic method* in algebra.

According to this concept, the study of a calculation (or, as it is also called, an *algebraic structure*) bases itself on the data of a set of objects (E) and of a certain number (n) of operations, each of which consists of joining to two arbitrary elements x, y of E a third element

$$f_i(x, y) \ (1 \leqslant i \leqslant n).$$

The result of each of these operations is usually indicated by separating x and y by a sign attached to the operation, such as +, ×, ·, or T (or even by juxtaposing x and y without any sign); the arbitrary choice of this sign is left completely up to the mathematician, who sometimes chooses it according to the applications he foresees for it: here once again, there are no "natural" (or traditional) signs imposed in advance. What characterizes the algebraic structures of the type we study are the diverse relations (called *axioms* of the structure) that are imposed a priori between the given operations. For example, a structure in which there are two operations written as + and · (this sign being able to be omitted at will), with two privileged elements written as 0, 1, and for each x in E (*resp.* $x \neq 0$) an element written as $-x$ (*resp.* $1/x$) in E, so that all the rules (R) are verified, is called a *structure of commutative field*. There is such a structure for the set of complex numbers, for the set of rational numbers, for the set of numbers $a + b\sqrt{2}$ where a and b are rational. and for many more. Then too, the arithmetic of displacements, which we have spoken of above, is a particular case of *structure of group*. In such a structure, there is only one operation, which we can agree to write as T, and a "privileged" element written as e, with the following axioms:

(G_1) $x\mathrm{T}(y\mathrm{T}z) = (x\mathrm{T}y)\mathrm{T}z$ for any x, y, z in E;

(G_2) $e\mathrm{T}x = x\mathrm{T}e = x$ for any x in E;

(G_3)   for every x in E, there is an x' in E such that $x\mathrm{T}x' = x'\mathrm{T}x = e$.

It will be observed that three of the rules (R) relating to addition in a commutative field are translations of the preceding axioms, made according to the following "dictionary": T is replaced by +, e by 0 and x' by $(-x)$. Similarly, three of the rules (R) relating to multiplication in the set of elements $\neq 0$ of the field are the translation of the axioms of groups, this time made according to another "dictionary": · replaces T (or is eliminated), 1 replaces e, and $1/x$ replaces x'. These examples can give an idea of the great variety of cases in which a structure of group is present; in fact, there is no longer a single branch of modern mathematics in which this structure does not occur, often in many ways. They also show how much, if one wants to attain a notion applicable to the greatest number of possible cases, one must be able to detach oneself, even in notation, from the particularities of each of these cases, and reason in a completely abstract way.

Therefore, through these examples one can take a glimpse at how the study of these structures can supply the mathematician with tools of universal use. Before the flood of mathematical publications of every kind, which grows more and more every year, only the axiomatic method can in some way channel new discoveries, classify and join them to previous discoveries, often even simplify their presentation, and sometimes increase their scope by analyzing fully their potentiality and by revealing their principles in a pure state. But in order that they fully fulfill this function, it has been necessary for algebraic structures to acquire their versatility and plasticity at the price of abstraction pushed to its limit, which requires a sustained intellectual effort.

Mathematics: Its Nature and Its Psychology

PART THREE

9 Mathematical Structures and the Operational Structures of the Intellect

JEAN
PIAGET

Jean Piaget was born in 1896 at Neuchatel, Switzerland, and educated in Zurich, Paris, and Neuchatel, where he obtained a doctorat ès sciences at the age of twenty-two. He has been a professor of child psychology and the history of scientific thought at the University of Geneva since 1929. He is also director of the International Bureau of Education and co-director of the Institut J. J. Rousseau (Institut des Sciences de l'Education).

As a psychologist trained in zoology whose interests are primarily philosophical, since 1927, Piaget has conducted an enormous number of experiments seeking to elucidate the theoretical problems of the genesis of intelligence in order to trace what he calls the main stages of the mental development of children. Formerly president of the Swiss Society of Psychology and recipient of honorary doctorates from Harvard and Cambridge, he has authored an extensive collection of papers and books on cognitive processes, and accumulated the largest store of theoretical and factual observations on children's behavior. All over the world, but especially in the United States, his theories about human cognitive development have aroused more intellectual excitement and stimulated more research than any comparable collection of theoretical propositions since John Dewey's formulation of the basic tenets of progressive education.

The article that composes this chapter is the summary of a lecture presented at the Colloquium of la Rochette near Melun in 1952. This conference, devoted to the study of mathematical and psychological structures, opened with a lecture by J. Dieudonné on the first of these two topics. The following is a reply, from the psychological point of view, to Dieudonné. This is why it refers frequently to the propositions of that author (not summed up in this volume) and agrees in general with those of the Bourbaki ("L'architecture des mathématiques," in Les grands courants de la pensée mathématique, *edited by F. Le Lionnais).*

In this account, Piaget attempts to provide a firm foundation for the theory of learning by the use of logic and mathematics. Taking a non-Platonic viewpoint—that mathematical connections are formed through activity of the intellect—he considers three fundamental mathematical structures (algebraic structures, structures of order, and topological structures) and their "correspondence" to elementary structures of the intellect. The reader interested in logic and the concepts of "group" and "net" may enjoy dissecting Piaget's construction of a possible organizational scheme for the intellect.

I

Whether one places oneself at the practical standpoint of the instructor entrusted with teaching mathematical truths or at the theoretical standpoint of the epistemologist reflecting on the nature of mathematical entities, the main problem in both cases seems to be to know whether mathematical connections arise from the activity of the intellect or whether the latter discovers the former as an external reality already present. However, this problem, as ancient as western philosophy, can be stated today in psychological terms and even in terms of child psychology: it is up to the study of mental development, among other things, to show us whether the interplay of the subject's actions, and then the workings of thought, suffice to explain the formation of mathematical entities, or whether the latter are discovered from outside, just as physical entities with their objective characteristics are, and also just as are those sorts of ideal entities formed by syntagms of the language imposed on the individual by the social group of which he is a part (and it is well known that the comparison between logico-mathematical entities and linguistic relationships is supported by a large number of logisticians, whether their allegiance be conventionalist or Platonist in nature).

Now, if the methods of approach to this eternal problem can be rejuvenated by appealing to genetic psychology, a restatement of the problem itself has recently been made possible by the perspectives opened by the Bourbaki to the architecture of mathematics and by the fundamental role attributed in these works to the notion of "structure."

At the base of the edifice of mathematics, men have long sought for some simple essences, conceived more or less atomistically. There were the whole numbers, which Kronecker attributed to God himself as opposed to all the other numerical varieties originating from human fabrication. There were points, lines, and so forth, whose arrangements would generate space. But these were always entities given in themselves, which the mind was called upon either to contemplate or manipulate, depending upon whether thought had yet become aware of the role of the operations or whether it superimposed these on simple essences, like the tools that a bricklayer uses to cement material given previously in order to construct a wall or a house.

But even though the foundations consist of "structures" and, thanks to them, construction proceeds both from the simple to the complex and from the general to the particular, there are implications of another sort. A structure, such as a "group," is an operational system; the question is then to know whether the elements of very diverse nature to which the structure applies exist prior to it—that is to say, whether they have sufficient meaning independently of it—or whether on the contrary it is the action of the structure— an action at first not explicit because the order of awareness reverses the order of creation—which confers upon the elements their essential characteristics. More accurately, the psychological problem (and this is the only one with which we have to concern ourselves) is to establish whether the entities serving as the elements of the structures are the product of the operations that give rise to them, or whether they exist prior to operations, which then apply to them afterward.

Now the alterations from which the idea of structure evolves in the interplay of definitions and demonstrations are significant in this respect. Instead of defining elements separately, by convention or by construction, the structural definition consists of characterizing them by the operational relations they maintain between each other as a function of the system. And such a structural definition of an element will take the place of a demonstration of the need for this element, inasmuch as it is presented as belonging to a system whose parts are interdependent. Thus a principle of totality is given from the beginning, and this totality is necessarily of an operational nature. Even in a system of pure relations like the structures of order, if the product of two relations is another relation, it is because the relations are coordinated with each other by the operations of the logic of relations.

No less revealing are the transformations introduced into the architecture of mathematics thanks to the notion of structure, which amounts to saying that in the order of construction or relationship of the innumerable classes, it is possible to distinguish one abstract entity from another. In this respect, one can say that the introduction of structures represents a progress similar to that which anatomy accomplished for biology by substituting a classification founded on internal genetic connections for a classification satisfied with external characteristics in all their static discontinuities. Starting from some fundamental structures, the course to follow consists of differentiating them, from the general to the particular, and in combining them, from the simple to the complex, from which a hierarchy is derived, substituting for the old juxtaposed areas a series of plans superposed according to these two methods of generation. From this there derives once again a principle of totality, wherein elements or classes of elements are subordinated to the dynamism of a real construction.

Let us also notice the importance the method of discovery of these structures has for the psychology of mathematical thought. This brings us back to our option at the beginning—that is, of continuity between intellectual work and mathematical construction, or of the externality of ideal entities that the mind would apprehend as from the outside. At first sight, examination of how the mathematician seeks to reach fundamental structures seems to speak in favor of the second of these propositions: far from deducing them at the outset, he starts from analogies discovered after the fact between forms of reasoning at work in areas without any apparent affinity; then, in a seemingly inductive manner, as one proceeds in the presence of experimental facts, he looks for common mechanisms until he uncovers the most general laws of the structure investigated; only then does axiomatization intervene, and after that exploitation—that is to say, the application of these general laws to particular theories by progressive differentiation. Furthermore, the passage from parent structures to secondary structures takes place through the combination of multiple structures. Here again, this combination is not a deduction, for in respect to each new structure, new axioms must be introduced in order to integrate new elements.

But this procedure for discovering structures, which is in some sense inductive, is on the other hand very revealing concerning the relations that these structures maintain with the diverse elements they regulate. If, historically, these elements seem to be given prior to the discovery of structure, and if the latter thus essentially plays the part of a reflexive instrument intended to reveal their most general characteristics, it must not be forgotten that, psychologically, the order of awareness reverses that of creation: what is first in order of construction appears last in reflexive analysis, because the subject becomes conscious of the results of mental construction before understanding its inmost mechanisms.[1] Far from constituting a decisive argument in favor of the independence of structures in relation to the work of the intellect, their late and almost inductive discovery would tend on the contrary to make one suspect their primitive and generative nature. But if what is fundamental appears in the final analysis, the converse in not necessarily true and the problem then remains open as to how to make clear the eventual connections among the parent structures of the mathematical edifice and the operational

---

1. Let one consider, for example, how late (not until Cantor) was the introduction of the operations of placing into one-to-one and reciprocal correspondence, even though these are the operations that generate the whole numbers for the child and for primitive man.

structures that the study of mental development allows one to consider as constituting logico-mathematical construction. This is what is now to be examined from the point of view of psychogenesis.

The three fundamental structures on which the mathematical edifice rests are, according to the Bourbaki, the algebraic structures, whose prototype is the "group," the structures of order, of which a variety commonly used today (even in some cases to excess) is the "net," and the topological structures. As a matter of fact, this number of three is not exhaustive, and the development of mathematics could continue to increase it. But, in the present state of knowledge, these three structures are the only ones that are irreducible to one another, and thus play the part of parent structures.

Now, it is interesting to observe that if one seeks to follow to its roots the psychological development of spontaneous arithmetical and geometrical operations of the child, and especially of the logical operations that constitute their necessary prior conditions, one finds at every stage first a fundamental tendency toward organization of totalities or systems, outside of which the elements have no meaning or even existence, and next a distribution of these *set* systems according to three kinds of properties, which correspond exactly to those of algebraic structures, structures of order, and topological structures. This is what we are going to try to show by examining them one by one, in order then to reveal the general lesson this convergence calls for.

II

First, it is proper to recall that in the last few decades the notion of structure has become, independently of the recent evolution of mathematics, one of the current notions of the psychology of cognitive functions (perception and intelligence). In the most diverse areas, psychologists have been led to acknowledge that the "natural" progress of the mind, which consists of seeking elements prior to totalities and of creating the latter by the composition of the former, rests on fallacious analogies with material manufacture. In particular, in the area of perception, where field actions are easily analyzed experimentally, it has been observed that the so-called elements are always the product of dissociation or segregation inside a previous totality and that no particular relation can be revealed without first starting from structural characteristics of sets.

In the special area of intelligence, which alone interests us here, this role of wholes is also constant, but the wholes differ in form from those in the area of perception. In fact, intelligence appears essentially as a coordination of actions. The latter are first merely material or sensory-motor (that is to say, without the intervention of the symbolic function or of representation), but are already organized into patterns that involve certain structured wholes. Then, with the help of the symbolic function, and particularly of mental images and of language, the actions are progressively internalized; and after a more or less lengthy phase of transition between sensory-motor acts and representations (a period which we will call that of *preoperational thought*, between 2 and 7–8 years of age), they are formed into "operations" and then present in a typical form the set structures characteristic of intelligence.

In order to understand the nature of these operational structures, one must start from the fundamental fact that, unlike perceptual processes that are irreversible because they are founded on a kind of "probabilist" composition, intelligence directs itself from the beginning toward a reversibility that constantly grows in importance during the course of development. Undoubtedly, the initial sensory-motor actions are still irreversible because they are directed only in one way toward the practical goal that is to be attained. But as soon as the coordination of sensory-motor patterns begins, the intellect becomes capable of a certain mobility characterized by detours and backtracking, which can be seen as a beginning of the more or less systematic reversibility that will appear again on the plane of representation. On this new plane, reversibility is far from being immediately imposed. During the entire preoperational phase, the subject reasons about configurations more than about transformations, and for him it is a question of learning to think about what he can do in action (for example, to represent to himself a system of positional places once he has learned how to treat them materially). In the same way, throughout this important phase of early childhood, the growing ability to represent still contains systematic obstacles to reversibility and therefore also to conservation of elementary invariants (lengths, distances, discontinuous sets, physical quantities, and so on). But already with this preoperational phase, a thicker and thicker interplay of regulations leads to progressive compensation for mistakes due to the initial irreversibility and thus foreshadows operational reversibility.

Thus the appearance of the first systematic operations (around the age of 7–8 years) indicates the arrival at the state of equilibrium toward which thought tended during the preceding inchoate phase, and one must have a good understanding of this relation of progressive equilibration between the preoperational phase and the first operational period (from the ages of 7–8 to 11–12) in order not to consider the latter as a kind of absolute beginning. The budding operations, descended from sensory-motor coordinations and from preoperational representational regulations, thus present the following characteristics: they are, correctly speaking, actions that extend previous material actions, but are internalized in thought owing to the symbolic function; they are essentially reversible—that is to say, the operation is an action able to unfold in two directions, and understanding of one of the directions means ipso facto the understanding of the other; and most of all, they are bound up right from the beginning with a system (there is no isolated operation, for an isolated action goes in one direction only and thus is not an operation). An operation is therefore necessarily associated with other operations, and the very nature of the operation is due to this capacity for mobile composition that is reversible within a system. Hence there is operational structure as soon as there are operations, and set structure is not a product, after the event, of compositions among previous operations, because the initially irreversible action becomes operational and reversible only within a structure and under the effect of its organization.

Before we can describe the types of structures in detail, we must also observe that reversibility, constituting without a doubt the fundamental law of compositions proper to the intellect, is present from the beginning (therefore as soon as sensory-motor patterns occur) in two complementary and irreducible forms: *inversion* (or negation) and *reciprocity*. When a baby of 10 or 12 months, who begins to organize in a systematic way the positional places in his immediate surroundings, moves an object from A to B, he can cancel this change by the inverse transformation of bringing the object back from B to A, which, in sum, is equal to no movement at all. But he can also leave the object at B and move himself from A to B, which will reproduce the original situation in which the object was in front of his own body; in this case, the moving of the object has not been canceled at all, but simply compensated for by a reciprocal moving of the body itself, which constitutes another change. Without wanting to put a baby's behavior in logistic formulas, let us nevertheless notice this essential difference between negation (or inversion) and reciprocity (or compensation) and bear in mind that these constitute from the beginning two essential kinds of reversibility, which we will come across again side by side throughout development, and which will not reach synthesis in a single system until the level of formal operations after the age of 11–12, when there will be constituted the group of four interpropositional transformations (which, to return to this example of positional change, will allow the child to coordinate in a single whole all the changes of place according to two systems of reference at once—one mobile and the other fixed).

Here we are, then, in a position to specify in what sense the three fundamental structures of the Bourbaki correspond to the elementary structures of intelligence (the former constituting the formalized extension and not, of course, the direct expression of the latter).

III

Algebraic structures, and notably those of the "group," correspond to the operational mechanisms of the intellect ruled by the first of the two forms of reversibility, which we have called inversion, or negation (the product of an operation by its inverse being then the identity operation or transformation).

One must insist strongly, in this respect, on the fact that, however delayed the discovery of the notion of the group has been for mathematics (nineteenth century), such a structure expresses in reality some of the mechanisms most characteristic of the intellect. From this point of view, let us notice the significance of four of the elementary properties of the group: (1) that the product of two group elements is another group element, (2) that every direct operation corresponds to one and only one inverse operation; (3) that there thus exists an identity operation; and (4) that successive compositions are associative. Expressed in the language of intelligent actions, these four properties mean: (1) that the coordination of two plans of action constitutes a new plan of action adding itself to the preceding; (2) that a coordination can be made or suppressed at will, and, expressed more simply, that an intellectual action (operation) can unfold in two directions; (3) that returning to the starting point makes it possible to find the latter unaltered; and (4) that the same goal can be reached by different roads without being modified by the road traveled. Generally speaking, the "group" is then the symbolic translation of certain of the fundamental characteristics of the act of intellect: the possibility of a coordination of actions, and the possibility of returns and of detours.

But there is more to come. The transformations appropriate to a group are always bound up with certain invariants, from which it results that the constitution of a group goes along with the construction of invariants that correspond to it. Now it is exactly the same for the spontaneous forms of organization that intelligence takes in the course of its development: to the initial irreversibility of actions corresponds an absence of conservation, and to the construction of reversible structures corresponds the elaboration of notions of conservation relative to the area thus structured.

Starting from the sensory-motor level, such processes can be observed by a kind of prefiguration (which is practical and linked to the immediate surroundings) of what the operations will be on the plane of representation or of thought. Thus, during the first months of existence, changes of place cannot yet be organized into a group because they are centered around the body proper and formed according to certain systematic mistakes as a function of this egocentrism.[2] At this level there are still no permanent objects with a trajectory independent of the action itself. On the other hand, toward the end of the first year, the experimental group of changes of place already invoked by H. Poincaré (which he believed to be innate, although it actually constitutes a final form of equilibrium of the sensory-motor organization) is constituted at the same time the schema of the permanent object is elaborated (as a function of successive localizations, such as detours and returns).

The development of representational thought, in the course of the preoperational phase and at the level of the first concrete operations (from 7 to 11 years of age), gives rise to a similar picture. As long as thought is irreversible, there can not be notions of conservation even in the most simple areas of observation (conservation of a set in the case of modification of the configuration of elements; conservation of the equivalence between two corresponding sets when the elements, after having been each opposite the others. no longer present an optical correspondence; conservation of the equality of length of two rigid sticks when one is slightly staggered in respect to the

2. See Piaget, *La Construction du réel chez l'enfant,* chap. I–II.

other; conservation of the distance between two immobile elements when new objects are interposed between them; and so forth). On the other hand, construction of the first reversible representational structures (around 7–8 years of age) effectively involves elaboration of corresponding notions of conservation.

It is useless to reproduce here the description of numerous reversible structures of an algebraic type, which we have pointed out elsewhere in the 6–8-year-old child's elaboration of notions of whole numbers, of projective or Euclidean lines, of geometric measure, of time, and so forth. The important thing is to remember that each of these constructions assumes a previous logical elaboration, participating among other things in the logic of classes, and that the first operations of this logic accessible to the child also assume, in order to constitute themselves, certain structures of an algebraic type, not yet identical with the group, but presenting some of its characteristics.

Let us take for an example the inclusion of a partial class A in a complete class B. Nothing seems simpler than to understand such a "fitting in," when all the elements are supplied simultaneously in the same field of perception (as when B = a visible collection of wooden beads, A = a part of B composed of 20 brown beads, and A' = another part composed of 2 or 3 white beads). However, it is sufficient to ask the child if the set B is more or less numerous than A ("Are there more wooden beads or more brown beads here?") to perceive the operational complexity of this inclusive fitting in of one part in a whole. Before the age of 7, on the average, the child answers that A has more beads than B, because, as soon as the set of B is split up into parts, this set no longer exists as such and what remains of B is now no more than the other part A' ("There are more brown ones than wooden ones because there are only two white ones left," the child will say despite knowing that the brown ones are also wooden). To establish the relation $A < B$, the child must go through the reversible operation $A + A' = B$, from which it is derived that $A = B - A'$ and $A' = B - A$. It is only when this reversibility of logical addition and subtraction of classes is acquired that the set B can be kept independent of the subdivisions that can be introduced into it. In other terms, inclusion of the part in the whole itself presupposes a previous algebraic structure.

Of what does this structure consist? Its simplest form, which we have called the structure of elementary "groupings," can be illustrated by the example of classification or additive grouping of classes. Its constitutive operations are

(1) $A + A' = B$; $B + B' = C$; $C + C' = D$; and so on, where all the classes of same rank (kind, order) are disjoint ($A \cdot A' = 0$; $B \cdot B' = 0$; etc.).

(2) $-A - A' = -B$, from which it is derived that $A' = B - A$; and so on.

(3) $A - A = 0$.

(4) $A + A = A$ (tautology).

(5) Associativity is limited to nontautological operations:
$(A + A') + B' = A + (A' + B')$, but $A + (A - A) \neq (A + A) - A$.

We recognize in this structure certain transformations common to the "group," such as $+A$, $-A$, and 0. But, first, associativity is restrained. Also, transformations take place only in a contiguous fashion—that is to say, by passing by the complementary class to the class immediately above. Of course, these two limitations greatly diminish the generality of this structure. But, from the genetic point of view, it is still important because it shows the undoubted need to go through an algebraic structure in order to reach the simplest logical constructions. Let us notice, moreover, that certain forms of scientific thought are restricted to structures of this type (for example, the zoological classification in which we again encounter each of these characteristics including contiguity: one cannot dissociate any two classes, such as the camel and the earthworm, to make a new class without first going through a series of dislocations of the kind $A' + C' = D - B'$, and so on).

Furthermore, we shall see that such structures also constitute, from the point of view of structures of order, incomplete nets, since all the lower bounds between classes of the same rank are zero. But, from the point of view that interests us here—that of the *relationship* of structures arising out of the mechanisms of spontaneous development of intelligence—it is even more valuable to find not only structures of considerable breadth and generality, but also certain inchoate forms of organization that, precisely because they have escaped the formulation of logicians and mathematicians, bear witness to their primitive nature.

IV

Structures of order, to which we can now return, are, we are told, structures of relations (such as, for example, the *net* or *lattice*) rather than structures of operations. But again we must make it clear what we mean. Undoubtedly, one can define the net entirely in terms of relations instead of introducing the operations $+$ and $\cdot$: in this case one considers the relations "x precedes y" or "y succeeds x" as basic, instead of deriving them from the operations $x \cdot y = x$ and $x + y = y$. But even when considering only relations between half-ordered elements, the fact remains that the transitivity of "x precedes y, and y precedes z, therefore x precedes z" consists in linking two relations into a single one, which we will treat as an additive operation that bears on relations.

But the net is not only an operational structure: it is by definition a reversible structure. However—and here is the great psychological importance of such systems—its reversibility is no longer, in the general case, inversion or negation (only certain kinds of distributive nets are complemented in a defined fashion and thus own "complementing elements of the first and second kind"); the general reversibility proper to the net is *reciprocity*. In fact, the net involves a *law of duality*, which consists of transposing the $\cdot$ and the $+$, as well as the connections of "precede" and "succeed." Let us then apply the law of duality to the following example, marking down here the relation of "preceding" by the symbol → and the relation of "succeeding" by the symbol ←:

(1) $AB \rightarrow A$ and $AB \rightarrow B$; $A \rightarrow (A + B)$ and $B \rightarrow (A + B)$ from which it follows

(2) $(AB) \rightarrow (A + B)$.

By duality, we obtain

(3) $(A + B) \leftarrow (AB)$.

Now we notice that (3) is not at all the negation of (2), but on the contrary a simple conversion of the relationship (2). In general, the law of duality proper to the net does not lead to an inversion or a negation, as is the case with algebraic structures, but to a change based on reciprocity—that is to say, on the permutation of order. Whereas inversion amounts to canceling the operation itself, independently of relations of order, reciprocity amounts to changing order without negating the operations at work.

The structures of order are thus just as fundamental to the mechanism of intelligence as the structures of group (or other similar structures), and it would be easy to show, as we have done for the latter, that structures of order are already beginning to be formed at the preoperational levels, as early as sensory-motor behavior and *a fortiori* throughout the entire period of *imaginal representation* (stretching from 2 to 7–8 years of age). But let us limit ourselves to characterizing the role that they play on the level of concrete operations (7 to 11 years old), before the appearance of propositional or formal operations (11 to 12 years), and to look for what their relationships are with algebraic structures at this first operational level.

The structures of order are constituted, during this stretch from 7 to 11 years of age, by systems of relations. While the elementary groupings of classes are based on the mode of reversibility that involves inversion or negation ($+A$ and $-A$), the groupings of relations are based on a second mode—that of reciprocity.

The simplest example of these spontaneous systems, whose development can be traced from the sensory-motor period forward, and which reaches equilibrium (that is to say, its operational level) as early as the age of 6–7, is that of the chain of transitive asymmetrical relations, or *qualitative seriation*. Already at the sensory-motor level, when a child of 1½ to 2 plays at building a tower by putting the largest of his blocks at the bottom and continuing in descending order of size, one can say that he is working out empirically and by a groping method (trial and error) a practical scheme that anticipates seriation. But as yet, it is only a question of an empirical scheme, based on a perceptual configuration and on the immediately perceived inequality of the few elements arranged there. If, instead of these elements whose relative dimensions are seen in a single glance, we present the child with elements that he has to compare two by two in a more careful way (for example, ten sticks of 10 to 19 cm arranged randomly), and if we ask him to place them in order of increasing length, we notice that the systematic seriation is different from this empirical seriation and that it supposes a complex interplay of operations. In fact, after a series of preparatory stages (couples of little uncoordinated groups, empirical series with corrections after the event, and so forth), the child ends up (but only around the age of 6½ to 7) by discovering a method that this time assures the construction of a complete and exact seriation, without groping or mistakes: he seeks, by comparing them two by two, the smallest of all these sticks (A) and puts it down; then he determines by the same comparisons the smallest of the remaining sticks (B) and places it beside A; in the same way he finds stick C, the smallest of all those left unseriated, and so forth. Thus, the method in this way constructed supposes understanding of the following relations: (1) that any element, such as E, is bigger then all its predecessors—that is, $E > A, B, C, D;$ (2) that the same element E is smaller than all its successors—that is, $E > F, G, H,$ and so on. Furthermore, it is essential to note that at the level of seriation by means of groping, the child is in no way certain of the transitivity of inequalities; after having found by side-by-side placement that $A < B$ and that $B < C$, he is not sure of the relation $A < C$ if A is hidden while leaving C visible. On the contrary, the discovery of the two relationships "$E > D, C,$ and so forth" and "$E < F, G,$ and so forth" involves ipso facto the transitivity (3) $A < C$ if $A < B$ and $B < C$.

Now if we try to formulate the relations used by the child in this seriation, we find a structure analogous to that of classification, but bearing only on relations. Let us call a the relation $A < B$, b the relation $A < C$, c the relation $A < D$, and so on, and let us call a' the relation $B < C$, b' the relation $C < D$, and so on. We then have

(1) $a + a' = b; \; b + b' = c;$ etc.

(2) $b - a' = a;$ etc.

(3) $a - a = 0$

(4) $a + a = a$

(5) incomplete associativity, as in p. 125.

But we notice that if the subtraction of the classes $A - A = 0$ gives the null class, which is the characteristic of inversion, subtraction of the relations $a - a = 0$ gives a difference of zero, which is not the same operation because a difference of zero is an equivalence. Thus, in the case of relations, composition consists simply of reading the relation between outer elements of two juxtaposed segments of a seriation: $A(a)B + B(a')C = A(b)C$ and the opposite operation of changing the order $A(b)C - B(a')C = A(b)C + C(a')B = A(a)B$. From such a point of view, the reversibility at work in such systems is thus based on reciprocity and no longer on negation; this is why $a - a$ leads to an equivalence and not to a null relationship.

We can then affirm that, from 7 to 11 years of age, at the level of concrete operations (elementary groupings of classes and of relations bearing on concrete objects, as opposed to verbal statements dissociated from all manipulation), structures of classes are dependent on inversion (algebraic structures) and structures of relations are dependent on reciprocity (structures of order). But do these two types of structures coexist in their inchoate period, without connections between them, or is there, on the contrary, some bond joining one of these systems to the other?

From the point of view of the psychology of operations of thought (without a concern for the eventual formalization of these primitive operational systems), it is appropriate to make an essential observation. If one refers to the classical distinction between the *extension* and the *intension* of concepts, one must atuomatically acknowledge (the whole world being in agreement on this) that the extension is made up of systems of classes that correspond to inversion and to the algebraic structures; but, psychologically, intensions are always made up of systems of relationships, and this is what is not always acknowledged. Whether the characteristics connoted in the understanding of a concept consist of predicates that are apparently not relative (trees are "ligneous," grass is "green,") or of explicit relations (the older ones are "older" than the younger ones), it is nonetheless impossible to think of the predicates of the first type otherwise than in relative terms: "green" means either a quality in the continuous series of hues leading from yellow or blue to green, or a quality common to different objects; "green" is thus, psychologically speaking, an asymmetrical or symmetrical relation, depending upon the context.

From such a point of view, there then exists between the structures of classes based on inversion and the structures of relations based on reciprocity, a close bond between the extension and the intension of concepts. This is why the four elementary groupings that we have been able to distinguish in the structures of classes at the level of concrete operations (comprising additive and multiplicative groupings, each of these in the form of one-to-one *into* and one-to-one *onto* correspondence) correspond exactly to the four elementary groupings of relationships. In other words, the same collections of elements can be structured either along the model of classes or along that of relations, a fact which insures the psychological unity of the system. But from the point of view of the operational structure, no structure exists at the level of the concrete operations, which unites the whole set of properties in a single system of transformations, and which thus assures the synthesis of inversion and reciprocity. This synthesis of two fundamental forms of reversibility will take place only at the final equilibrium state in the development of logical operations—that is to say, at the stage of interpropositional operations, about which we will speak in part VI.

V

If algebraic structures and structures of order thus appear to be deeply rooted in the psychological functioning of intellectual operations, can one say as much for topological structures?

It is interesting to notice first, in this respect, that the order of construction of geometric concepts and operations in the spontaneous development of the child[3] does not conform at all to the order of the historical stages of evolution of geometry and is closer to the logical order of priority of the fundamental groups on which the different types of spaces are based. Historically, metric or Euclidean geometry preceded projective geometry by many centuries, and topopogy has become autonomous only much more recently. On the other hand, from the standpoint of the fundamental groups, topology is first, and one can derive from it simultaneously metric Euclidean geometry (through the intermediary of a general metric) and projective geometry (the latter joining metric Euclidean geometry by the intermediary of affine geometry and of similitudes). Now, although the child does not start out with general topological schemes (for his topological intuitions are subordinate to certain perceptual conditions that are rapidly structured along Euclidean lines),[4] it is nonetheless striking that from the beginning of drawing the child does not distinguish among squares, circles, triangles, and other metric figures, but he differentiates very well between open or closed figures, situations of externality or internality in relation to a border (including the position on the border), separations and proximities (without conservation of distance), and so forth. Furthermore, starting thus from fundamental topological intuitions, he then directs himself simultaneously in the direction of projective structures and metric structures.

From a strictly operational point of view, it is appropriate to add that, side by side with operations of classes and relations that constitute the only "logical" operations at work on the level of concrete operations, we must consider what we have called "infralogical operations." The logical operation begins with the individual object and extends to classes that are always independent of the spatial configuration of the elements composing them, whereas the infralogical operation decomposes the object into its component parts or puts the object back together from its components. This mode of composition therefore differs from logical operations because it invokes the continuum and configurations. Although distinct in their structure from the logical operations, infralogical operations do not precede them in time: at the preoperational level there is no differentiation between the first infralogical intuitions and the first logical intuitions, whereas at the level of concrete operations two kinds of structures exist parallel to each other. It is interesting

---

3. *Spontaneous* means independent of school instructions but not, of course, of the stimuli of the social surroundings in general.

4. However, one would like to be able to study the perceptive space of the first weeks.

to observe this parallelism at the level of the first spontaneous operational
structures, for, however modest and insufficiently structured the elementary
forms of operational organization may be, one may discern in them the roots
of this parentage, or rather of this profound complementarity between topological structures and algebraic structures, which certain recent developments
in topology have revealed.[5]

VI

Thus it is not presumptuous to assert that operational structures of the intellect, while in formation, manifest from the beginning the presence of three
major types of organization, corresponding to what will become in mathematics algebraic structures, structures of order, and topological structures. It
is also appropriate to bring up the fact that very rapidly the parent structures
are coordinated and give rise, through their interstructural compositions, to
certain later structures, whose importance for the construction of logical and
mathematical ideas is just as great.

At the level of the concrete operations, which are linked to the manipulation
of objects and thus involve only certain operations of classes and relations
(elementary "groupings"), there does not yet exist any set structure that fuses
into a single system of transformations the inversions proper to algebraic
structures and the reciprocities proper to the structures of order. But, around
an average age of 11–12 years, a set of new operations is added to the concrete operations, the new operations bearing on propositions rather than on
objects. These *interpropositional operations* constitute a double structure
of group and net, each of which reconciles the inversion proper to algebraic
structures with the reciprocity proper to structures of order.

The group that therefore comes into play involves four transformations
(Klein group), which one can define in the following way for the particular
case of interpropositional operations:

(1) The *inverse* or *negation* (N) of an operation is its complement under
the set of associations of basis. For example:

$$N(p \vee q) = \overline{p \vee q} = (\overline{p} \cdot \overline{q}) \text{ or } N(p \supset q) = (\overline{p \supset q}) = (p \cdot \overline{q}).$$

(2) The *reciprocal* (R) of an operation is the same operation, but between denied propositions. For example:

$$R(p \vee q) = (\overline{p} \vee \overline{q}) = (p/q) \text{ or } R(p \supset q) = (\overline{p} \supset \overline{q}) = (q \supset p).$$

Let us notice that the reciprocal thus amounts to changing the order of the
terms of an implication. This fact offers a general way of conceiving a recip-

---

5. See the works of Pontrjagin interpreted by B. Eckman (*Topologie u. Algebra*,
Viertel j. Naturf. Ges., Zurich: 1944, p. 26) on the sense of a "complementarity" between the topological and algebraic meanings.

rocal, because every propositional operation can take the form of an implication!

Example:

$$(p \lor q) = (\overline{p} \supset q). \text{ Therefore } R(\overline{p} \supset q) = (q \supset \overline{p}) = (p/q).$$

(3) The *correlative* (C) of an operation results in the permutation of (v) and (·) in the normal form of this operation. For example:

$$C(p \lor q) = (p \lor q) \cdot (p \lor \overline{q}) \cdot (\overline{p} \lor q) = (p \cdot q)$$
$$C(p \supset q) = (p \lor q) \cdot (\overline{p} \lor q) \cdot (\overline{p} \lor \overline{q}) = (p \cdot q).$$

(4) The *identical* transformation (I) leaves the operation unchanged.

We then have the commutative group:

$$NR = C; \quad NC = R; \quad RC = N \text{ and } NRC = I.$$

For example, in the case of *p, q* we have

$$N(q \supset p) = (\overline{p} \cdot q) = C(p \supset q) \quad \text{that is, } NR = C$$
$$N(\underline{p} \cdot q) = (q \supset \underline{p}) = R(p \supset q) \quad \text{that is, } NC = R$$
$$R(\underline{p} \cdot q) = (p \cdot \underline{q}) = N(p \supset q) \quad \text{that is, } RC = N$$
$$R(p \cdot q) = (p \cdot q) \text{ and } N(p \cdot \overline{q}) = (p \supset q) \quad \text{that is, } NRC = I.$$

It is the same for ternary operations, and so on.[6] But, in certain cases (diagonals of the table of binary, tertiary operations, and so forth), we have R = N and C = I, or R = I and C = N, but the inverse, N, is, of course, always distinct from I.

We see then that this group INRC, which constitutes an algebraic structure, nonetheless incorporates into itself reciprocities, and these constitute the form of reversibility of structures of order. Thus, in psychological terms, this group constitutes both the synthesis and the form of final equilibrium of these two previously distinct series of operational structures, one based on inversion and the other on reciprocity.

The system of interpropositional operations also constitutes a net: every couple of operations involves a lower bound defined by their common part (·), as, for example,

$$(p = q) \cdot (p \lor q) = (p \cdot q)$$

and an upper bound defined by their union (v), as, for example,

$$(p \cdot q) \lor (\overline{p} \cdot \overline{q}) = (p = q).$$

However, from the very fact that it is complemented, this net admits inverse operations. Besides (and this is important to point out), for any two oper-

---

6. See Piaget, *Essai sur les transformations des coérations logiques*, Paris (P.U.F.), 1952.

ations, their lower bound (LB) and their upper bound (UB) together constitute a group; this is not the same as the group INRC, but is isomorphic to it and involves the transformations that we will call IaNaRaCa. We will define this group in the following manner.

Take a binary operation such as $p \vee q$. It can be perceived as being composed of two unitary operations (p and q) linked by a composite operation ($\vee$). In the same way, a ternary operation such as

$$(p \cdot q \cdot r) \vee (p \cdot \overline{q} \cdot r) \vee (\overline{p} \cdot \overline{q} \cdot r) \vee (\overline{p} \cdot \overline{q} \cdot \overline{r}) = [(q \supset p) \cdot (p \supset r)]$$

can be perceived as being composed of two binary operations ($q \supset p$) and ($p \supset r$) linked by a composing operation ($\cdot$). The transformations I, N, R, and C applied to the composing operation will be called Ia, Na, Ra and Ca. Now if x and y are any two operations of the net, LB their lower bound and UB their upper bound, we have the following group:[7]

(Ia) $x \cdot y$ (= LB)	and	(Ia) $\underline{x} \vee \underline{y}$ (= UB)
(Na) $\underline{x/y} = \overline{x} \vee \overline{y}$		(Na) $x \cdot y$
(Ra) $x \cdot y$		(Ra) $x/y = \overline{x} \vee \overline{y}$
(Ca) $x \vee y$ (= UB)		(Ca) $x \cdot y$ (= LB)

We thus have

$$Ca(LB) = UB \text{ and } Ca(UB) = LB.$$

We have further

$$Na(LB) = Ra(UB) \text{ and } Na(UB) = Ra(LB).$$

And we also have all the usual transformations of the group:

$$Na(x \cdot y) = RaCa(x \cdot y);$$
$$NaRaCa(x \cdot y) = x \cdot y;$$

and so on.

In other words, if the group INRC incorporates reciprocity, the net of interpropositional operations (including inversion and the fundamental relation among their bounds and the operations they link together) has a group structure.

Now, from the genetic point of view, this double structure of group and net that interpropositional operations constitute is just the end point of the elementary structures of "groupings" (which represent, we have seen, imperfect groups, because of lack of total associativity, and semi-nets). The passage from the groupings of classes and relations to the group-and-net structure of the propositional operations can, in fact, be thought of as the result of the intervention of combinatory operations, substituting for merely additive and multi-

---

7. See Piaget, *Essai sur les transformations des coérations logiques,* p. 159, prop. 247. See also the following prop. and prop. 263.

plicative operations. In other terms, for the simple inclusion hierarchy of a classification, for example, the net substitutes a "set of parts" by combining these parts *n* by *n* with each other. But such a combinatory composition is itself only a generalization of the classification process: the set of parts, which constitutes the double structure of the net and the group under discussion, results from the set of the possible classifications of the elements of the grouping, themselves translated into propositional language.

VII

In our conclusion we will consider both the general interpretation of mathematics—which necessarily influences the educator, whether he wishes it to or not—as well as its practical application.

Concerning the first of these two subjects, the essential problem is to know whether the educator, to be loyal to the spirit of contemporary mathematics, must take his inspiration from a rigorous logicism that is Platonist in orientation, or whether he can consider mathematical thought as an extension of the spontaneous constructions of the intellect, in which case he can have recourse to the teachings of psychology as well as to those of logic.

However, if the preceding psychogenetic data are indeed valid, the conflict between logicism and psychologism could at least be somewhat attenuated if one were to introduce a certain number of distinctions, which amount mainly to dissociating psychology itself from "psychologism," and logic itself from "logicism."

"Psychologism" is an attempt to found logic on psychological laws. In this respect, L. Apostel said, "For psychologism, the laws of logic are laws of psychology and describe true reasoning, whether the most frequent, or the most normal, or the most practically efficient."[8] Stated more familiarly, psychologism is a way of applying psychology to an area to which it is not relevant, since psychological laws are based upon factual observations, and laws of logic derive from deductive or normative necessity.

Reciprocally, "logicism" is an intrusion of the logician's thought into the realm of facts. It may consist, for instance, in affirming that the intellect of humans (whether of scholars themselves or of students just beginning in mathematics) achieves logical rigor only by following specific routes, such as intuition of entities, or the individual's submission to the rules of a language acquired from outside.

But, if one agrees to leave the job of studying facts to psychology and the job of analyzing foundations to logic, it appears that these two sciences together offer more points of contact than do the "psychologism" and "logicism" with which people have sought to identify them. Moreover, these points

---

8. L. Apostel, *Logique et breuve,* Methods, vol. 5 (1953), p. 303.

of contact are more useful to the educator than the doctrinal oppositions, which are alien to the very progress of such sciences.

Actually, psychology holds out a hand to logic by showing that the intellect is spontaneously oriented towards the organization of certain operational structures that are isomorphic to structures or to parts of structures that mathematicians place at the beginning of their constructions and logicians find in systems they elaborate. But this partial isomorphism does not mean that rules of logic are laws of thought. The set structures toward which the intellect is oriented in the course of its development correspond neither to preformed nervous structures (or to forms a priori) nor to physical structures empirically registered. They are only laws of equilibrium presenting themselves under the form of systems of possible operations, of which only some are actualized as a function of surrounding physical and social conditions. Logic studies the complete set of all these possibilities, and logic is free to furnish them with whatever foundations are needed. Thus, we would not know how to conceive of points of friction between the deductive and exhaustive analysis of possible logics on the one hand, and, on the other hand, the experimental determination of possibilities or impossibilities that characterize the forms of equilibrium corresponding to different levels of organization of the intellect. Without a doubt, the logician's algebraic techniques can be useful to the psychologist in his description of forms of equilibrium or of structures, but that does not mean that he has the effrontery to assimilate without further ado laws of logic to those of thought.

As for knowing whether logic in turn will seek some point of contact with psychology, that will be up to future research. Certain logicians remain dominated by distrust of psychologism in general. But here one needs to know whether the fear of psychologism results from the logical attitude itself or from a residue of logicism that, without his realizing it, leads the logician to opt in favor of one rather than another psychological conception of the manner in which an individual manages to grasp logical connections. Other logicians, like Apostel, distinguish between traditional psychologism and a more subtle resort to psychology: "we do not, like the 19th century psychologists (Sigwart, Heymans, Wundt, Erdmann), affirm that rules of logic are laws of thought. We only say: there are laws of thought such that, in a certain social structure and for individuals possessing certain characteristics, we can infallibly (with physical necessity) force these individuals to accept our conclusions if they accept our premises, providing that we also perform certain operations, whose stages are described by the rules of correct demonstration."[9] Generally speaking, it is quite possible that current work on the

---

9. L. Apostel, *loc. cit.,* p. 305. Apostel's position thus tends to appeal to "the psychosocial concomitants of logical operations" (p. 305), which defines a problem for collaboration, on which work in psychology is not, in fact, as nonexistent as he supposes. On the contrary, the psychologist's difficulty will be to admit, for real operations, a physical necessity distinct from psychological necessity, unless this notion should be reducible in the final analysis to what we call (with Gestalt theory) the laws of equilibrium.

relations between logic and language will end up by concluding that language itself sinks its roots, precisely to the extent that its structures reflect those of logic, in operational systems deeper than the connections existing between mere verbal signs.

In short, the future of the relation between psychology and logic remains wide open and cannot be prejudged as a function of past mistakes. Thus, from the practical point of view, there cannot be any question for the educator of a choice between formalist methods founded on logic and dynamic methods based on psychology: the purpose of mathematics instruction will always be the attaining of logical rigor as well as comprehension of an adequate formalism and only psychology is in a position to furnish instructors with data on the manner in which this rigor and this formalism can most surely be obtained. Furthermore, there is no proof that starting with formalism is an effective way to end up with an authentic kind of formalism; on the contrary, the ravages of pseudo-formalism and formalism that remains purely verbal because it is too precocious show the dangers of a method that ignores the laws of mental development.

In reality, if the edifice of mathematics rests on "structures" that correspond to the structures of the intellect, it is on the progressive organization of these operational structures that mathematical teaching must be based. And, psychologically, the operations derive from actions that are coordinated with structures as they become internalized. Thus it is wrong to imagine that the initial appeal to actions compromises subsequent rigor and favors treating mathematical truths as factual rather than logical truths. Such empiricism occurs when the educator substitutes for a mathematical demonstration a physical experiment accompanied simply by a lecture on the results obtained. But when the experiment serves as an opportunity for the coordination of actions, and when abstraction is from the actions themselves and not objects, the experiment paves the way for the deductive approach instead of hindering it.[10] If all acquisition of knowledge by the child presupposes a participation in experience, this psychological fact does not justify empiricism at all, for there exist two kinds of experiences: the physical experience (experiment) leading to an abstraction of characteristics drawn from the object itself, and the logico-mathematical experience leading to abstraction from actions or operations effected on objects, rather than from objects as such. Thus, recourse to experience and to action (and generally, among the procedures of mathematical initiation, the pedagogy called "dynamic") does not compromise subsequent deductive rigor at all; on the contrary, it prepares the way for such rigor by supplying it with foundations that are real and not merely verbal.

---

10. For example, in the experiments on order (direct order, inverse order due to a change in direction or a rotation of the apparatus, and so on), the child abstracts order not from objects as such, but from the actions or operations through which the objects were arranged. The subject's understanding will naturally be better if he has intervened actively and has not been limited to passive contemplation of the result of actions performed by others.

10 Algorithmic Approach to Curriculum Construction in Mathematics

*Joseph M. Scandura is currently an associate professor
of mathematics education and structural learning at
the University of Pennsylvania. A graduate in mathematics and in educational psychology, he completed
his doctorate in mathematics education at Syracuse University in 1962, at which time he started his
post-doctoral work in both mathematics and the
psychology of learning mathematics. The holder of
several scholarships, fellowships, and distinguished
awards, Professor Scandura has demonstrated both
his talent for scholarly research and his pedagogical knowledge in reference to mathematics teaching
through his active participation as a consultant
for several university-affiliated mathematics learning
projects, the Conference on Mathematics Education of the Pennsylvania Department of Education,
and the Philadelphia schools.*

*Author of a great number of valuable books and
articles in mathematics education (particularly in the
psychology of learning mathematics), he is the recipient of a large number of federal, state, and non-
governmental research grants.*

*Before presenting his theory of mathematical knowl-
edge, Scandura discusses the increased interest in basic
research in math education and the question of behavioral versus subjective goals as it relates to mathematics curricula.*

*Regarding his theory of mathematical knowledge,
the author believes that all mathematical behavior
(even creative behavior) can be considered as a rule-
governed activity. He outlines here his theory em-
ploying rule sets and combinations of rules.*

JOSEPH M. SCANDURA

Preparation of this report was supported in part by grants
NSF-GW6796 and OEG-3-71-0136 to the author.

*The casual reader is encouraged to press on to the
final section concerning curriculum construction,
as Scandura, using rules to characterize a curriculum,
illustrates the process of distilling tasks, devising
rules for each task, and finding a higher-order relationship between rules. He feels that this rule-based
curriculum effectively deals with the "goal definition" problem.*

For the past fifteen years, most of the research activity in mathematics education has been concentrated in curriculum development. During that time,
only a small handful of people have been actively engaged in basic research on
mathematics learning.

Today the situation is changing rapidly. While there are still only a few
centers actively engaged in fundamental research on mathematics learning,
mathematics educators are turning, more and more, to basic research as
a basis for further development. This is, it should be noted, in direct contra-
distinction to the earlier views of some of those engaged in curriculum
development—those who made a special point of downgrading the importance
of basic research in education.

The goals of this paper are (1) to attempt to explain and account for the
new interest in research in mathematics education during the last few years;
(2) to identify a basic problem with curriculum construction in mathematics
education; (3) to describe a new theory of mathematical knowledge; and
(4) to describe how this theory might be used to provide an algorithmic base
for curriculum construction.

1. WHY THE INCREASED INTEREST IN BASIC RESEARCH IN MATHEMATICS EDUCATION?

The question of why interest in basic research in mathematics education
has been increasing is perhaps best answered by tracing the history of basic research and development in this country over the past four decades.

It seems that successful scientific and technological development requires
the presence of two vital ingredients: first, an adequate scientific base, usually obtained through basic research; and second, adequate financial and social support, most frequently by governmental agencies.

As a case in point, consider the space program. Here, a well-worked-out
scientific base goes as far back as Newton's theory of mechanics and includes,
as well, Goddard's more recent work during the 1920s on liquid-fuel rocket
technology. Yet, in spite of the ready availability of this ground-breaking
work, full-scale development of space technology did not come about for
many years. Such development began only after considerable governmental

pressure and concomitant economic pressure were brought to bear. The United States did not move into the space field seriously until the launching of Sputnik by the Soviet Union was coupled with the supposed "missile gap" of the 1960s. In short, it was public pressure and continued Soviet accomplishments that prompted President Kennedy's pledge for a moon landing before 1970.

Today, almost a decade later, after the spectacular achievements of Apollo 11, it is questionable whether the nation is willing to commit itself so single-mindedly to landing men on Mars in the near future, despite the technological feasibility of such a goal. At the present time, domestic issues have taken priority with a large percentage of the American public and, as a result, much of the money that would normally be earmarked for space projects will undoubtedly be diverted to other areas.

In the late 1950s, the situation in mathematics education was much the same as it was in space research. Sputnik also gave realization to the American people that mathematics education in this country was woefully inadequate.

Furthermore, fundamental advances in mathematical research in the preceding fifty to one hundred years did, in this instance, provide a more than adequate scientific base for revolutionizing the content of school mathematics. (It is worth noting in this regard that the so-called new mathematics was *not* an invention of curriculum developers of the last decade.)

More recently, though, major improvements in mathematics education have come more slowly; it has been much harder to come up with new programs that are really better than what already exists. At best, the most recent programs have simply been refinements of other programs and, at worst, they have been unrealistic and/or philosophically indefensible. Some mathematics educators, for example, would have us teach high school students the same material that is at the present time offered in the junior and senior year to students at our better universities. This idea is completely feasible and perhaps even desirable for extremely gifted students; but it can be applied to the teaching of our more numerous "top 20 percent" only by overemphasizing the relative role of mathematics in the high-school curriculum.

One obvious reason for the slowdown is the economic pressure of the Vietnam war. This has resulted in greatly decreased support for research and development, and has made it extremely difficult, if not impossible, to maintain the pace of the late fifties and early sixties. Perhaps the most fundamental reason, however, is the lack of an adequate base in the behavioral sciences (and educational philosophy) for making significant further improvements in curriculum development.

In effect, when adequate basic knowledge is available, the relative gains from developmental activity are likely to be greater than those from basic research. However, after development has progressed for a period of time, the payoff from basic research is likely to be much greater. Figuratively speaking, developmental activity without basic research is much like living it up on past savings without any concern for the future. This is the situation in which mathematics education finds itself today. The reservoir of knowledge about mathematics as it relates to mathematics teaching in the schools is largely exhausted, and an all-out effort must be made to build up a new body of knowledge to prepare the way for breakthroughs in development similar to those of the past. This is particularly true in the areas of teaching methodology and curriculum construction.

The situation is not unlike that in the field of atomic energy where, on the basis of the knowledge provided by Einstein's Theory of Relativity and the work of other pioneering physicists like Rutherford and Fermi, scientists and engineers were able to produce in the late 1930s the world's first sustained chain reaction. Later, given the added impetus of World War II, scientists were able to create the atom bomb. Later still, on the basis of the same basic know-how, they were able to produce the hydrogen bomb and even to go on to harness the atom for peaceful purposes. However, when it came to harnessing hydrogen power (the fusion process), the situation was quite different. In spite of the billions of dollars that have been spent on development, the field is at a relative standstill, and many scientists believe that taming hydrogen power must remain theoretical until much more is known about the processes operating inside the nucleus of the atom.

2. WHAT SHOULD BE INCLUDED IN A MATHEMATICS CURRICULUM?

In curriculum construction, the inevitable question arises as to what should be included—that is, what should the objectives of the curriculum be? This question of objectives has led to a good deal of controversy.

There seem to be two fairly well defined, but opposed, points of view. On the one hand, many educational psychologists hold that stating objectives is worthless insofar as educational planning is concerned, unless the objectives are stated unambiguously and in operational terms—that is, in terms that make it possible to determine, by testing the learner, whether or not an objective has been attained. Only then, it is argued, can objectives serve any real purpose. Proponents of this view have organized curricula on such easily tested objectives as "Counts orally from one to ten"; "Supplies the number that is one more, one less, or in between any two given numbers less than 200"; "Adds two numbers with sums up to 20, using expanded notation when required"; "Writes any given date in terms of the month, day, and year"; and "Uses an inch ruler in measuring real objects or pictures to the nearest inch."

The other group, composed primarily of mathematicians and mathematics educators, has been just as firm. It is useless to specify objectives, they would argue, since only the most trivial objectives can actually be specified. A typical comment might go something like this:

> The ability to make intelligent guesses, the ability to think mathematically, and so on, are the important objectives of mathematical education,

but we are, as yet, unable to define them operationally. We think it is important for people to appreciate mathematics, to develop intellectual independence, to develop effective habits of thinking, to appreciate the importance of deductive thought; and furthermore, we feel that we can make good judgments as to which kinds of instructional situations may be helpful in achieving these ends. Do not try to pin us down prematurely as to just what is involved.

My own view is somewhere in between. On the one hand, I feel that complete reliance on operationally defined objectives has led some to a fragmented curriculum—a curriculum based on discrete bits of knowledge with little or no attention to basic relationships that may exist in the subject matter—or to general processing skills that are important in learning and doing mathematics. On the other hand, I feel that the nonobjectivists have not gone as far as possible in pinning down the vague and nonoperational aims of mathematics education that they propose.

What is needed is an explicit and operational way to characterize mathematical knowledge (and processes) that is consistent with what we "feel" knowing mathematics is all about. Until this is accomplished, curriculum construction will continue to be based either on inadequate behavioral concepts or on "seat of the pants" intuition. Where the former view predominates, we can probably expect little more than what the increasing number of new profit-motivated curriculum concerns (such as Independent Learning Systems and Westinghouse Learning Corporation) have to offer.
The approaches being proposed all seem to revolve around this fragmented view of operational objectives. Where the latter view predominates, curriculum construction will remain subject to only subjective or at best inadequate objective evaluation. (Most mathematics educators agree, for example, that current techniques for measuring creativity and problem-solving ability in mathematics are less than adequate.)

3. A THEORY OF MATHEMATICAL KNOWLEDGE: CAN RULES ACCOUNT FOR CREATIVE BEHAVIOR?

Mathematics is perhaps the most highly organized body of knowledge known to man. Yet, in spite of its clarity of structure, most of the basic research done on mathematics learning and behavior has been strictly empirical. To be sure, there has been a fair amount of research in the area, and the amount seems to be growing rapidly; but there has been no superstructure, no framework within which to view mathematical knowledge and mathematical behavior in a psychologically meaningful way.

A number of psychologists seriously feel that the mechanisms involved in language, mathematical behavior, and other subject-matter behavior may be accounted for within the confines of S-R mediation theory. This may be possible in principle (62)(100), but the networks of S-R associations required to do the job would almost certainly be so complex as to provide little intuitive guidance in formulating research on complex mathematical learning.[1]

As a way around these problems, linguists, like Chomsky (10)(11), have introduced rules and other generative mechanisms to account for (idealized) language behavior. Although many details still need to be worked out, it is generally agreed that some sort of analysis in terms of rules will prove adequate to account for most language behavior.

During the past few years, I have been attempting to develop a similar approach to mathematics learning (80)(85)(86)(87)(88). No comprehensive scheme for classifying mathematical behaviors has been proposed, however, and most (but not all) of the experimental research has been based on relatively simple mathematical tasks (87). The basic supposition has been that if we can understand what is going on here, we will be in a better position to understand more complex mathematical learning. While there has been increasing support for this contention among behavioral scientists (4)(48)(64), many of my colleagues in mathematics education have been skeptical. Presumably, they have taken a position similar to that which I have with respect to S–R mediation theory—the position that any interpretation of complex mathematical learning in terms of simple rules will surely be inadequate.

In reaction, I would propose and defend the rather strong thesis that rules *are* the basic building block of *all* mathematical knowledge, and that if looked at in the right way, *all* mathematical behavior is rule-governed. More specifically, it is proposed that the mathematical behavior any given subject is *potentially* capable of, under *ideal* conditions of performance, can be accounted for precisely in terms of a finite set of rules.

This statement is clearly meant to imply more than just a *post hoc* account of a given finite corpus of behaviors. If limited to this, the claim would be trivially true, since any given subject during his lifetime is necessarily limited to a finite number of behaviors. (A finite number of behaviors can obviously be generated by a finite number of rules.)

Furthermore, this is not a thesis to be proved, since it is basically empirical in nature. The problem is that we have no operational way of determining the potential behavior of a subject independently of the rules we use to characterize his knowledge. Unfortunately, it would be extremely difficult and time-consuming to obtain an adequate sample of mathematical behaviors to work with under the ideal conditions envisioned—that is, conditions under which the subject is unencumbered by memory or his limited capacity to process information.

What we shall do instead is to propose and evaluate alternative characterizations of given finite corpora of behavior in terms of their relative power or parsimony. That is, given a large class of behaviors, such as those associated with mastery of a given school curriculum, the idea is not only to come up with a finite set of rules that characterizes the curriculum, but to come up

---

1. For arguments pro and con, see Arbib (3), Scandura (85) (90) (91), and Suppes (99).

with the best possible set. (Loosely speaking, power refers to the diversity of behaviors that the characterization accounts for; parsimony refers to the number and intuitive simplicity of the rules in the characterizing set.) Such criteria, of course, have been an essential part of formal linguistics ever since Chomsky's influential *Syntactic Structures* was published (11).

In order for a characterization to have maximal relevance to psychology, however, these criteria alone are not sufficient. It is also important that a theory of knowledge (that is, a characterization) be compatible with the mechanisms that govern human learning and performance. Specifically, it is important, in addition to specifying finite rule sets, also to specify *how* the constituent rules may be *combined* to generate behavior. It is such "rules of combination" that must find parallels in the way learned rules are put to use in particular situations.[2]

The basis of my present argument is that, given suitable rules of combination, much of what normally goes under the rubric of creative behavior can be accounted for in terms of finite rule sets. In order to limit the scope, we shall concentrate primarily on those kinds of rules that are more properly associated with mathematical or logical content—specifically, with mathematical systems and axiomatic theories. In each case, we begin with a mathematical characterization and then show what it means to know the underlying mathematics in a behavioral sense.

Relatively little attention is given to so-called mathematical processes.[2] Thus, for example, inference rules are discussed, but relatively little is said about heuristics and other higher-order rules by which inference rules may be combined in constructing proofs. This does not imply, however, that such processing skills cannot be formulated in terms of rules. On the contrary, it is basically a simple matter to formulate such heuristics as "organize (arrange) the data" and "work backward from the unknown" as rules (73). What *is* hard is to show explicitly how these rules may be combined with other rules to solve problems. Even this problem is not insurmountable, however, and some illustrative analyses of this sort have been worked out.[2]

What is a Rule?

Let us first agree on exactly what we mean by a *rule*. In spite of an increasing amount of research on the subject, it is perhaps surprising that the term has no clearly defined meaning among behavioral scientists.

The first thing we need to do is to make a sharp distinction between underlying rules—or, as we shall see shortly, generative procedures composed of rules—and rule-governed (RG) behavior. Intuitively speaking, a class of be-

---

2. This question of relationships between different levels of theorizing is extremely important, but we cannot go into it here. For details, see Scandura (81) and my forthcoming books with Gordon and Breach Science Publishers, *Theory in Structural Learning* and *Mathematics and Structural Learning*. A taxonomy of processes is given in Scandura, *Mathematics: Concrete Behavioral Foundations.* (N.Y.: Harper & Row, 1971).

haviors is said to be RG if the behavior can be generated by a common algorithmic (generative) procedure of some sort. This means, in effect, that a person who has mastered *any* underlying procedure should, ideally speaking, be able to generate each and every response, given any particular stimulus in the class of stimuli.

More specifically, RG behavior involves the ability to give the appropriate response in a class of functionally distinct responses to each stimulus in a class of functionally distinct stimuli. The class of S–R pairs, defined in this way, is called *S–R instances*. To see what this means, consider simple addition. The proposed definition says that the behavior is RG if each pair of numbers is attached to a unique number called the *sum*. Thus, for example, the numbers 5 and 4 can be paired with any overt representation of the number 9, but not with any representation, say, for the number 6.

Ideally, then, RG behavior corresponds precisely to the notion of a function in the mathematical sense. That is, *every* stimulus is paired with a unique response. When looked at in this way, it is clear that what psychologists call *concepts* and *associations* can be viewed as special cases of rules. Concepts are simply rules in which each stimulus in a class is paired with a common response. Associations are further restricted to a single stimulus-response pair. Thus it may turn out that the goal of some psychologists to reduce complex learning to S–R associations may be quite misplaced. Rather than reducing complex learning to association theory, it may be more sensible to view the sort of learning studied by neoassociationists as a relatively useless restriction of learning in general. These matters have been discussed at length elsewhere (85) (86) (87), and there is no need to repeat the details here.

Let me now turn to the idea of a rule, or generative procedure. Originally, I viewed a rule as an ordered triple (D, O, R), where D is the set of (*n*-tuples of) stimulus properties that determine the responses and O is the operation or generative procedure by which the responses in R are derived from the critical properties in D (80) (85) (88) (90). Although it suggested a number of fairly interesting experiments on rule learning (83), this characterization still leaves much at the intuitive level when the procedures are at all complex. More of the detail involved can be represented by adopting ideas taken from recursion theory. In particular, a generative procedure is a sequence consisting of at most four kinds of rules:

1. encoding rules by which essential properties of stimuli are put into store;

2. transforming rules by which things in store are transformed into something else in store;

3. decoding rules by which things are taken out of store and made observable; and

4. rules for selecting other rules, given the output of some previous rule (which is in store).

Church (14) proposed that any set of behaviors that mathematicians would be willing to classify as partially recursive could be generated by a procedure composed of just these four types of rules. In general, this would include just about all the mathematical behaviors one normally expects of the school-age child, the ability to perform arithmetic computations, the ability to construct geometric figures with ruler and compass, and so forth.

Characterization of Mathematical Knowledge

The main purpose of my paper is to show how complex mathematical behavior might possibly be accounted for in terms of finite rule sets. Do not expect a complete formulation.

Mathematical Systems. Every mathematical *system* consists of one or more basic sets of elements, together with one or more operations and/or relations and/or distinguished elements of the basic sets. By capitalizing on certain logical equivalences, it is possible to reduce the characterizing elements to one basic set and one or more relations. Consider a simple example: the system whose basic set consists of three "undefined" elements A, B, C (denoted $\{A, B, C\}$), with A being distinguished in the sense that it serves as an "identity," and whose defining relation is

$$o = \{(A, A) \to A, (A, B) \to B, (B, A) \to B, (A, C) \to C, (C, A) \to C,$$
$$(B, B) \to C, (C, C) \to B, (B, C) \to A, (C, B) \to A\} .$$

This is a system in which the distinguished element A "maps" every element it is paired with into itself. When B is combined with B, the result is C, and when C is combined with C, the result is B. Finally, B combined with C in either order results in A. Notice that no meaning is specified for any of the elements A, B, C, or the operation. They are "undefined terms."

What may be called an *embodiment* of a mathematical system results on assignment of meaning to the undefined elements. Thus, in the example just cited, the undefined terms might correspond to certain rotations with A corresponding to a rotation of $0°$, B to a rotation of $120°$, and C to a rotation of $240°$. In this case the operation would simply be "followed by." That is, the result of combining two rotations is a single rotation that results in the same action as first doing one rotation and then the other. For example, a rotation of $120°$, followed by one of $240°$, results in the same action as a rotation of $0°$.

These definitions of systems and embodiments say something about the nature of the objects we are studying, and in that sense they are extremely important. They do not, however, tell very much about their psychological nature.

What kinds of behavior are implied by knowing systems and embodiments of this sort? And how can such behaviors be accounted for in terms of rules?

First, knowing a system certainly implies the ability to compute within the system. Thus, for example, given the pair A, B, the knower should be able to give the "sum" B. He should also be able to do more complex computations, such as

$$[(AoB)oA]oC \rightarrow (BoA)oC \rightarrow BoC \rightarrow A,$$

which involve combining individual facts (that is, associations). In addition, the knower should be able to give "differences" (that is, given the sum and one of the "addends," he should be able to generate the other addend).

If these were the only kinds of behavior to be accounted for, we could simply list the facts (rules) involved. But clearly, any reasonable interpretation of "knowing a system" must also deal with relationships as well. For example, mastery of a number system would surely include the ability to generate the subtraction (difference) rule from the addition rule (and vice versa). Knowing that $B + C = A$, for example, should be a sufficient basis for generating the corresponding subtraction fact, $A - B = C$.

Relational rules of this sort provide a simple way to account for such behaviors. Thus, instead of listing all of the subtraction facts separately, it would be sufficient to know the addition facts together with the relational rule (assuming, as is traditional in formal linguistics, that individual rules can be composed, that is, performed in succession).

The obvious way to account for such relationships—the way taken by curriculum developers of the operational-objectives persuasion—is simply to add more rules to the characterization. There are, however, major problems with this approach (89). For one thing, listing a new rule for each kind of relationship would have a *post hoc* flavor that would not likely add much in the way of understanding more creative behavior. For each *new* system (of the same type) considered, for example, there would be a new relational rule for each one in the original system. Even granting the economy obtained by eliminating inverses and the like, the number of rules could grow large very fast. This would not be bad in itself, assuming that this is the best one could do. The important question, however, is this: Can we come up with a more efficient account that at the same time is more powerful and allows for some measure of creative behavior?

To answer this question, first note that knowing how one or more systems are related to a given one may provide a basis for knowing how to compute in the new systems, given how to compute in the original. The relationships of interest will generally be mathematical, but they need not be limited to morphisms. For example, one system may be a simple *generalization* of another, as with cyclic 5 and cyclic 3 groups.

Because of the way particular relationships are defined, however, this advantage will generally be limited. With homomorphisms, for example, the ability to compute in the new system applies only to the defining operations themselves and not, say, to their inverses or to relationships between the operations. It is worth noting, nonetheless, that knowing even a relatively simple set of interrelated rules such as this would make possible a certain degree of creative behavior (what might be called "analogical reasoning"). For example, suppose that a subject has learned how to add in system A and that he knows the homomorphism that connects A to system B (that is, that he can generate the elements in B that correspond to those in A). Then the subject should be able to add in system B without ever being told how. If we let the homomorphism be one to one (an isomorphism), let system A be the embodiment of the illustrative 3 group above, and let system B be the illustrative system itself, then one might generate a sum in the abstract system B by (1) using the isomorphism to determine the corresponding elements in A, (2) adding in A, and (3) using the isomorphism in reverse direction to determine the element in B corresponding to the sum (in A). (Notice that this follows as long as our rules of combination allow for composition of rules.)

We can get a far more powerful and parsimonious characterization, however, by simply allowing rules to operate not only on ordinary stimuli, but on other rules as well. Such rules may be said to be acting in a higher-order capacity or, for short, to be *higher-order rules.* Although functions on functions are common in various branches of analysis (and their formalization is routine), the idea seems not to have pervaded formal linguistics. The closest linguists have come in this regard has been to introduce the notion of a *grammatical transformation* between phrase markers (11), which closely parallels what we have here called *relational rules* (that is, rules between addition and subtraction).

There are two reasons why this has probably not been done in the past: first, grammatical transformations have resisted mathematical treatment (65) insofar as this relates to computer science; and second, no existing approach to psychology that I know of provides any real motivation for introducing them.

This is unfortunate, since there is a very simple and intuitively sound reason for including higher-order rules: the idea of allowing rules (in rule sets) to operate on other rules is compatible with the following intuitively appealing hypothesis concerning performance. If a subject does not have a rule available for achieving a desired goal, then he typically will try to construct a rule that does work (81). There is a good deal of introspective evidence in favor of this hypothesis, and we have already collected some empirical support for it. In a recent study (82) it was found that the ability to use parentheses was a sufficient basis for combining learned rules so as to solve the given tasks that involved interpreting new statements of mathematical rules. Later analysis of these tasks showed that use of parentheses may be viewed as a higher-order rule (90). We now have a study underway in which we have succeeded in generalizing this result to a number of different kinds of situations and populations. Further discussion would be out of place here, however, since a relatively complete treatment of this idea and related issues concerned with psychological theory will soon be available (81).

Allowing rule sets to act in this way makes it possible for them to "grow" in ways not possible by just forming simple compositions (of rules). Thus higher-order rules may generate completely new kinds of rules, and these rules, in turn, may be used to generate still other rules.

Let us see what higher-order rules might do for us in the present situation. To make things definite, suppose that a subject has learned a higher-order rule that connects each operator (rule) with its inverse. Such a rule would connect not only, say, addition of numbers with subtraction, but composition of all sorts (such as permutations, rotations, rigid motions, and so on) with the corresponding inverse operations. The defining operation of each system and its inverse may be thought of as being distinct rules that are mapped one onto the other by this higher-order "inverse" rule. Assume, in addition, that the subject has learned how to add in system A, has learned the relation (such as a homomorphism) between system A and system B, and also has learned how to form the composition of arbitrary rules (in the rule set).

In this case, there are all sorts of behaviors that the (idealized) subject would be capable of. For example, he would be able to subtract, not only in system A but in system B as well. To see this, we need only observe that he can form the composition of the rule between systems A and B and the higher-order inverse rule. This composite (higher-order) rule in turn would allow the subject first to generate an addition rule in system B and then to generate a subtraction rule in system B. This subtraction rule, in turn, would allow the subject to subtract. Translated into more meaningful terms, a rule set of this sort would imply such abilities as finding inverses with rigid motions, given only the ability to add numbers. But then, isn't this just the sort of thing we have in mind when we think of creative behavior?

Axiomatic Theories. There is clearly more to knowing systems than simply knowing the rules and interrelationships within these systems. This amounts to internal knowledge of the systems, but it says nothing about the systems in the descriptive sense.

Axiomatic theories are concerned with properties of systems. As an example of one such property, notice that in the illustrative system it does not make any difference in which order two elements are combined. The system satisfies the commutative property; in fact, it satisfies all of the axioms (properties) of a commutative group of order three.

In order to define precisely what we mean by an axiomatic theory, the next thing to observe is that a set of axioms or properties defines a family of systems—namely, that family consisting of all and only those systems that have each of the given properties. Therefore, an *axiomatic theory* may be defined as a set of properties that holds in the family of systems defined by a given set of axioms. The set of axioms, of course, belongs to the set of properties.

Paralleling the discussion of systems, we now ask, "What kinds of behavior are involved in knowing axiomatic theories, and what kinds of rules are needed to account for these kinds of behavior?" Due to the complexities involved, the discussion is restricted largely to lower-order rules.

The *sine qua non* of mastering a theory is knowing the axioms and theorems of that theory. In behavioral terms, this ability may be thought of as being able to give on demand the conclusions associated with each set of premises. Thus, as with knowing the particular addition facts of the illustrative system, one might be tempted to characterize knowledge of particular theories as sets of discrete associations. This would be wrong, however, on two counts. First, the number of theorems associated with any given theory (including trivial ones) is infinitely large, so that they could not all be learned in this way. (Of course, the number of important theorems is usually much smaller.) Second, and more basic, such a characterization, while feasible in part, would not be very parsimonious or powerful. Many more rules would be needed than might be desired, and important relationships would simply be ignored.

One problem has to do with *not* knowing proofs of the theorems, but there is more to it than just that. Proofs can be learned in a strictly rote fashion, and being able to generate one may signify little more than simply knowing the theorem itself.

The kind of rule we have in mind may act not only in any given theory, or even in any class of theories, but in any theory whatsoever—indeed, in any situation at all. They are closely related to *inference rules* of formal logic, but they do not act on strings of symbols, nor do they generate strings of symbols. Neither do they *all* map properties of systems into properties of systems as one might expect in view of the relationship between formal systems and axiomatic theories. (Strings of symbols of formal systems correspond to properties of mathematical systems.)

Some inference rules are of an entirely different sort. Instead of operating on properties of systems and generating new properties, what are called *suppositional inference rules* map logical arguments into properties. In present terminology, they correspond to rules that map instances of other inference rules (or combinations thereof) into properties. For example, from *any* specific argument in which property B follows directly from property A, one can infer the property $A \supset B$. In an important sense, then suppositional inference rules correspond to what we have referred to above as relational rules (and transformations), and not to higher-order rules (since they do not operate on other rules, but on instances of other rules).

The stimuli of RG behavior may be viewed as families of systems, and the responses may be viewed as derived properties of these families, called *theorems*. Thus the RG behavior associated with any particular logical procedure involves a class of families of systems and a class of corresponding theorems of these various families. If the procedures are sufficiently unique, as for example in proving many nontrivial theorems, the class of RG behaviors may be quite small; in fact, it could include only one instance.

In effect, a logical procedure may act on corresponding properties of *dif-*

ferent families of systems, and produce other properties of the respective families, or other theorems. Some idea of the way in which complex logical procedures operate can be obtained by considering familiar rules of inference. *Modus ponens* provides a simple illustration. Suppose that the statements "If *G* is a finite group and *S* is a subgroup of *G*, then the order of *S* divides the order of *G*" and "*G* is a finite group and *S* is a subgroup of *G*" are properties of one family of systems (actually, of pairs of systems); and suppose the statements "If a function is continuous over a closed interval of the real line, then it is uniformly continuous" and "The function is continuous over a closed interval of the real line" are properties of another family. Then, application of the logical rule (of inference) *modus ponens* tells us that the statements "The order of *S* divides the order of *G*" and "The function is uniformly continuous" are also properties of the respective families. The corresponding premises and conclusions are quite different, but the logical rule of inference by which they are related is the same.

The same general idea may be extended to more complex logical procedures. In this case, decoding rules involve accepting or rejecting properties (axioms and theorems) of families as appropriate to given goals the subject might have. Rules of inference correspond to transforming rules (type two), and stating theorems correspond to encoding rules (type three). Branching rules (type four) may also be involved in logical procedures, as when repeated application of a rule of inference is required. For example, the conclusion *D* can be inferred from the premises $A \supset [B \supset (C \supset D)]$, *A*, *B* and *C* by repeated application of *modus ponens.*

Since inference rules and the generative procedures that may be constructed from them apply in all conceivable situations—that is, apply to properties of all situations—it may be that they can be discovered at an early age from instances, in the same way as many other rules. This possibility moves me to remark that *deduction may be viewed as induction on a logical rule.* If this is true, it could have important implications both for the study of mathematical reasoning and for teaching it.

Of course, no one individual has mastered, or ever will, all the logical procedures that might be constructed. Such knowledge constitutes an ideal that can only be approached. The behavior involved in proving any nontrivial class of theorems is necessarily partial. According to Church (14), there exist classes of theorems for which no generative procedure can possibly exist. This does not necessarily mean, however, that theorems in such classes can never be proved. Some procedure might exist for deriving any particular theorem; Church's thesis is simply that no *one* procedure will do for the entire class.

Nonetheless, many logical procedures, even reasonably complex ones, are apt to be common to a number of different theories. The number of more-or-less-unique procedures in any particular theory is likely (according to the present view) to be relatively small. Hence, assuming prior mastery of most "standard" logical procedures, a skilled mathematician may gain mastery of a new theory in relatively short order by concentrating on those procedures associated with some of the deeper theorems of the theory. (Note that logical procedures correspond roughly to proof schemas—that is, to classes of proofs of the same general form.)

In order to prove most theorems, of course, and to engage successfully in complex deductive reasoning of any sort, a subject must know more than just rules of inference, or even a large number of relatively complex logical procedures. The subject must also have higher-order rules available, by which he can combine known inference rules and other logical procedures into new forms—that is, so that he can *create*. One type of higher-order rule that is frequently used in constructing proofs is closely associated with the heuristic, "Work backward from the conclusion." In this case, the learner attempts to derive a procedure for generating the conclusion from the premises (that is, to construct a proof) by first selecting an inference rule that yields the conclusion and then by trying to derive a logical procedure (by using this or some other higher-order rule) that yields the input of the first rule selected. Presumably, the subject continues in this way until either he succeeds or the whole approach breaks down. The widely used technique of proving theorems indirectly by assuming that the conclusion is false provides a particular example of a higher-order rule generated by application of this heuristic (a still higher-order rule). In this case, the problem reduces to one of constructing a proof of $\sim A$ from $\sim B$. (The final step in constructing such a proof just amounts to selecting what might be called the contrapositive inference rule, by which the theorem $A \supset B$ can be inferred from the argument from $\sim B$ to $\sim A$.)

More could be said about such things as formal systems and metamathematics, but space does not allow. In the first case, it suffices to say that formal systems are easier to work with than axiomatic systems. Nothing new is required, except that the allowable inference rules are specified, and no decoding rules are needed. The axioms and theorems are themselves the stimuli and responses. In the second case, metamathematics turns out to be nothing more than an axiomatic type of theory in which only noncontroversial rules of inference are allowed.

In conclusion, I would like to reemphasize that we have dealt primarily with what it means to understand an existing body of mathematics. Relatively little has been said about intellectual skills of the sort that must inevitably be involved in *doing* real mathematics. Nonetheless, we have shown that what appears to be creative behavior might well be accounted for in terms of growing rule sets. The key idea in making this a feasible and rather attractive possibility is that of the higher-order rule. Although space limitations have made it necessary to ignore many details, and there obviously are still a good many important questions left unanswered, I hope that enough has been said to convince the reader that my basic conjecture must be taken seriously: All mathematical behavior is a rule-governed activity, and the basic underlying constructs are rules.

4. ENGINEERING A VIABLE AND OPERATIONAL MATHEMATICS CURRICULUM

As suggested in the previous section, there is very little difference between thinking of a set of rules as characterizing a person's knowledge and thinking of it as characterizing a curriculum. The task of curriculum construction, then, is reduced largely to the identification of a finite set of rules that provides an efficient account of some larger class of behaviors.

In this section, I shall describe an approach to curriculum construction in mathematics that is both operational and, in my opinion, mathematically viable.

The plan itself is a variant of one used by members of the Mathematics Education Research Group (MERG) in analyzing my book, *Mathematics: Concrete Behavioral Foundations*, and I shall describe the method used there first. In that case, the task was to characterize explicitly, in terms of rules, knowledge (content) that was implicit in some 400 pages of text material. The immediate, practical goal was to construct a workbook that might be used to facilitate learning of the material.

In the process of constructing this workbook, an experiment was conducted by Walter Ehrenpreis as part of his dissertation, in which two types of rule-based characterization were contrasted. The *discrete* characterization consisted of a set of discrete rules that were designed to reflect directly what was in the text. The *higher-order* characterization, which was the main goal of the development, also included higher-order rules that reflected relationships between the discrete rules. The introduction of the higher-order rules allowed a sharp reduction (about 40 percent in the total number of rules, since many of the discrete rules could be derived by use of the higher-order ones. Equally important, a large number of rules that were *not* dealt with in the original text could also be derived in this way. (The actual procedure used is described below.)

The standard design for comparing two curricula was used, but unlike the results usually obtained, ours were extremely encouraging. Not only did the subjects in the higher-order-rules group have less to learn, but they were able to perform the untaught rules just as well as the discrete-rules group. Furthermore, these subjects were able to solve other tasks (beyond the original text) that the discrete-rules subjects could not. Unfortunately, the data for this experiment are still being analyzed and more detailed information is not yet available.

Returning to the engineering itself, the plan we used was as follows. First, we went through the original text and identified, as far as we could, all the kinds of tasks that were implicit in the text material. These tasks were then formulated directly in terms of the observable behavior a learner would have to exhibit in order to demonstrate his ability to solve such tasks. For illustrative purposes, three sections of the text, *Mathematics: Concrete Behavioral Foundations*, and the tasks implicit in them, follow.

EXCERPT A (from chapter 8, pages 286–87)

For one reason or another, most people learn to add integers in the following manner:

1. If both signs are +, add the magnitudes (as if they were whole numbers) and affix + to the result.
2. If both signs are –, add the magnitudes and affix – to the result.
3. If the sign of the integer with the larger magnitude is + and that of the smaller magnitude is –, then subtract the smaller magnitude and affix + to the result.
4. If the sign of the integer with the larger magnitude is – and that of the smaller magnitude is +, then subtract the smaller magnitude and affix – to the result.

[If both integers are of equal magnitude, either may be picked as the smaller (larger) in order to apply the algorithm.]

When written in this way, we see that the algorithm is composed of what essentially amounts to four distinct algorithms, one corresponding to each possible combination of signs: + +, + –, – +, and – –. For this reason, we call this algorithm the *four-case algorithm*.

Task A: Given integers m and n, find the sum $n + m$.

EXCERPT B (from chapter 7, pages 255–57)

Multiplication. The product of two fractions,

$$\frac{x}{y} \text{ and } \frac{z}{w},$$

is defined to be the fraction

$$\frac{x}{y} \times \frac{z}{w} = \frac{xz}{yw}.$$

The product of two fractions may be thought of as the result of superimposing two (corresponding) fractional *amounts* on one another in the sense described below. To be specific, let us represent the fractions

$$\frac{3}{5} \text{ and } \frac{2}{3}$$

as parts of squares as shown in figure 1. The product

$$\frac{3}{5} \times \frac{2}{3}$$

in this case corresponds to the ratio of the *crosshatched* area (6 sections), formed by superimposing the two representations, to the area of the whole square (15 sections). This is shown in figure 2. Our definition of multiplication, then, gives us precisely what our intuition has led us to suspect: the fraction

$$\frac{3}{5} \times \frac{2}{3} = \frac{3 \times 2}{5 \times 3} = \frac{6}{15}.$$

Task B: Given two fractions r_1 and r_2, represent in concrete terms the action involved in generating the product $r_1 \times r_2$ denoted by $r_1, r_2 \rightarrow r_1 \times r_2$.

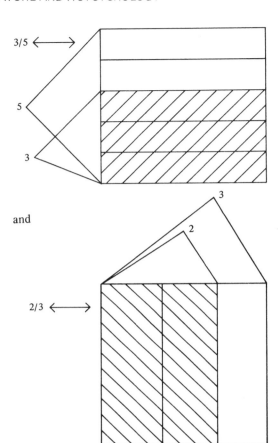

and

Figure 1

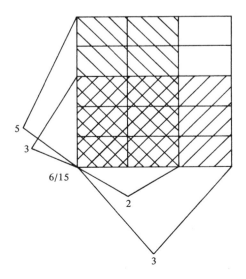

Figure 2

EXCERPT C (from chapter 1, page 42)

Logical inference may be viewed as a higher-order skill that operates on ideas, facts, and rules. In particular, by drawing inferences one may "deduce" (that is, arrive at) new ideas (rules) on the basis of given ones. Such skills are used every day by most people to draw conclusions about their worlds from things they already know or believe to be true. Thus, if we know that the zoo is always closed on holidays, and that today is Thanksgiving, we would immediately conclude that visiting the zoo is not a possible after-dinner activity. The conclusion follows naturally and without effort. We do not need to go to the zoo to double-check (although, of course, there is always the chance in real life that someone might break the rules). No one who is able to reason deductively would seriously question the conclusion, given the same facts. In short, the process of making logical inferences provides a third, and fundamentally different, way to acquire new knowledge.

Task C: Given a set of statements, draw an obvious (logical) conclusion.

The second step was to identify and eliminate any obvious redundancies. Actually, very few of these were found in the text. Perhaps the main reason for this was that we deliberately wanted to maintain the original sequencing of ideas (rules) in the text. Hence, we did not eliminate rules that were prerequisite [in the sense of task analysis, Gagné (42)] to rules that occurred later on. In constructing an idealized curriculum, on the other hand, one might want to systematically determine (that is, engineer) the most efficient sequencing of rules, and this can be done only after all the desired terminal objectives (rules) have been identified.

Third, an efficient rule was devised for solving each kind of task. Rules for solving the illustrative tasks above, for example, can be stated:

Rule A: Determine the signs of m and n. Then,
1. If m and n are both positive, add the magnitudes and affix + to the sum.
2. If m and n are both negative, add the magnitudes and affix − to the sum.
3. If the sign of the integer with the larger magnitude is + and that of the smaller magnitude is −, then subtract the smaller magnitude and affix + to the result.
4. If the sign of the integer with the larger magnitude is − and that of the smaller magnitude is +, then subtract the smaller magnitude and affix − to the result.

(Notice in this case that the rule statement closely follows the original text).

Examples
1. Add $^-3$, $^-4$.
Since m and n are both negatives, use case 2 of the 4-case rule. Adding the magnitudes, $3 + 4 = 7$, and affixing − gives $^-7 = {}^-3 + {}^-4$.
2. Add $^-3$, $^+4$.
Since m and n have different signs and the positive magnitude is larger, use case 3. Subtracting the magnitudes, $4 − 3 = 1$, and affixing + gives $^+1 = {}^-3 + {}^+4$.

Rule B: Draw two equal squares. Represent the fraction

$$\frac{m}{n}$$

by partitioning one square into *n* congruent horizontal rectangular regions. Then shade *m* of the regions, adding more to the *n* available regions when necessary. Next represent

$$\frac{c}{d}$$

by partitioning the other square into *d* vertical regions of the same type, and then shading *c* of them as above. The product is represented by superimposing one square upon the other. The product is given by

$$\frac{l}{L}$$

where *l* represents the total number of boxes in the doubly shaded region, and L represents the number of boxes formed within the boundaries of the square.

Example

1. Multiply $\dfrac{4}{3}, \dfrac{2}{5} \rightarrow \dfrac{4 \times 2}{3 \times 5} = \dfrac{8}{15}$

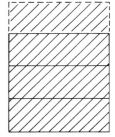 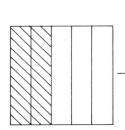 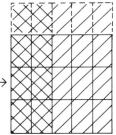

Rule C: For logical inference, there is no single rule that will apply in all cases. However, a relatively small number of simple rules, three of which are given below, exhaust most common cases.

Rule 1. If two true statements are of the form
  1. "If *P*, then *Q*" and
  2. "*P*,"
  then the conclusion (given by *modus ponens*) is "*Q*."

Example
  1. "If today is a holiday, then the zoo will be closed."
  2. "Today is Thanksgiving (a holiday)."
  The conclusion is "Today the zoo will be closed."

Rule 2. If two true statements are of the form
  1. "Either *P* or *Q*" and
  2. "not *P*" (or "not *Q*"),
  then the conclusion is "*Q*" (or "*P*").

Example
  1. "Either Joey returned his books to the library by the date they were due or he paid a fine."

2. "Joey did not return his books to the library by the date they were due."
The conclusion is "Joey paid a fine."

Rule 3. If two true statements are of the form
      1. "All P's are Q's" and
      2. "x is a P,"
then the conclusion is "x is a Q."

Example
1. "All squares are rectangles."
2. "This figure is a square."
The conclusion is "This figure is a rectangle."

Next came the most crucial step of searching for higher-order relationships among the rules.[3] The essential idea is to look for parallelisms among different rules. One basic type of relationship occurs where a number of pairs of rules may be combined in the same general way to generate third rules. As a simple example of this, consider the following classes of tasks and rules, which are variants of those used in an experiment with elementary school children.

Simple Rules

Example A
  Task: Find the number of candy bars to be traded for a given number of balloons.
  Iconic representation of rule:

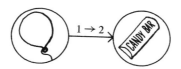

  Statement of rule: For each balloon, trade 2 candy bars.

Example B
  Task: Find the number of suckers to be traded for a given number of candy bars.
  Iconic representation of rule:

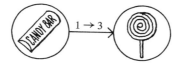

  Statement of rule: Trade 3 suckers for each candy bar.

---

3. Quasi-systematic methods for doing this are described in Chapter 5 of *Mathematics and Structural Learning* (83).

Example C

Task: Find the number of bobby pins to be traded for a given number of sticks.

Iconic representation of rule:

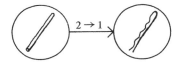

Statement of rule: Trade 1 bobby pin for each 2 sticks.

Composite Rule

Example

Task: Find the number of pieces of paper to be traded for a given number of sticks.

Iconic representation of composite rule:

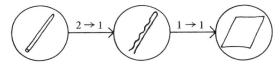

Statement of composite rule: Trade 1 bobby pin for each two sticks, and then trade 1 piece of paper for each bobby pin.

Higher Order Rule

Example

Task: Find the composite rule corresponding to two given simple rules in which the output of one matches the input of the other.

Iconic representation of higher-order rule:

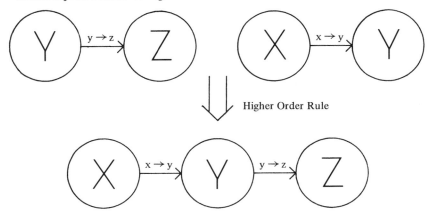

(where *X*, *Y*, and *Z* may be any type of object whatever, and *x*, *y*, and *z* any natural numbers.)

Statement of higher order rule: Given two simple rules in which the output of one matches the input of the other, combine the two rules so that the output of the former matches the input of the latter, thereby constructing the composite rule.

Notice in this illustration that given any pair of simple rules in which the output of one matches the input of the other, application of the higher-order rule yields a (new) composite rule that can be used to solve new kinds of tasks. For example, given the simple rules depicted in examples A and B, application of the higher-order rule yields the composite rule represented by

This composite rule can be used for trading suckers for balloons. As indicated in the related experiment, knowledge of this higher-order rule was both a necessary and a sufficient condition for this type of transfer.

It is important not to be misled by the artificial nature of these tasks. Similar relationships abound in mathematics and in other structured subject matter. Furthermore, these relationships are what provide an explicit basis for engineering transfer potential directly into a curriculum.

Consider, for example, the following rules for certain specific kinds of "computing."

Specific Solution Rules

1. Given $+m + +n$, add the magnitudes of *m* and *n* and affix + to the sum.
   Example: $+2 + +6 \rightarrow 2 + 6 = 8 \rightarrow +8$

2. Given

$$\frac{a}{b} \times \frac{c}{d},$$

   multiply $a \times c$ and $b \times d$. Write the product of *a* and *c* in the numerator and the product of *b* and *d* in the denominator.

   Example: $\frac{3}{4} \times \frac{4}{5} \rightarrow 3 \times 4 = 12, 4 \times 5 = 20 \rightarrow \frac{12}{20}$.

3. Given $m° \bigcap n°$, where *m* and *n* are rotations of between 0° and 360°, add $m°$ and $n°$. Then, if $m° + n° \geq 360°$, subtract 360°.
   Example: $270° \bigcap 180° \rightarrow 450° \rightarrow 450° - 360° = 90°$

Clearly, there are any number of such rules in mathematics, and learning them all individually would become a terrible chore.

This task is greatly simplified, however, for a subject who has learned the following two rules.

1. *General Transformation Rule.* In a statement of the form $m * n$, where $*$ represents an operation and m and n specific elements, replace $*$ by its inverse operation, $*'$, and n by its inverse element under $*'$.

$$Examples: \ ^+3 - {}^-5 \rightarrow {}^+3 -' {}^+5 = {}^+3 + {}^+5$$
$$8 \div \frac{1}{2} \rightarrow 8 \div' \frac{2}{1} = 8 \times 2$$

2. *Higher Order Rule.* Replace the operations $*'$ and $*$ in the transformation rule with the operation indicated in the given specific solution rule and its inverse, respectively. Combine the obtained transformation rule and the specific solution rule so that the output of the former becomes the input of the latter. Notice that application of the higher-order rule to the general transformation rule, together with any computational rule, yields an inverse rule for successful computation on inverse tasks. This effectively cuts in half the number of specific solution rules that need to be learned. Consider the following examples:

1. Given rules } General Transformation Rule: Specific Solution Rule 1

Higher Order Rule

Derived rule } In the statement $^+m - {}^-n$, replace $-$ with $+$, and ^-n with ^+n; add the magnitudes m and n, and affix $+$ to the sum.

Example of derived rule } $^+3 - {}^-5 \rightarrow {}^+3 + {}^+5 \rightarrow {}^+8$

2. Given rules } General Transformation Rule: Specific Solution Rule 2

Higher Order Rule

Derived rule } In the statement $\frac{a}{b} \div \frac{d}{c}$ (where $b,\ d,\ c \neq 0$), replace $\div$ with "×" and $\frac{d}{c}$ with $\frac{c}{d}$; multiply $a \times c$ and $b \times d$; write the product $a \times c$ in the numerator, and $b \times d$ in the denominator.

Example of derived rule $\left.\right\}$ $\dfrac{1}{2} \div \dfrac{2}{3} \rightarrow \dfrac{1}{2} \times \dfrac{3}{2} \rightarrow \dfrac{3}{4}$

3. Given rules $\left.\right\}$ General Transformation Rule: Specific Solution Rule 3

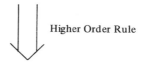

Higher Order Rule

Derived rule $\left.\right\}$ In the statement $m°\ \curvearrowright\ n°$, replace $\curvearrowright$ (clockwise rotation) with $\curvearrowleft$ (counterclockwise rotation) and $n°$ with $(360 - n)°$; add $m°$ and $(360 - n)°$, and subtract $360°$ if $m° + (360 - n)° \geq 360°$.

Example of derived rule $\left.\right\}$ $180°\ \curvearrowright\ 270° \rightarrow 180°\ \curvearrowleft\ (360° - 270°)$
$= 180°\ \curvearrowleft\ 90°$
$\rightarrow 180° + 90° = 270°$

The fifth step in the engineering plan is to eliminate those rules that can be derived by application of the higher-order rules to other rules in the characterizing set. In the experiments reported above, we used derivable rules to test for transfer. In developing an actual curriculum, some of the derivable rules might be used to provide learners with additional practice—specifically, *practice in how to transfer.*

Notice that in describing this procedure, the *mode* of presenting the rule-based curriculum was determined externally: that is, the book company involved wanted a workbook to accompany the text[4]. In working with young children we would almost certainly not want to limit ourselves to just that mode.

Although the engineering plan described above was used to construct a curriculum for teachers, it should be clear that the plan is perfectly general and could also be used to engineer a rule-based curriculum for school or college students. That, in part, is what is being proposed. In order to accomplish this, of course, a first crucial step would involve selecting an appropriate set of materials and tasks to analyze. Among other things, this would involve making value judgments concerning the relative importance of the various kinds of material that might reasonably be considered.

---

4. Any of the illustrative rules above closely parallel those included in J.M. Scandura, J. Durnin, Walter Ehrenpreis, and George Luger, *An Algorithmic Approach to Mathematics: Concrete Behavioral Foundations* (New York: Harper & Row, 1971).

CONCLUDING COMMENT

In the first section of this paper I argued that bringing about further substantial improvements in mathematics curricula will necessarily require a deeper behavioral base than that which existed during the 1960s. Next, one important problem with present-day mathematics curricula was identified. This problem involves the relative advantages and disadvantages of operationalizing objectives versus not operationalizing them. Third, a new theory of mathematical knowledge (competence) was described. Finally, a technology called *algorithmic analysis*, which is based on this theory, was described and applied to the engineering of mathematics curricula. This technology potentially, at least, provides an effective way of dealing with the aforementioned problem.

11 Learning Research and Mathematics Instruction

Robert M. Gagné received his undergraduate educa-
tion at Yale University, and obtained his doctor's
degree in experimental psychology from Brown Uni-
versity in 1940. He has been actively engaged in
research on human learning for many years. His
college teaching career began at Connecticut College
for Women. During World War II he served as an avia-
tion psychologist, engaged in the development of
tests of motor and perceptual functions in the classi-
fication of aircrew.

He returned to college teaching at Pennsylvania
State University and later went to Connecticut College,
where he also carried out a research project on the
learning and transfer of skills. For eight years there-
after, he held the position of technical director in two
Air Force laboratories that were engaged in research
programs dealing with learning and methods of tech-
nical training.

From 1958 to 1962, Dr. Gagné was a professor of
psychology at Princeton University, where he carried
out a series of studies on the acquisition of knowledge,
and collaborated with the University of Maryland Math-
ematics Project in studies of mathematics learning.
From 1962 to 1965, he was the director of research
of the American Institute for Research, where he was
concerned with general supervision of research pro-
grams on human performance, instructional methods,
educational objectives, and design and evaluation of
curricula and educational procedures. His writings dur-
ing this period deal primarily with methods of instruc-
tion, problem solving, and the conditions of learning.
From 1966 to 1969, he was a professor in the Depart-
ment of Education at the University of California,

ROBERT M. GAGNÉ

*Berkeley, in the field of educational psychology. In
this position, he directed the effort toward establishing
a regional educational laboratory, managed a program
of graduate training in educational research, and continued his research on the learning of school subjects.
He is currently a professor in the Department of Educational Research and Testing at Florida State University.*

*In regard to mathematics education, Professor Gagné
feels that although numerous studies on mathematics
learning are being done, there is still much to be learned
that could improve mathematics instruction. In his
opinion, learning research will undoubtedly continue
to provide this necessary knowledge, but we need to
consider the kinds of questions that it can answer.*

*The most general question considered in this paper
is, What can learning research tell us about mathematics learning? The question will not be answered by
attempts to apply existing knowledge gained from the
findings of various studies, but by consideration of
what the psychologist sees as requirements for obtaining knowledge about learning.*

*In his discussion of the requirements for obtaining
knowledge about human learning, he deals with three
basic concerns: the requirements for research, the
nature of the answerable research questions, and the
application of learning research to mathematics instruction.*

*Within each of the above concerns, Gagné discusses
several important topics. Definition of the problem
and the nature of performance objectives form the
major categories within the section on the requirements
for research. The four areas of investigation of learning are (1) prerequisites of learning, (2) conditions of
learning, (3) conditions for retention, and (4) learning
styles. In the realm of applications of learning research,
Gagné suggests that findings might illuminate the areas
of sequence of topics, selection of topics, usable retention, and individual differences.*

*Gagné asks many questions, and he attempts to alle-
viate the reader's frustration concerning the lack of
answers in two ways. First, he presents a breakdown*

of the problem concerning investigation of learning
research. Second, he discusses "the dynamic verbal ex-
change" between teachers and students as the one area
that will not be affected by results of learning research.

Studies of how students learn have often used mathematical content in the design of prototype tasks to be learned. Often, such investigations are conducted to answer some very basic question about the nature of learning, the conditions required for learning, the basis of memory, or the variables affecting learning transfer. Less often, they are concerned with some more specific problem of mathematics instruction, such as whether greater retention of the subtraction operation will be generated by one method of presentation than by another. However, regardless of the degree of specificity expected of the results, it is reasonable to suppose that they will in some degree or other throw light on the problem of designing effective instruction in mathematics.

A recent publication by the National Council of Teachers of Mathematics (88) presents an interesting selection of research studies on mathematics learning, illustrating several different approaches to the subject. There also appears to be an increasing number of investigations of the learning process reported in a variety of scientific journals, all of which employ mathematics problems as material to be learned. At the same time, however, there seems to exist a rather widely held opinion that we have hardly scratched the surface of theory or practical information that could be put to use in improving mathematics instruction.

Surely it is true that we need to know a great deal more about instruction of all forms of mathematics and about how considerations of the process of learning might enter into the design of such instruction. It does not seem unrealistic to expect that learning research will, perhaps at an increasing rate, provide the systematic knowledge and theory that will make improvements in mathematics instruction possible. While maintaining this view, however, we may need to take a closer look at the kinds of questions that are likely to be answered by research on learning.

QUESTIONS IN LEARNING RESEARCH

The investigator of human learning, understandably enough, shares with mathematics scholars and teachers the belief that mathematics instruction is an essential part of the school curriculum. Every student needs to learn to think within his environment and to act upon his environment in terms of numbers and number operations. The issues to which the investigator of learning is likely to respond most readily arise when one begins to ask such questions as what kinds of mathematics, what sequences of topics in mathematics, and what sort of presentation procedures can aid mathematics instruction?

The most general form of the question I wish to consider is, What can knowledge about human learning contribute to making the student's acquisition of mathematics more effective? This is not a new question; in fact, it is one that gets asked all the time by students of learning and instruction. It is also a question that can be answered in more than one way. For example, an attempt can be made to answer this question, as a number of authors have done quite well, by searching out, evaluating, and summarizing the findings of studies on learning various mathematical topics and by describing how these apply to classroom or other types of instructional situations. A great deal of information is conveyed in this type of answer, but it tends also to be rather fractionated. Investigators who study learning do not necessarily stick to one kind of mathematics, nor to a single level of mathematics instruction. Conducting experimental studies of human learning is not a simple thing to do; it is, rather, a highly complex activity. So perhaps one should not be too impatient about the fact that the nuggets of empirically based truth do not often come in neat packages.

In contrast to this kind of answer, I should like instead to take a different approach to the question, What can learning research tell us about mathematics learning? The person who does research on learning is usually a psychologist, who carries around with him a set of broad views and attitudes about the discipline he pursues. These in turn determine the kinds of questions he asks about human learning and the kinds of requirements that must be met in finding the answers to these questions. Accordingly, I should like to try to answer the major question not in terms of existing knowledge, but in terms of what the psychologist sees as *requirements for obtaining knowledge* about human learning. Three parts to this question may be distinguished:

1. What essential conditions must be met to seek scientific knowledge of human learning?
2. What kinds of questions concerning mathematics instruction can theoretically be answered by experimental learning studies, and what kinds cannot?
3. By what means and under what conditions can results of scientific studies of learning be applied to mathematics learning and teaching?

REQUIREMENTS FOR RESEARCH ON LEARNING

What conditions have to be met in order for an investigator to obtain verifiable knowledge about how human beings learn, including how they learn mathematics?

The first condition is quite easy to state, but quite difficult to achieve. It is simply that the investigator must have a good definition of the problem, How do students learn? Actually, there might be several variations of this question:

1. Perhaps the question is, How can students learn mathematics more rapidly, so that, for example, most students could begin the study of calculus

in the eighth grade, or linear algebra in the tenth? The question might be, Would it be possible for second-graders to learn to deal with decimals, and fifth-graders with analytic geometry? Actually, there are many studies that show that children can learn almost any mathematical topic at any time, provided the proper groundwork has been laid. So this question may resolve itself into another and different one: rather than how soon *can* the student learn a particular topic of mathematics, how soon *should* he learn that topic, considering all the other things he should also learn? This, then, becomes a very different kind of concern, and not at all a matter of speed of learning. But in any case, the question of learning rapidity remains as one particular kind of query.

2. A second possible question, and quite a different one, is, How can the learning of mathematics be arranged so as to prevent the occurrence of obstacles and emotional blocks to learning? The problem is certainly different in this case, and the psychologist of learning would undoubtedly approach it in a different way. For example, under some circumstances, it might even be found that time pressures cause emotional blocks. Thus it is conceivable (speaking quite hypothetically) that the variables of speed of learning and absence of emotional blocking would turn out to oppose each other in their effects. However, the occurrence of learning obstacles seems likely to have a more complex cause than this.

3. Still a different question is this: How can instruction be arranged so that a higher proportion of students achieve mastery of certain specified mathematical topics? One sometimes hears of surveys of samples of American adults, in which they are asked to add such fractions as one-seventh and one-fifth, and frequently they cannot do it. Have they forgotten how? It seems more likely that they never learned how. Why not? Can one conceive of a set of conditions in which, say, 90 percent of students would learn such things in a fully retainable way, rather than an estimated 60 percent of students? Again, this is a different kind of question about learning, and requires a different kind of research study to answer it.

These examples all support the idea that the investigator of learning must have a clearly defined question in order to do his work. The generally stated question of how mathematics learning can be improved does not provide all the necessary information. The student of learning must necessarily design different kinds of studies to answer different kinds of specific questions, and to do this he must know what "improvement" means in equally specific terms.

The second requirement is simply an extension of this first one. If learning is to be investigated, one must know what the student is expected to be able to do both before and after learning. As I have pointed out previously (43), learning is an inference made from a change in human performance, and such a change must first be observed between time x and time $x + 1$. Accordingly,

the learning psychologist must know, or be told, the nature of the performance he is to observe.

Sometimes this requirement is stated in terms of "educational objectives."
But if this phrase is not sufficiently communicative, the idea need not be
stated in these terms. One can simply say, if an investigator is going to study
learning, that he must begin by identifying the human performance he is
going to observe. It is as simple as that. If a chemist is going to observe elec-
trolytic phenomena, he must have a defined solution of chemicals. If the
psychologist is going to observe learning phenomena, he must have a defined
performance. For a subject with as much inherent clarity of content as mathematics, one would think the question of the performance outcomes to be attained from studying the subject would be equally clear and even more or
less unarguable. Yet there seem to be many arguments, and not much consensus.

When one speaks of mathematics in terms of topics, as is often done, there
are many things to puzzle the investigator of learning, things which keep him
from a clear definition of the performance to be observed. For example, take
fractions. Is the desired performance one of formulating fractional problems,
of performing fractional operations, of transforming fractions to decimals, of
deriving a system of rational numbers, or of estimating fractional quantities?
Of course, the answer may be, all of these. If this be the case, then one must
seek further specification of the performances. Is the desired performance
transforming all fractional expressions to decimals, or just some of them? Is
the student expected to do this without computational aids, or with them? Is
he to do it at the rate of about one per second, or at the rate of one per thirty
seconds? Such questions are not simply academic ones to the learning investigator. He must have an agreed-upon answer before he begins his investigation.

Consider another example: finding the roots of algebraic equations of the
second degree. Does this mean demonstrating the basic logic of equations?
Does it mean showing in a step-by-step fashion what is meant by a root? Does
it mean finding roots by inspection? Again, it is often difficult to tell what
the desired performance is. It has also been my experience that the answer
"all of these" seldom actually stands up under serious questioning. At any
rate, here is another instance of the difficulty experienced by the investigator
of learning in meeting even one of the first requirements of a scientific
investigation.

The Question of Performance Outcomes

This topic should not be dropped without consideration of a further point or
two. Many people seem to find questions concerning performance outcomes
difficult to answer. Does the mathematics teacher know the answer? Does he
know what the student should be able to do after he has learned? Perhaps he
thinks he does, but it is usually because someone else has told him. Who can
provide the answer to such questions?

It may be of particular importance to point out that the investigator of learning, so long as he is playing that particular role, does not pretend to know the answer. But if he is also a psychologist, he does know how to find the answer. When he suggests a method for studying this problem, he is not being a learning investigator, but is rather playing the role of a personnel psychologist, or one who deals with human performances in tasks and jobs.

Fundamentally, the suggestion of the personnel psychologist is this: To find out what kinds of mathematics performances are needed, find out what people do with these performances—that is, what more general goals they serve. Does the individual use the mathematics performances he has in order to learn certain specified kinds of advanced mathematics? If so, the particular performances required for such advanced learning are the ones he needs. Does the person use the mathematics performances to solve problems concerning the normality of chemical solutions? If so, the particular performances required for the chemical problems are what he needs. Does the individual use his performances in mathematics to compute the resistances in electric circuits? If so, that particular set of performances is the one he needs.

I may possibly seem here to be emphasizing what has been so often deplored as the "social usefulness" idea of mathematics, which led at one time to projects in compound interest, check balancing, and home budget preparation. In part, I admit to the charge. It seems to me that the basis for deciding what mathematics is to be learned *must* be largely one of social usefulness. Mathematics is much too important to serve only the goal of esthetic enjoyment. But I simply do not see why a criterion of usefulness must lead to the trivialities that seem to have been largely the case, say, forty years ago. Mathematical skills are highly important in our society, and I should expect that the capability of formulating and solving quantitative problems of a wide variety is one of the most important of these activities. It seems to me that the criterion of social usefulness, if that's what it was, was previously used to disparage *any* really useful mathematics, by reducing such activities to the lowest common denominator of routine procedures. It should have done just the opposite; it should have given increased emphasis to the general and transferable problem-solving skills that can be applied widely in human affairs. I cannot believe that this degradation into trivia resulted from the criterion of social usefulness itself. Something else must have been added, such as "personal adjustment."

To return, then, to the original question, I have surely emphasized sufficiently that the first question to be answered when one seeks verifiable knowledge about mathematics learning concerns "what mathematics," or what kinds of capabilities are desired. Once this question is answered, the investigator of learning can proceed to ask a number of other questions, most of which can be answered by means of empirical evidence. Briefly, his procedure is approximately as follows. Knowing that the objective is, let us suppose, rapid mental addition of two-place numbers, he makes one or more, probably several, hypotheses concerning the conditions that will produce this capability most efficiently. One of these hypotheses might be that rapid mental addition of one-place numbers is essential for the two-place number task to be learned. He can then proceed to do an experimental study, in which differing rates of rapidity of adding one-place numbers are learned by several comparable groups of students. Following this, it is possible to measure the ease with which mental addition of two-place numbers is learned. If such an experiment is done properly, and due account is taken of the other conditions under which the results occur, a conclusion can be drawn that is highly reproducible, whose applicability can be stated with a great deal of confidence. Other hypotheses, subjected to other kinds of experimental treatments, can yield results of similar value.

By repeating this process, the investigator is gradually able to build up a sound and well-established set of generalizations about mathematics learning. Eventually, these can all be put together in a kind of grand design, tried out, and evaluated as a total system of mathematics instruction. This may sound like a slow process. It is, relatively speaking; but this is the way research proceeds. Of course, it is always possible to take some shortcuts. New methods of mathematics instruction are often built partly upon guesses, rather than upon systematically accumulated evidence of the sort I have described. I should by no means recommend that this *not* be done. But ultimately, our truly dependable knowledge of how mathematics is learned must come by piecing together principles of learning that are individually determined on the basis of experimental evidence.

INVESTIGATION OF LEARNING AND INSTRUCTION

If this is the way an investigator of mathematics learning proceeds, what kinds of questions can he expect to find answers to? What the learning investigator hopes to be able to learn about are the following kinds of variables.

1. The Prerequisites of Learning

What does a youngster have to know how to do before he can be taught to add single-place numbers? What does a student have to know how to do before he can learn to make a graphic plot of a function, or solve simultaneous equations, or formulate a differential equation?

2. The Conditions of Learning

There is a whole complex of variables pertaining to the stimulation coming to the learner from the outside. What kinds of variables are there?

a) There is the variable of amount of drill or repetition. Although this is an old question, no one has answered it satisfactorily—that is, in a way that provides useful results. Let me put the question this way: Suppose a student has just learned to derive an expression for a straight-line graphic plot. How many examples must now be provided before we can be sure he knows how to do

this? Two? Five? Twenty? And does this number vary with the kind of problem or with the nature of the student's past experiences? These are questions
that I believe can be given generalizable answers; they do not need to depend
on guesswork. Yet we do not have these answers at the present time.

b) A related variable is the amount of variety in examples, and the effect
this has on the retention of a newly learned principle. Under some conditions
it appears that variety promotes both retention and transfer to other related
tasks, but this effect is not always obtained [see Gagné and Rohwer (47)]. We
need additional research aimed at a more precise definition of this variable, as
well as its effects.

c) The discovery method of instruction is another kind of instructional variable that can be reasonably investigated in educational settings. Actually,
there have been a number of studies, many of them on mathematical subject
matter. On balance, I believe they tend to show an advantage for what has
come to be called "guided discovery." The evidence is reviewed by Wittrock
(112). Cronbach (16) has reviewed these studies critically, and believes they
do not provide dependable evidence for or against discovery. In particular, he
believes that such studies must encompass longer periods of instruction than
has been the case in the past, in order for the most important of the hypothesized effects to show themselves. A recent study by Worthen (1968) indicates
that discovery methods of classroom teaching promote improved retention
and transfer of learning.

d) The scope or generality of principles learned is an interesting variable of
potentially great importance for the design of sequences of instruction. Scandura, Woodward, and Lee (94) investigated this variable in connection with
the number game called NIM. The generality of the rule was found to have a
highly significant effect on the generality of application in later problem solving. Transferability of a principle, in other words, must be built into the instructional process. It does not occur, according to these authors, because of
superficial stimulus resemblances among problems.

e) Familiarity with components of a principle is another variable that may
be shown to have a considerable effect on the learning of these principles. Here
is another variable that has been of interest to Scandura (82). He used a set of
artificial principles, unfamiliar to college students majoring in education, to
investigate this variable. The principles were based upon the notions of greatest integer, sign notation for sequential addition, vector, and partial derivative.
One group learned them in verbal form, another in symbolic form. The degree
of familiarity the learners had with the symbols making up the principles was
varied in the study. A major finding was that principles in symbolic form are
applied successfully if and only if the learners have been taught the constituent symbols.

My list of possible variables is perhaps getting overly long. Surely it is apparent that if we can find dependable results dealing with learning conditions such
as repetition, variety, discovery, scope, prior familiarity of components, and
visual versus verbal representation, we shall, in fact, know a great deal about

how to communicate with a student for learning purposes. Properly designed research can give us such information.

3. The Conditions for Retention

A variety of questions are currently being asked [see Gagné and Rohwer (47)] about the retention of organized meaningful material. What kinds of principles are retained best? What circumstances, such as review and usage, tend to maintain retention of what has been learned? It is, of course, true that retention studies are not easy to do, and that they inevitably take a certain amount of time. Yet, it is remarkable how little is known of the factors affecting retention, beyond strictly anecdotal evidence.

4. Individual Differences in "Learning Styles"

The idea that there are such styles is such an appealing one that people begin to think they *must* be there. Yet the evidence, recently reviewed by a group of outstanding learning psychologists, shows that there are a few established learning styles, and many suggestions that have not yet been even explored. There seem to be many directions in which we can look for the kind of variables that might cause an individual to learn more readily one way than another. The method for finding them is fairly clear, but they have not yet been discovered.

Here, then, are four different areas of investigation, each of which can be tackled by methods of experimental study that are well understood. However, such findings will not be obtained overnight. What is most needed, it seems, is highly dedicated investigators who will take up these problems and pursue them vigorously until some reasonably complete answers are found. Teachers of mathematics can help this process along. The greatest help will come not by demanding answers that the investigator is not yet prepared to give, but rather by giving him active help in understanding what the problems are, as seen from the teacher's point of view, and in coming to a mutual agreement about the applicability of the variables he works with.

Another point should perhaps be made at this juncture. There are relatively few generalizations to be uncovered by the experimental method that are unique to mathematics; many of them are common to various school subjects. It is not specifically mathematics learning that is studied by this method, but the learning of concepts and principles and learning by problem solving, whether they occur in languages, social studies, science, mathematics, or some other school subject. One does not really expect to find, for example, that the amount of repetition required to establish a given amount of retention applies to mathematics content but not to geography or to physics. This is not the level of generalization aimed for, and it is not the level of generalization expected from such investigations. One hopes by these methods to find and to verify principles about repetition, about variety of examples, about scope of generality, about retention, and also about individual differences, all of which are highly applicable to all school-subject learning. There is no reason to suppose that such general findings cannot be obtained or that they will not be as applicable to the learning of other subjects as they will be to mathematics learning. The psychology of mathematics learning, in other words, can be expected to have a great deal in common with the psychology of science learning, or even with the psychology of language learning.

APPLICATION OF LEARNING RESEARCH TO MATHEMATICS INSTRUCTION

The third question I mentioned earlier is, Under what conditions can the results of studies of learning be applied to mathematics instruction?

It may be desirable to mention first one of the sets of conditions that the results of learning studies should *not* be expected to affect very much. This is, in fact, the crux of the learning situation itself: namely, the dynamic verbal interchange between the teacher and a class of students. Learning studies should probably not be expected to illuminate to any great extent the communication between the teacher and a class, insofar as this communication forms a part of the process of learning (as opposed, for example, to motivation or the maintenance of discipline). Why is this so?

1. First, learning does not take place in a group or class; it takes place in the nervous systems of individuals. In a strict sense, there is no such thing as the learning of a class, and the findings of learning studies apply only to individuals. It is true that the investigator of learning sometimes uses groups to study learning, but he does this only in order to obtain an average finding that applies to individuals. In a basic sense, then, one can apply the findings of learning studies only to individuals.

2. Second, learning inevitably involves individual idiosyncratic components. The individual process by which a student gets from the idea of multiplication to the idea of factoring numbers, for example, can probably not be predicted with complete specification of the mental steps involved. The reason for this is that these steps depend on individual factors in the student's past experience, and no one thinks these can be controlled in any exact sense. The steps in the mental processing can be predicted only in a probabilistic way— that is, in the sense that we know, for example, that the word *black* will probably evoke the associated word *white* in more than 90 percent of instances, but *not* in 100 percent.

3. Third, in large part because of these considerations, we cannot expect learning studies to help us specify exactly what the teacher should say, what question he should ask, or how long he should pause for a student answer, for every particular instructional situation. Few, if any, natural situations are predictable to this extent, and we cannot expect the practice of instruction to be any more predictable than, say, the building of a bridge.

4. Since the process of instruction can be described only in somewhat general terms, the corresponding descriptions of essential communications be-

tween teacher and student turn out to be remarkably unsurprising. There is nothing at all mysterious about them, and it is difficult indeed to see how to improve them. For example, suppose children are learning to add directed numbers, using the number line along with the idea of "taking a trip" in different directions. At some point, the teacher must say something like this: "Now, if our trip takes us two units in the positive direction (+2) and one unit in the negative direction (-1), where would we be at the end of the trip?" The teacher must make this basic communication. Assuming that the children know what the words mean, very little change can even be imagined in this statement. True, it may be phrased as a statement rather than a question, but that may not make much difference. The teacher can use a different idea rather than "trip" to convey direction, but that is unlikely to be important. Several different kinds of symbolic representation of positive two and negative one can be used, but this hardly seems a likely variable. In other words, while it is essential for instruction that this *idea* be expressed, the kinds of variations in the *way* it is communicated appear likely to be trivial in their effect upon learning.

What this means, then, according to my reasoning, is that the results of studies of learning cannot be expected to illuminate to any remarkable extent the essential activities involved in the core communications between teacher and student. If this is so, what then can be expected of learning studies? Where and in what ways can the findings of such studies be applied to the process of instruction? There are some possible answers to this question.

1. First, one can see that studies of learning can throw light on what a *proper sequence* of topics ought to be, to be most effective. Thus, the question of what specific kinds of capabilities an individual needs to have in order to learn about solving simultaneous equations, for example, is a legitimate one, whose answer can be determined by suitably designed research. It is not the kind of question that is to be answered by a mathematician, except insofar as he may be a shrewd guesser. The question is one of what particular learned capabilities exhibit the greatest transfer of learning to the defined task (that is, solving simultaneous equations). This is exactly the kind of question investigations of learning can be designed to answer. I refer to studies of mine and my colleagues [Gagné (42); Gagné, Mayor, Garstens, and Paradise (46)], which attempted to determine successful sequences of instruction for such mathematical tasks as finding the sum of terms in a number series, and demonstrating the addition of integers.

2. Second, learning studies can shed light on the question of the *selection of topics* in mathematics curricula, which is perhaps an even more basic matter than their sequence. They can do this because the question, again, is one of the degree of generalizability, or transfer, that certain topics have. Some kinds of mathematical content will doubtless have greater transfer value for certain useful performances than will others. I have previously pointed out, for example (44), that the number line appears to be, to one who is not highly trained in mathematics, a highly generalizable idea that can transfer readily not only

to the learning of negative numbers but also to the more advanced principles involved in graphics representation of functions, analytic geometry, and calculus. Thus the value of the number-line idea lies not so much in its immediate effects as in its value as a prerequisite way of thinking about numerical quantity, which can bring about markedly greater ease of learning of more advanced mathematical ideas. This is a hypothesis that can be subjected to test via learning experiments.

3. Third, studies of learning may be expected to throw light upon the question of the *amount and nature of review* of learned principles. This is, in other words, the question of how to maintain usable retention of initially learned capabilities. How often should one return to the transformations of trigonometric relationships, once they have been initially learned? Naturally, the answer to such a question depends on what one intends to do with these relationships and how often one expects it to be done. But the other part of the question pertains to the human memory and to the degree of retention that can be measured after various periods of disuse. This is the kind of question that suitably designed learning studies can be expected to answer.

4. What to do about *individual differences* is surely another area on which light could be thrown by experimental investigations. What kind of difference is it that produces the block in the ninth-grader first encountering algebra when he has apparently up to that time had no particular difficulty with mathematics? Or how about the block in the third-grader encountering long division for the first time? Such questions can presumably be answered by means of the methods I have described. However, it is perhaps worth saying also that there are not likely to be easy answers. It is quite unlikely, for example, that one will find a simple key to these difficulties, such as a simple namable "trait" measured by some single "test." Our methods of measurement, in fact, need to become a good deal more sophisticated than that. For one thing, they probably need to depend on a sequence of tests, each of which gets closer and closer to the specific capabilities involved, instead of focusing on a single measurement. But that is too long a story to get into here. The method of experimentation, if used ingeniously, seems capable of providing some useful answers about how to adapt instruction in mathematics to the great variety of differences displayed by individual students.

In summary, it appears that there are questions of considerable importance that can be answered by experimental studies of learning. In fact, there are some questions that probably cannot be answered validly in any other way. These are questions that have to do particularly with the selection of mathematical topics, the ordering of these topics, the relative emphasis of the topics in repetition and review, and the means and rapidity of presenting the topics for different individuals. These are questions that should not be answered by opinion in any ultimate sense, although they may have to be so answered as a temporary expedient. As long as one can be clear about what kinds of human capabilities one wants to produce by instruction in mathematics, these subordinate questions fall into place as having answers that can meet the test of scientific validity.

12 Some Peculiarities of Calculative Thinking and Their Consequences

John Williams was born on June 15, 1931. He received **JOHN D.**
a B.Sc. in psychology and logic from London Uni- **WILLIAMS**
versity and has since carried out research in the philos-
ophy of science (at Oxford University), in problem
solving (at Edinburgh University), and a variety of
other subjects, ranging from programed instruction to
the evaluation of mathematics courses (at the National
Foundation for Educational Research in England and
Wales). At present he is working with the Centre de
Recherches en Psycho-Mathématique at Sherbrooke
University in Canada, where he is mainly concerned
with laboratory studies of the learning of mathemati-
cal structures.

In the two books and more than forty papers he has
written, Williams has focused primarily on research
design, educational evaluation, programed instruc-
tion, and a variety of topics on mathematics learning.
Through his writings he has always demonstrated a
genuine concern for the learning of abstract terms,
their relationships, operations on these terms, and op-
erations on other operations.

Thus the difficulties involved in the learning of cal-
culation form the basis of Williams's paper. Features of
the calculative process are described in terms of arith-
metic, and they include the following topics: remote-
ness from reality, conceptual prerequisites, many
strands and steps, terseness, and prescription of opera-
tions. To him, these features may create problems in
the forms of compulsive indifference, anxiety, in-
ability to see meaning, loss of the thread of the argu-
ment, and possibly the disinclination to understand.

Some of the sections of this article have been taken from the author's article, "Barriers to Arithmetical Understanding," *Mathematics Teaching*, 28, 1964.

Emotional reactions to arithmetic often occur be-
cause calculation offers no "degree" of failure; each of
the many steps draws blame when the result is incor-
rect. Abstractness has a great deal to do with what
Williams calls the "thought-block," in that symbols are
used for a long time without direct reference to ex-
perience, and there is no parallel imagery to keep the
learner from losing his place in the calculation. In the
area of compulsive indifference, the author feels that
a person cannot temporarily withdraw and expect to
succeed later, because arithmetic is a cumulative sys-
tem and the precision requirement remains.

Diminishment of understanding is the result of dif-
ficulties discussed in the paper, and failure to under-
stand contributes to the ascending spiral of difficulty
for the learner. Although Williams does not suggest
remedies for problems, his analysis of calculative
thinking may enable teachers to foresee learning
problems.

In this article I hope to formulate some of the features that characterize a
kind of thinking and learning that occurs a great deal in mathematics and
much less elsewhere. This is the learning and thinking required for mastering
and operating the techniques of the formalized routine called *calculation*. All
the examples I shall give will be taken from elementary arithmetic, but they
will illustrate processes that can be expected to occur wherever humans try to
delegate the moves of a thought-game to a calculative procedure.

We shall consider what is involved both in learning to calculate and in calculating and shall consider this from the point of view of the education of the
child. We shall be particularly concerned with the difficulties involved in these
activities, for it is naturally this aspect that gives the most cause for concern.

Pervading the article is the assumption that our objectives, in teaching the
child to calculate, are that he should master the necessary skills, understand
the mathematical generalities that underlie these skills, and develop attitudes
toward calculation that promote the quality of both his skill and his understanding. (The fact that this last statement is cliché-ridden suggests perhaps
that our objectives are likely to be shared by a substantial number of present-
day educational practitioners.) At the end of the article, we shall use these objectives as a framework within which to summarize the observations we have
made.

REMOTENESS FROM THE REAL

One does not need to be professionally concerned with the education of children to recognize that they find great difficulty in handling notions that are not directly connected with concrete experience or behavior. Yet arithmetic, while it is capable of an infinity of concrete applications, consists entirely of abstractions. In fact, it is because it consists of abstractions that it can be applied in so many concrete situations. But one might argue: "I agree that 3 is abstract by virtue of the fact that it applies not only to one particular set of things, but to any such set. But are there not other similarly abstract terms, such as *blue*, *running*, and *laughter*, with which children have little difficulty?" This is a legitimate misgiving, and leads us to ask why it is that the abstractness of arithmetical terms presents children with such difficulties.

Two related explanations come to mind. First, while in everyday language the child uses abstract terms even in direct relation to concrete situations, it is usually necessary to do more than this in the case of a device for calculating such as arithmetic, for in the arithmetical "language" the point is not only to describe things, but also to be able to pass from one statement to another without referring to things in the process. The essence of calculation consists largely of this kind of procedure. It is a prerequisite of this calculative function of the arithmetical language that much of the meaning of its terms be given by the terms' relations to *one another* rather than to *things*. Consequently, before the arithmetical language can be intelligible to the child, he must grasp quite complicated and rigorous relations between different abstractions— a feat that is different from, and in many ways much more difficult than, seeing relations between abstractions and things. For example, in learning the meaning of 3, the child has more to do than merely to learn to be able to attach 3 to any of the concrete situations to which it applies. He must also learn how this term relates to the other terms of arithmetic: this is what gives 7 when added to 4, or this is what gives 15 when multiplied by 5, and so forth. Thus, by virtue of the fact that he must learn the complicated "internal" relations that exist among the terms of arithmetic, the pupil is forced to operate on a plane above the concrete.

This brings us to our second point. Many of the moves of the arithmetic-game require us to retreat still further from the concrete. Consider an expression such as

$$4 \times \frac{5}{6}$$

Here, we are not referring to just the simple abstraction 4, but to a 4 that is multiplied by a 5 that is divided by a 6. Before we can understand the implications of this expression, we must be able to think at a level that is three flights above the concrete, for the objects to which we are here referring are qualified by the symbol 4, which in turn is qualified by its relation to 5, which in turn is qualified by its relation to 6.

Apart from the foregoing kinds of abstractness, there is one kind of remoteness from the real that derives from the fact that even fairly simple arithmetic often refers to situations that do not make *perceptual* sense to us. While we can easily imagine the size-relationship between a group of 3 and a group of 4, it is virtually impossible to do this in the case of, say, groups of 35 and 37. Yet, in quite ordinary arithmetic, numbers of this size are encountered and their relations formulated.

CONCEPTUAL PREREQUISITES

Before arithmetic can be said to make sense at all, certain basic notions must be appreciated, and, as the research of Piaget has shown, such an appreciation is often absent in children of the age at which arithmetic is attempted. For example, without the appreciation that quantity is conserved (an appreciation that many five-year-olds are lacking) there is little assurance that the child will realize how 3 + 1 is numerically the same as 2 + 2.

But even when such basic concepts have been grasped, there is still a danger that the pupil will be faced with arithmetical learning that he is ill-equipped to handle with insight. This is because arithmetic is conceptually what might be called a *cumulative* system in which there are more elaborate structures that incorporate more elementary structures, and unless the *elementary* structures have been grasped, those that incorporate them will not be intelligible. For example, we cannot understand the long division procedure unless we understand the subtraction procedure, because the former incorporates the latter. This might seem to pose difficulties enough, especially where the pupil's learning has been inadequate at certain stages in the system; however, there are difficulties in addition to these, for even where a part of arithmetic *has at one time* been fully understood, it might well have become automatic and meaningless by the time it is to be incorporated into a more elaborate part. Learning very naturally tends to follow a course towards mechanization, in which a procedure might well be interpreted, "sorted out," or understood on first acquaintance, but is likely to be performed without attention once it has been mastered. Eventually the learner is able to perform it without an awareness of its meaning, and, in some cases, without even being able to recover his original understanding of it.

MANY STRANDS AND MANY STEPS

Part of the power of arithmetic is derived from the fact that it enables us to break down complex situations into many manageable parts, and complex processes into many manageable steps. As an example of the former, we can take long multiplication, in which we multiply first by the units, then by the tens, and so on of the multiplier, and only at a later stage combine the results of our operations. Compound interest could be cited as an instance of the breaking down of a process into steps. Here we form a conclusion about part of the situation, then a further conclusion that incorporates our first conclusion, and so on. Now, before one can be said to know fully what is going on in these *multistrand* and *multistep* procedures, he must realize how the strands are brought together and how the stages articulate to form the procedure. The child is at a great disadvantage in both cases, because realizations of the former kind tax his span of attention, while those of the latter kind tax his immediate memory (both of which are likely to be very limited compared with those of the adult).

Another consequence of what might be called the "composite" nature of arithmetical calculations is that the pupil will find it difficult to understand, when he has made a mistake, precisely *where* he has erred. In which strand has the string been weakened? At which link has the chain been broken? To have failed without being able to establish precisely *how*, will discourage the pupil in his attempts to render calculations intelligible to himself and leave him with little hope of being able to improve his performance.

TERSENESS AND INTELLIGIBILITY

In the language of arithmetic, we are concerned with representing only a very limited aspect of the environment. This has made great economy in the construction of the language possible, while at the same time our use of this language for complicated calculations has made such economy desirable. However, the resulting terseness of arithmetic has sometimes reduced its intelligibility, and the precision required in using so terse a language is likely to conceal from the pupil the degree to which he has succeeded in understanding the general techniques of its use. Some examples will make these points clear.

a) Economy of Notation. We do not use a different digit for every different number. Instead, we make do with the symbols 0–9. In order to understand to which number any one of these is referring, the pupil must grasp the conventions of a fairly complicated system of positional notation. Again, the same symbols are used for a variety of different purposes. In $4 + 2$, the 2 stands for a set of 2 units. In 2×4, the 2 stands for a number of sets of 4 units. In 4^2, the 2 stands for the number of 4s we are multiplying together. Because the same symbol is involved in all cases, it is quite likely that the pupil will regard the cases as less distinct from one another than they actually are.

b) Shortcuts. In many of our formulations and calculations, we economize at the expense of explicitness. For example, in dividing 4,256 by 8, we should normally behave in our first step as if we were dividing 42 instead of 4,200.

c) Precision. If the correct answer to a calculation is 43, then 44 will usually be wrong, just as will 84. In most kinds of calculation, degrees of correctness are not acknowledged, and even slight incorrectness is not accepted. This is a direct result of the fact that the components of arithmetical statements are so essential to the meaning of these statements (there being so little redundancy in the arithmetical language) that precision of less than 100 percent in any of these components could often change the meaning to a disastrous degree. As a consequence, although the pupil may have been following a perfectly correct procedure, he might well get his sum wrong because of carelessness, incomplete knowledge of his tables, and so on—reasons that may be peripheral to his grasp of the essence of the skills involved and unrelated to his understanding of them. Because of the important part that precision plays, mastery and understanding of basic skills sometimes go unrewarded and are sometimes even unjustly brought into question.

PRESCRIPTION AND PASSIVITY

While arithmetic is obviously an admirable vehicle for certain kinds of thinking, it tends (as do the more literal kinds of vehicles) to be conducive to a kind of laziness. Let us look at what typically happens in arithmetical thinking. Initially, we are faced with a problem, as for example: "How much money do I need in order to pay each of my 32 employees £48?" We can analyze our treatment of this problem into three steps. Step 1 consists of a translation of the problem-situation into a form that is amenable to arithmetical calculation. Here a certain amount of discrimination is required; a suitable form would be £48 × 32. Again in the final step, step 3, a certain amount of judgment and discrimination is often required; this consists in the translation of one's results back into terms that are relevant to the situation with which one is dealing. But it is in the intermediate step 2 that we are interested. In this step, the pupil follows a calculative procedure, which he would probably write out thus:

$$
\begin{array}{r}
48 \\
\times 32 \\
\hline
96 \\
1440 \\
\hline
1536
\end{array}
$$

Here, not only is very little discrimination involved, but the student needs to be very sure indeed (in view of the precision that arithmetic requires) that he follows the procedure obediently. Since the form that this procedure should take has been worked out in advance, he is likely to proceed automatically in following it. The interpretative activities usually required in the everyday working out of problems are not needed here. He does not need to work out his conceptual route, for he is carried along by a preplanned calculative procedure. He does not need to search for general principles for guidance or engage in the kinds of analysis that problems usually demand of him, for his course is cut and dried. Because his program is so closely prescribed and so little interpretative initiative is required, it is not surprising that he may often be tempted to cease trying to interpret his behavior and, consequently, develop an attitude of what might be called *cognitive passivity*. Such an attitude, once it appears, takes root quickly, for once the struggle to interpret has been relinquished, arithmetic becomes less and less intelligible; failure to understand some moves renders the understanding of others impossible.

EMOTIONAL REACTIONS

It is not unusual, in response to the difficulties with which arithmetic confronts him, for the learner to react in a strongly emotional way and develop behavior patterns that are sufficiently maladaptive to be described as neurotic. We shall consider first the details of how such behavior is instigated and then some aspects of the form it often takes.

Number neurosis can be considered similar to other kinds of neurotic behavior in that it usually results from a situation in which the learner is highly motivated to solve a problem that is insoluble for him.

We can account for the initial strength of this motivation if we consider the unpleasantness of failure in calculative activity. As we have seen, there tend not to be shades of failure in calculation; one is either as successful as one can be, or as unsuccessful as one can be. Frequently, the learner is in the position of failing repeatedly, drastically, and without hope of being able to remedy this state of affairs. Furthermore, the emotional effect of the outcome of a calculation is likely to become attached to each move in the series of moves leading up to this outcome, because on the one hand, the outcome of an arithmetical calculation can be seen to be a direct effect of the moves that culminate in it, while on the other hand, it can be difficult to establish which of these moves is responsible for the outcome being wrong.

We have already examined some of the features of arithmetic that can contribute to the inability to perform calculations correctly. Two of these are—

1. Where component understandings and skills have not been learned properly, there is often no hope that the learner will be able to achieve a mastery of the composite technique. Attempts to do so, without the necessary background learning, will be futile.
2. The difficulty of identifying the guilty move in a complex procedure impedes improvement.

The neurotic behavior resulting from these conditions manifests itself in at least two forms:

1. compulsive indifference
2. anxiety

Compulsive Indifference

In this case, the learner manages to "withdraw from the field," often integrating his failure with a none-too-pleasant conception of his ability. Perhaps it is because failure at arithmetic is so unambiguous that there are comfortable, clearly defined, ready-made roles in our culture for those who fail in arithmetic. Many children have parents who appear to be perfectly capable and competitive in other ways, but who are very ready to concede that they are "no good at figures."

In the case of some subject matters, such a withdrawal might place the learner in a better position to succeed. Withdrawal might release him from a crippling anxiety, after which partial or occasional success might ignite interest. However, the likelihood that this will happen in arithmetic is, for two reasons, very small indeed:

1. In view of the high degree of precision demanded by this subject, success in it will not come, even occasionally, to those who are not both attentive and extremely careful to make the correct moves.
2. Since arithmetic is cumulative—that is, later learning depends on earlier learning—withdrawal, even temporarily, can present great difficulties for subsequent learning.

It is likely, therefore, that indifference will produce circumstances conducive to its own consolidation, and once it is established, it will feed upon its consequences and thrive.

Anxiety

In a subject like arithmetic, anxiety serves the learner no better than indifference. Where simple tasks are to be performed, high anxiety can be an effective motivator, but as tasks become more complex for the performer, so does it become more likely that high anxiety will disrupt his performance. This effect could be brought about in many ways, but probably the following factors substantially contribute to it:

1. High anxiety produces unpleasant feelings, some of which are physical, that can distract the performer's attention.
2. Perhaps as a consequence of this, but also as a result of the part played by anxiety as an emergency drive in the motivational economy, the performer's field of attention narrows considerably. This simplifies the environment for him, and thus facilitates the direct action that is needed in an emergency. However, it can also oversimplify situations that require complex appreciation.
3. Finally, the learner's ability to suspend responses is reduced; one can see the advantages of precipitate reaction to emergency conditions, but one can also see how such precipitateness could impair the performance of complex tasks requiring detour-behavior, and particularly that of tasks of an arithmetical nature, which require careful and exact compliance with complex and rigorous rules.

As if this kind of disruption were not sufficient to place the learner under a severe handicap, anxiety is also likely to produce an attitude of passivity, for the blind pursuit of well-learned, clearly prescribed routines would be much less inhibited by such a state than would the more complicated kinds of behavior that are involved in constructive thinking.

Like indifference and passivity, anxiety is likely to perpetuate and amplify itself. The less successful the anxiety-prone pupil becomes, the greater will be his anxiety to succeed; and the greater his anxiety, the smaller his chances of success. Were it not for this "positive feedback" effect, anxiety would probably seldom reach heights that would cripple arithmetic performance, but thus "stepped up," it occasionally reduces the pupil to a state approaching complete arithmetical impotence.[1]

THE THOUGHT BLOCK

This phenomenon seems to occur much more frequently in arithmetic than in many other areas of the curriculum. While it sometimes manifests itself conspicuously, it more often dogs the performer in a sub-acute form, impairing the efficiency of his calculating without noticeably interrupting it. There appear to be two kinds of thought blocks:

1. an inability to "see meaning" in arithmetical statements
2. a tendency to "lose the thread" in an arithmetical calculation or argument

Meaning Blindness

In these cases, the pupil seems to feel no associations with an arithmetical statement. Such a statement triggers off neither images nor dispositions to behave; it "leaves him cold," just as a statement in an unfamiliar language might. A comparison of arithmetical symbolism with the words of our everyday descriptive language might well provide us with some insight into the origins of this "meaning blindness."

In the first place, arithmetical symbols are used for a great deal of the time in detachment from any reference to experience; it could be claimed that part of the utility of arithmetic is that it enables us to come to conclusions about our experiences without direct reference to them. This, coupled with the fact that the meaning of these symbols is extremely abstract, tends to develop in the learner the habit of thinking about and manipulating the symbols without any accompanying imagery of situations to which they might refer. This is far from so in the case of our everyday language. Here the purpose of the language is largely to refer to situations. Usually it is used for this purpose and, consequently, it is much more likely to be accompanied by images of such situations.

---

1. For an excellent and detailed treatment of number anxiety, see J. B. Biggs, *Anxiety, Motivation and Primary School Mathematics*, National Foundation for Educational Research, 1962.

There is another reason why arithmetical symbols often fail to evoke a referent. When we see or do things, we automatically process our experiences in
such a way that they fall into categories that are suitable for the kind of interaction we are likely to have with our environment. For example, we usually
categorize a flat tabletop and its long legs as a single entity and see them as
such, whereas we usually categorize the flat tabletop and the flat breadboard
as different entities and see them as such. We find it easy to bring to mind
images that represent our experience "divided up" in these customary ways,
and the categories implied by our everyday statements closely parallel those
underlying this imagery. Consequently, everyday statements are likely to
find corresponding referents in our usual imagery. Number symbols, by contrast, refer to an aspect of the environment in terms of which we do not
usually, for purposes of perceiving the environment, need to categorize it.
(This is not to say, of course, that there are not some circumstances in which
we can profitably use numbers as a means of discriminating between different entities; for example, we often use this means when we wish to make
particularly fine distinctions, when we wish to relate experiences in a particularly abstract and stable manner, or when, as in the case of monetary dis-
criminations, we are working within a man-made set of conventions.) Since
our perceptual categories thus tend to be irrelevant to numerical categories,
we do not naturally have available an imagery to which to refer our number symbols. It is, of course, possible to use our everyday kind of imagery
for this purpose, but we cannot do so very readily, for we must first go to the
trouble of re-sorting our experiences into categories that are relevant to
numbers.

As was stressed earlier, the reference of number symbols to situations outside the system in which they are used is certainly not the only source from
which they gain meaning. An important part of their meaning resides in
their interrelationships with one another. Unfortunately, meaning of this
kind is also likely to be inaccessible. There is nothing about number symbols
that will betray their relational implications; indeed, it is often necessary to
give the symbols a concrete or imaginal reference before their relations to one
another become apparent.

From these points, it should be gathered that the learner must often engage
in a certain amount of searching before he can give meaning to arithmetical
statements. It is in bridging this gap between symbol and meaning that he often
fails. Conditions of stress, such as anxiety, are likely to disrupt the searching
process (a kind of thought process that is patently incompatible with precipitateness of response) and thus reduce the likelihood that meaning will be
found. Here lies the association between meaning blindness and such states as
number anxiety.

Losing the Thread

We can to some extent explain this kind of blockage in the terms we used for our explanation of meaning blindness. At some point in a calculation, the search for the meaning of a statement can fail. If this happens, the learner is held up at this "implicationless" statement, for there is insufficient indication of how to proceed to the next. It might be observed that if we were proceeding in a concrete or imaginal medium, this kind of interruption would be less likely to happen, for, in a sense, "statements" in such media actually embody their implications and are therefore less likely to become detached from them.

There is another respect in which the progression through a series of "statements" in a symbolic medium (rather than a medium that is concrete or imaginal) is likely to be vulnerable to interruption. When we are carrying out a series of manipulations of real things or images of real things, there is usually a redundancy of "threads," over and above the arithmetical "thread," by means of which the steps can be held together in an orderly sequence. Concrete instances of our moves have many aspects, apart from their numerical aspect, which will enable us to fit them together into a coherent story. If, instead of just subtracting 4 from 10 and then dividing the remainder by 2, we are taking 4 oranges from a basket of 10, placing them in a bowl, and then dividing the remainder between two children, there are many ways of relating the moves to one another, for each of these components of the sequence can be related to others, along a multitude of dimensions. For example, we have removed something orange in color from something brown in color, placed what is orange in something white in color, and then divided between two pink things the something orange that remained. Other alternatives include something spherical being taken from something shapeless, something rough being placed into something shiny, something vegetable being divided between two animal things, and so on. Now if in the course of calculating in this kind of medium the arithmetical thread is lost, there will be several other guidelines to follow, so that the calculator will have at least a general idea of where he is in the sequence, what has happened, and what must be done. In contrast, the symbolic language is abstract, not in this way multifaceted, and offers relatively little opportunity for parallel progression; once the learner loses hold of the slender arithmetical argument, he is lost. Like a tightrope, it is economical but also precarious.

As in the case of meaning blindness, the difficulties resulting from losing the thread can be aggravated by stress. Once the thread has been lost, search activity will be necessary before it can be regained. We have seen how the narrowing of the span of attention and the need for a precipitate response might reduce the effectiveness of this kind of activity.

UNDERSTANDING

We have seen that every one of the difficulties mentioned tends in some way or other to reduce the likelihood that arithmetic will be understood. A failure to understand brings with it many unfortunate effects: the amount of material to be memorized will be much greater than it would otherwise have been; in assimilating material, the learner will be less well equipped for interpreting it; material that has been learned will be less accessible and less easy to transfer; the selection and modification of techniques and information will pose problems; and learned material will probably be retained less permanently than it would have been had understanding been brought into play in its acquisition.

All the factors that discourage understanding encourage an attitude of passivity, and, as this attitude grows, difficulty in understanding joins forces with a disinclination to understand. Such an alliance is particularly formidable in arithmetic, a subject in which these enemies will gain strength with every victory.

SUMMARY

A system such as arithmetic that consists of procedures for facilitating calculation causes certain characteristic difficulties for those who learn and use it:

1. It is abstract, in that it involves both symbol relationships into which objects do not enter and operations that are performed on other operations. It is remote, in that many of its statements refer to situations that are not easy to appreciate perceptually.

2. As Piaget has shown, children are often introduced to arithmetic at an age at which their appreciation of its underlying concepts is too poorly developed for them to be able to understand it. Again, the parts of arithmetic are interdependent in such a way that composite skills cannot be performed without the mastery of component skills, and cannot be understood without the grasp of certain basic concepts. Consequently, in certain cases, the pupil is in a position in which he cannot master or understand the arithmetic to be learned. This difficulty is aggravated by the deactivation of once-present insights.

3. Calculations often involve many strands and many stages. This places obstacles in the way of error detection and the examination of the parts of a calculation.

4. Shortcuts in calculation and economy in notation result in a terser, but less intelligible, calculating system. Moreover, such a system is unusually precise, and, as a consequence, leaves very little room for the use of a learning strategy of "progressive approximation": the alternative to complete success is often complete failure.

5. In calculation, the learner's procedure is closely prescribed. Consequently, he tends not to engage in active interpretation of the course he follows and develops an attitude of "cognitive passivity." This particularly impairs performances involving the selection or adaptation of techniques.

6. Failure, with little hope of success, provides negative motivation, which

produces compulsive indifference or anxiety. Both of these will perpetuate themselves, and both impair performance. Anxiety impairs performance on complex tasks by distracting, reducing the field of attention, and prematurely precipitating responses.

7. Thought blocks may be due to either "meaning blindness" or "losing the thread." Meaning blindness results from the failure of number symbols to evoke a relationship either with other symbols or with a referent. Loss of the thread can be due to meaning blindness or to the precariousness of the pursuit of a symbolic course of which the learner has little understanding. Both kinds of thought blocks are aggravated by stress.

8. In one way or another, all the above factors tend to reduce the learner's understanding of what he is doing. Failure to understand in turn adds to the learner's difficulties.

Mathematics: Its Language and Communication

PART FOUR

13 Mathematics as Human Communication

Paul B. Johnson, born in Lewistown, Idaho, received his A.B. and M.A. from the University of Washington, and his Ph.D. in mathematics from the California Institute of Technology in 1947. He left his position as chairman of the Mathematics Department at Occidental College to go to the University of California at Los Angeles, where he is currently a professor of mathematics.

Author of several publications in mathematics as well as in mathematics education, he has been on the faculty of an experimental junior college, has worked in the actuarial department of the Occidental Life Insurance Company, and has served as consultant in medical research and business management with Capitol Records and General Electric. His major interests are geometry, statistics, mathematics for engineering executives, and the communication and learning of mathematics. In addition, Professor Johnson has been director and instructor of a number of conferences for high school and college teachers of mathematics, and he has lectured on "Mathematics for Engineering Executives" at UCLA, the University of Texas, and for General Electric and Kaiser Industries. Currently, he serves as consultant to a number of school districts on curricular problems of mathematics, and he is a member of the American Mathematical Society and the Mathematical Association of America. He is a past member of the board of governors, past president of the California Mathematics Council, and a current member of the National Council of Teachers of Mathematics.

One of Professor Johnson's main concerns is the process of communication in mathematics. In mathe-

PAUL B. JOHNSON

*matics, he feels, this communication is second in
importance only to individual thinking. Yet massive
blocks impede the mathematician's communication
with those outside the field and even with other mathematicians. By analyzing the components of communication—the sender, the receiver, the medium,
and the message—we can begin to remove these blocks
and encourage an active flow of ideas. Johnson's paper scrutinizes these four main components of communication. Most of his examples lie in the realm of
university mathematics, though his views apply to
the communication process in general.*

*Tracing the course of an idea from the sender to the
receiver, Johnson discusses characteristics of each.
These characteristics include background and knowledge of material, attitude toward the subject, use of
learning and communication tools, and the point of
view (arithmetic or geometric) that is held. This last
characteristic has significant implications in the teaching of mathematics, but is often overlooked.*

*The sections of the paper dealing with the medium
cover the standard topics (text, lecture, discussion,
and so on), but the lengthy portion concerning journal articles as communicators may be new material
for many readers.*

*A subjective, but possibly revealing, analysis of cer-
tain content material in calculus and arithmetic texts
comprises most of the discussion on the message. Here,
Johnson classifies reasons for student acceptance of
any particular sentence, and he judges the sentences
in each of several selections on the basis of this classification. General conclusions as to whether communication consists of authoritative statements or
reader participation are hard to make, but the author
hopes to stimulate investigation of this area and the
whole process of communication.*

Second only to individual thinking, communication is perhaps the most important mathematical activity. For example, the question "What do mathematicians do?" is faced by every mathematics lecturer talking to junior high

students, college students, parents, or lay people. The usual answer is "He studies, he does research, he teaches, or he applies mathematics to a field such as actuarial science, engineering, or computing." This answer sounds impressive. The questioner and answerer both nod sagely, and the conversation moves elsewhere. It isn't that the audience has learned any useful knowledge, but the questioner doesn't know how to ask the next question. If he did, the lecturer probably wouldn't know how to answer it in a way the questioner could understand.

What is often overlooked is that if a mathematics major or even most Ph.D. mathematicians ask questions of other mathematics experts, the answers received are often only slightly better. There are massive blocks in the communication channels. Are these blocks necessary? Many people are convinced they are. They say there is no point in talking to anyone who is not an expert on the topic at hand. Others feel that the blocks can be whittled drastically if a vigorous attack is made on them. This paper will explore the situation. New criteria for evaluating communication in terms of student cognitive level and student involvement are suggested in the later sections.

First we must describe what we mean by communication in the most general sense. In mathematics, some individual has an idea. After a while, another individual has an idea related to the first idea by some causal process occurring in time. This process is communication. Looking at a process in this general way will not only allow us to see the places where obvious room for improvement exists, but it will also probably turn up otherwise overlooked possibilities of even greater fruitfulness.

There appear to be four major components in the communication chain. They are the sender, the receiver, the medium, and the message.

The sender is the person who has the idea. Under this heading comes, for example, discussions of his knowledge, personality, background, sense of purpose and obligations, skill at conceiving and expressing ideas, and the actions he takes.

The receiver is the person who gets the idea. How well prepared is he for the message? Is he skilled at receiving (listening and reading)? Is he eager, enthusiastic, bored, or resentful? Does he know the sender's intended meanings of words? How recent and at what level is his mathematical background? The receiver may be the same person as the sender. Talking to oneself is not a mark of insanity, but a way of clearing ideas.

The medium refers to the physical process. It includes—

1. Sound (Lecture and discussion.)
2. Writing (Notes, articles, and books.)
3. Apparatus (Material objects, models, and structures.)
4. Persons (Many ideas are conveyed secondhand. Some are difficult to verbalize. We "wrap them up in a person" and then send the person.)
5. Situation (This gestalt concept states that an idea is conveyed by putting the person in a situation. He gets the idea from the situation.)

The message is the idea being communicated. Is it exposition, or a description of something? Is it inspirational encouragement to some action? Is it a direction, an order to take some action? Is it a 95-percent message, a 5-percent message, or something in between? No message includes all the details of the idea. While no accurate measurement is possible, a 95-percent message means that practically all the details are in the message, with only a few obvious ones left for the reader to deduce. A 5-percent message contains only the barest outline of the idea, leaving a rather strenuous task to complete the story. What is the level of the idea—introductory, middle, or advanced? Is the idea from arithmetic, algebra, geometry, analysis, or one of the other umpteen branches of mathematics? Are there affective, or feeling, components? Is the message long or short? Is the idea given all at once or separated into several messages? Is it given via a spiral approach?

The test of communication is how well the idea got through. That is, how close is the idea in the receiver to the idea in the sender? Any difference is usually a flaw, so steps are taken to correct these. Having human frailties, the sender customarily blames the flaw on the stupidity of the receiver, and the receiver blames it on the poorness of the sender. Sophisticates may blame it on the "noise" in the communications channel or process. Sometimes the new idea is better than the one in the mind of the sender. It is not clear where the credit for the improvement should go.

Sometimes the message is not a specific theorem, but an exhortation to work harder or more effectively. Such messages almost always get through verbally, but they are judged by the actions of the receiver.

Tests of the adequacy of communication are difficult to come by. Most common, and perhaps best, is the judgment of a trained observer. This permits taking account of many levels of cognitive ability. Such evaluations are subject to the personal biases of the observer. Many people desire a more objective evaluation. This is done by comparing the behavior of the sender with that of the receiver, and this leads to the idea of "behavioral objectives" and "operational definitions." Such comparisons are quite helpful to the artistic observer mentioned above as well. The concept of evaluating in terms of behavior is a step forward, but it does not eliminate judgment. Judgment tells whether the behavior reflects rote recall or deep understanding. The same behavior may lead to these different judgments in different situations.

To optimize is one of the fundamental drives behind mathematicians: "Find the maximum." "Do it once and for all." "Determine the best curriculum and teaching method." "Make it elegant." "Simplify." "Generalize." These and similar phrases motivate much of what we do. Frequently we are successful, when the situation has been simplified sufficiently.

Only a superficial consideration is necessary to see that no optimum exists in general in mathematics communication. There is no such thing as the best teacher, the best student, the best curriculum, or the best teaching method or medium. What is one person's meat is another person's poison. A dem-

onstration or phrase may be best in one situation for one sender and one receiver, but some entirely different activity may be better in another. Optimi-
zation purposes and goals still exist, of course, but only in sufficiently restricted situations. To achieve them requires thinking of a variety of possibilities. Most classes are too varied for a single maximum. The "best" teaching
strategy may be a combination of "better," rather than "best" methods. Criteria of desirability include not only the quality of communication but also
the resources in time, materials, and people that are available.

THE SENDER

The sender in mathematics communication is the person who has the idea and
desires to transmit it. Among other roles, he may be a lecturer, a writer, a dis-
cussant, a conversationalist, an administrator, or an editor. Probably the
last person in the chain before the idea hits the receiver is the most useful person to consider. However, it is worthwhile to realize that Euclid, Newton,
Gauss, and many others were also prime senders of the mathematics being
learned today. This is not too important to the student of parallelism, calculus, and curvature, but it is salutary for the person to consider now who in
fifty or a hundred years will play a similar role for learners of that time. Just
like Euclid, we are today sending messages that will be received only after
being filtered through a long channel of people and papers, by people unsym-
pathetic to the originator's purpose.

The persons most concerned with the characteristics of a sender are the receiver and an administrator or editor who has the responsibility of bringing
the receiver and sender together. Qualities of importance are—

1. Does he know the material? This is often difficult to tell. The requirements vary with other factors. If a person is writing a paper, or delivering
a lecture without questions, mere accurate knowledge of the topic is sufficient. If there are questions to be answered, or if discussions are held, a much
broader and deeper knowledge is required. Sometimes a person will give a
well-worked-out lecture, with correct definitions, airtight proofs, and relevant
examples. Then, when a misunderstanding occurs, it is seen that all he can
do is repeat what he said before. This is not as deep an understanding as that
shown by giving a wider variety of examples and alternative proofs that may or
may not be as rigorous.

While it is true that a person does not understand an idea he has never studied or used, and that he only partially understands something he has studied only once, it is also true that he may not understand material that he uses
correctly and expertly. Mathematicians delight in poking fun at cookbook
engineers. There are surveyors who can lay out or plot a highway, who have
only the vaguest ideas of trigonometry. Some mechanical engineers will
use transfer functions and be utterly unaware of Laplace transforms and differential equations. What is not so well known is that most college mathe-

maticians have cookbook skills in arithmetic and other very elementary topics. They do not understand arithmetic in sufficient breadth to be able to communicate it well, even though they can do any computation and are experts in advanced topics.

2. Does the sender like the material? Does he like sending, writing, or lecturing? Affective, or emotional, components are traditionally frowned on in mathematics. In ways that are not completely understood, they do rub off and make a difference in communication. This facet is hard to measure; yet somehow it is easier to understand and to learn from a person who is enthusiastic and enjoys what he is doing.

It is hard to compare the importance of knowledge versus enthusiasm. In a short exposure, knowledge is overwhelmingly the more important. In a long period, enthusiasm can compensate. The enthusiasm or boredom infects the receiver so that he may fill in gaps in the enthusiastic presentation, while he may miss important points in the bored presentation.

There is little, if any, hard data comparing classes having joyful teachers with those having bored teachers. Comparative research is extremely difficult. The variables are hard to define and measure, even in obvious situations. Further, the mere fact of making a study may upset conditions so that the results are not valid.

3. Does the sender have a drive to communicate? Does he understand how to use the tools? Does he understand how his receivers will react to his message? Does he regard his task as giving a logically exact presentation, with the receiver responsible for understanding what is sent? Does he evaluate his work by the quality and amount of learning shown in the behavior of the receiver?

4. There is a story that it was German academic tradition for college professors to give beautiful, clear, well-organized lectures that neither required nor allowed any audience response. One day no students came to class. The professor gave his lecture in full and complete detail to an empty room. He said his responsibility was to give the lecture. From there on, it was the students' responsibility.

It would not be fair to claim that this professor had no desire to communicate. He doubtless was very sad, but he felt there were other important principles at stake. However, occasionally there are people who don't seem to care whether they have an audience and are understood or not. Frequently, such people are not understood.

5. The tools of communication include chalk, paper, pencil, voice, printing and duplicating equipment, pictures, models, apparatus, overhead projectors, slides, films, texts, references, and even in a subtle way personal dress and bearing. Most mathematicians have the tool competence of the auto mechanic who learned by fixing the neighbors' cars. After several years of experience

he gets quite good with a few tools on certain models. Many mathematicians are quite good at writing what they say word for word on the chalkboard. For others, a piece of chalk is a security blanket with which they write a few tiny marks that are illegible beyond the first rows. The overhead projector has been in use for several years, and it is indispensable for large lecture halls. Still, many speakers need to be shown how to use it, do not know how big to write, or use only one projector.

There is a great variation in people's ability in rudimentary skills such as writing legibly, not standing in front of the blackboard, and speaking distinctly. Such skills are now recognized as desirable and worth developing. The use of more advanced tools is in its infancy in mathematics.

6. Does the sender have an arithmetic or geometric point of view? Does he think in the language of numbers or pictures? Mathematics developed from these two quite different types of experience, as well as from nature.

Many mathematicians have a decided leaning towards one rather than the other. The arithmetically slanted person is inclined to think and express his idea in terms of arithmetic and algebra. The geometric-minded person thinks and expresses himself in terms of geometry. While no individual is completely one way or the other, certain questions may reflect the difference. Did he find algebra or geometry more exciting in high school? When he thinks of "sin x," does he think of a table or infinite series, or does he think of a curve or projection of a revolving segment? Does he think of a real number as an infinite decimal, an equivalence class of Cauchy sequences of rationals, or does he think of it as a point on a line?

There has been a decided trend in the last century toward expressing ideas in terms of numbers. This may be a style trend, or perhaps it is easier to break a complicated argument into little steps in an arithmetic proof than in a geometric proof. As a result, arithmetic analysis has uncovered gaps and errors in demonstrations suggested by geometric thinking. Since mathematicians love nothing so much as pointing out errors and filling in lacunas in others' arguments, there has been a rush to arithmetic analysis, even by the geometric thinkers.

THE RECEIVER

The receiver is the person who learns or is taught the idea. He may be the end of a chain starting with Euclid, or he may be the latest link planning to pass on what he learns. The quality of the communication depends overwhelmingly on his ability to receive. His qualifications fall into four categories.

1. How adequate is his technical background? There is no point in teaching advanced calculus in the sixth grade. One teaches elementary arithmetic to a Ph.D. in much different fashion than to a ten-year-old child. It is a very difficult task to describe what an adequate background is for a given commu-

nication, and it is even more difficult to see if it exists. Being prepared cannot be completely described in terms of courses taken, materials studied, former professors, age, papers written, recent employment, or former students. All of these are perhaps indicators. Being prepared, however, is not only an intellectual knowledge of words and theorems that will be used, but also an appreciation of, or readiness to accept, the patterns and concepts that will be presented. History is full of cases where people have understood the words and logic but were unwilling to accept the pattern. It is said that Gauss had developed non-Euclidean long before anyone else, but he did not publish it because he felt people would not accept it.

Many interesting ideas require a background in several fields. Some receivers may be very well qualified in one field and woefully ignorant in another.

2. Does the receiver like the material? Interest and enthusiasm are like wheels on a railroad car. The mass can be dragged without wheels, but it is so much better with them. There is a decided difference between a required course and a voluntary one. Indeed, many people say if the receiver dislikes the experience, very little communication will take place.

If the receiver is eagerly searching, successful communication occurs with only the barest outline and suggestion of proof. A Leakey gets the message of a whole culture and race of men from a few bones in the eroded banks of a desert stream in Olduvai Canyon in Africa. Many mathematicians find even larger structures with less of a start.

If the receiver is passive, more details, examples, and analogies are useful. If the receiver is antagonistic, more attention to basic human satisfactions are useful. These include being sure the receiver is successful, that he sees a value in what is learned, that he recognizes its relevance, and that he has opportunity for a success image with his peers.

3. Does the receiver know the tools of learning? These include abilities such as reading, listening, taking notes, paying attention, participating in discussion, working problems, checking, asking questions, rewriting discussions in different words, thinking up examples, illustrations, generalizations and simplifications, telling the ideas to others, and taking examinations. Many students believe they are behaving appropriately if they take copious notes, memorize them, work homework assignments, and take examinations. This is not enough. More personal involvement is needed if efficient learning is to occur. Often such students look back at their education and are amazed at how little they remember and how pointless their experience seems. They then blame the instructor, the system, and the establishment.

Many students need help in learning to use the tools of receiving. This includes not only becoming aware of the tool and how it works, but also being convinced that the tool is valuable. Checking, for example, seems to be a very difficult tool to teach. The author had occasion to give a repeat examination to a class after a ten-day interval. During this period an impassioned plea was made for checking on an exam, along with certain other mind- and time-freeing tricks such as using one side of the page only, leaving lots of white space on the paper, starting problems at the top of the page rather than at the bottom, and using complete sentences. The appearance of the papers showed that about half the class adopted these tools, and half rejected them. Both good and poor students took both positions. However, a plot of grades on the second test versus grades on the first showed that those who adopted the tools increased their grades about 10 percent more than those who rejected them.

At some mathematics field days (a mathematics competition), a contest is held that emphasizes checking. Teams of two enter, with each person checking his partner's work (and his own, if he wishes). Papers are scored in terms of the number correct minus the number incorrect of those answers recorded. As much time is allowed for checking as doing the problem. Despite the most explicit instructions, zero is an above-average score. Our good students appear to have severe blocks against checking or acting appropriately after checking.

4. Is the receiver arithmetic or geometric oriented? Comments similar to those about the sender apply here. While quantum theory tells us that relatively few, if any, things are actually continuous, most of our human images and models are continuous. Geometric imagery such as shapes, curves, and graphs appear more suited than arithmetic imagery. Many people are more receptive to continuity (geometric type presentations at least) for introducing intuitive basic concepts. For example, years of trials by many dedicated persons have proved that using arithmetic ($\epsilon - \delta$ discussions) to introduce continuity is not successful. The receiver needs to have a good geometric feeling for continuity and then be placed in a situation where his geometric feelings fail before he is convinced of the value of $\epsilon - \delta$.

THE MEDIUM

Perhaps the most common media for communicating mathematics are texts, journal articles, treatises, lectures, class discussions and seminars, individual discussions or tutoring, small-group discussions, programed presentations using teaching machines, computers, television, movies, slides, film strips, phonograph or tape audio presentations, and demonstrations with models and laboratory equipment. People are also media.

The text is perhaps the most satisfactory medium. A very substantial amount of material can be included. Ideas can be developed in detail, including alternative approaches, motivating material, appropriate illustrations, and problems and exercises. The text lasts a long time, is easy to consult, and is a satisfactory reference. It is not surprising that to perhaps most classes the text is the curriculum, the guide, and the arbiter of the course.

The wide variety of texts shows that no text is perfect. Different senders and receivers will desire different attitudes and approaches to the same body of material. Texts vary in the level of language and the amount of illustrative background and historical material they present. Authors differ in their affection for different proofs of the same theorem. Which and how many of the hundreds of proofs known to the Pythagorean theorem should be included is a typical author's editorial problem. How much detail should be included? Too much detail is boring; if there is too little, no message gets through. Texts in the same subject will also vary in the topics discussed and their order. It usually pays to take these ideas into consideration in the selection of a text.

Journal articles are the accepted media for broad communication of new developments. There has developed a journalese style that tends to be succinct, include elegant proofs, and present background by reference to other articles. The high cost and large volume of publication has led to this style, which requires an excellent background and dedication from the reader. Editors try very hard to have articles that are interesting and intelligible. However, the emphasis is on the idea rather than the exposition. The prestige of research has caused this style to spread even to places like class notes where expense is not important. Some journals are working to improve the quality of exposition, and special recognition may be given for excellent exposition.

Good exposition implies an absolute standard that is hard to define. Better exposition is comparative and can be judged by the ease with which the reader catches the idea. While the final standards are external rather than internal to the writing, still there are some internal criteria that appear useful. Every journal and every publisher has a style manual. These manuals are more a cry of despair on the part of the publisher than a guide to exposition, since they deal with only the most rudimentary ideas. Part of each manual is usually a statement of the conventions of the publisher. But the bulk of each consists of embarrassingly obvious statements like "use consistent notation" or "illustrations should relate to the textual material." The fact that many mathematicians need guidelines like these suggests that a high level of exposition is not possible. There appears to be no discussion in print on the principles of writing clear expository mathematics. Such a discussion might suggest that good exposition requires redundancy—that is, the same idea is expressed several times from several points of view. The central presentation is a clear statement of the idea with a rigorous proof. Alternative ways would include—

1. A historical discussion that humanizes the development of the idea, if possible, in ways paralleling the rigorous proof in some manner

2. Alternative wordings

3. Alternative proofs

4. Illustrations that tell the story visually

5. Examples that show how the idea appears in other garb than mathematics verbalisms

6. Counterexamples

7. Similar ideas related to this one but differing slightly from it

Better exposition often makes it easier for the reader to become personally involved. Perhaps obvious simple examples are suggested for the reader to complete. It is often very valuable for the reader to copy the article, rewriting ideas in different language, making up different examples, asking and answering slightly different questions from those posed in the article. Some suggestions for this activity may be useful.

Sometimes problems are given with the implication that the reader will benefit from doing them. This is true, but these problems are often an extension of the ideas in the article and are put in to show how far the idea may develop. Exposition requires problems that help the reader develop the idea of the article for himself in ways at least vaguely similar to that in the article. Extension of the ideas in problems is valuable and makes some, but a rather small, contribution to exposition.

The great verbal media are person-to-person discussions and lectures. Personal discussion is excellent for short topics, clarifying recognized difficulties, jointly exploring an idea, and expressing personal concern. It is not so good for communicating extensive ideas. Personal conversation requires both parties to talk in turn. Grasping of mathematical ideas requires a certain amount of mulling over, experimenting, and trial and error. Discussions rapidly reach the point where the receiver needs to do a bit of this. Mulling something over involves repeating and rephrasing the idea in one's own terms, making guesses, testing them, and otherwise fitting the new idea into the receiver's personal intellectual background until either the idea fits satisfactorily or there is an obvious difficulty. Then the conversation can continue. The sender is an expert; he has to be quiet during the mulling period. But few senders can be. They rephrase the idea, give examples, point out errors in the receiver's guesses. The receiver either ignores the sender and does private mulling, or he listens and becomes confused by multiple approaches, none of which he has had time to absorb.

Sometimes the discussants explore an idea together. This is useful. The roles of sender and receiver switch back and forth and both leave the discussion enriched. Such exploration can cover extensive ground over long periods of time. This is different from a situation in which a sender who knows is communicating with a receiver who is seeking.

The lecture is the classic way in which a man who knows tells someone who doesn't. The sender usually speaks in front of a chalkboard and writes various things. Sometimes he writes the entire lecture, sometimes the outline of key points, diagrams, illustrations, dates and references. Usually, the sender writes as he speaks, although some lecturers put their visual aids on the board ahead of time, or prepare transparencies and slides for projection.

The lecture has many advantages. It is flexible. The sender can change the lecture to fit the mood and background of his listeners. It can be prepared quickly—in much less time than an equivalent amount of writing. Class size can be varied within wide limits. The lecture can bring in recent ideas that the sender finds exciting. The pace can be set to allow note taking and some mulling time. Ideas can be repeated several times with the listener not being embarrassed because he does not respond immediately or because he is thinking about an earlier statement. Questions can be asked and answered. It is not surprising that with all these advantages, the lecture associated with a text has become the prime media for communication.

There are temptations and pitfalls to lectures. Everyone moves at the same pace. There is little chance to look back or ahead. Because listeners have no overtly active role, there is a temptation for them to fall asleep, either openly or inwardly. Some discouraged people feel that at any given moment in a lecture, only about a third of the class will be paying attention. This dullness can easily result from the lecture being just a repetition of the text, too difficult for the class, material the lecturer feels is dull, read from a manuscript, or presented in a monotonous fashion. Sometimes the lecturer loses contact with the class; he is unable to tell that the class is not with him.

Successful lecturers usually make somewhat of a show. Mathematics is presented as an adventurous search, with delightful, unexpected treasures turned up in the caves and haunted houses left by our buccaneering forebears. "After all," as one mathematician said, "If Clark Gable can make 6,000,000 women think he is making love to them personally, one mathematician should be able to make a class of 60 feel that they personally are discovering mathematics."

Small-group discussions, or tutorials, have a great power, especially with elementary mathematics where topics are short. The sender gives a question to a group of, say, four receivers. The students talk it over, ask questions of each other, and explain points to each other. Each group should include at least one "talker" who is willing to keep conversation flowing.

Good results are more likely when a sender can circulate among groups, asking leading questions, settling questions of definition and convention, and demonstrating the use of learning aids.

The learning theory of small peer-group instruction is that excellent learning occurs when a receiver teaches someone else. A great part of learning in depth comes from asking questions. Once the question is phrased, the answer may come quickly or a peer may help answer it. Experience shows that many students feel easier about asking a peer a question that really gets at the point bothering them because they feel afraid to ask the professor such elementary, "stupid" questions.

Many builders of educational taxonomies feel that most mathematical learning is learning for recall on examinations. They say that a much higher level of understanding comes when the learner can ask questions and when he can explain the idea to others. Small peer-group instruction promotes this higher level of understanding.

Four appears to be an excellent size for a group. Each person can talk easily with each of the others. One can write on a piece of paper, and all can read.

Much of the discussion will be a dialogue, and four splits easily into two pairs in three different ways. With five, one person tends to be left out. Six tends to overwhelm the shy person, who doesn't quite get his question out and who can't quite see what the fellow on the other side is doing.

Programed learning, individualized instruction, and computer-assisted instruction have some staunch advocates and some serious enemies. Usually, a sequence of questions is presented to the receiver in a book or by a machine. The questions can be answered easily. Each question is only slightly more difficult than the preceding one, and the learner is supposed to get practically all of them correct. Sometimes an audio channel will supplement the written material.

In places where the material is used by enthusiastic teachers and where the teacher had a part in making the program, there have been some real successes. In places where the teachers are not excited about the method, the children tend to get bored if such material is used too extensively. Even here, however, this material can be useful for particular students who get help from an entirely different mode of presentation or who wish special help on particular topics.

Some teachers feel that students need peer stimulus to keep going. Individualized instruction may cause a heavy teaching load for the teacher, since he may have a class with everyone working on a different topic, requiring separate testing, and needing special stimulation to keep their interest high.

Laboratory apparatus is very helpful where appropriate. The use of counters, toothpicks, gumdrops, and the like is helpful in elementary arithmetic and geometry. The use of adding machines and desk calculators helps in understanding advanced arithmetic and geometry. Problems of convergence, approximation, and error analysis are aided by high-speed digital computers. An analog computer will help in studying differential equations. People's ideas tend to develop from concrete objects, through pictures of the objects, to abstractions. Often we present a learner with an abstract idea. The use of multisensory aids helps undergird these ideas with experiences closer to concrete reality.

"If you want to send an idea, wrap it up in a person, and mail him" is a motto of many religions and political leaders. It also applies to mathematics. Administrators, department chairmen, and teachers all use this tactic. This is the purpose behind administrators hiring mathematics teachers and teachers recommending tutors, assistants, and readers. It is probably beyond the purposes of this article to discuss possible criteria for choosing an assistant who will carry the message you want to send. This responsibility cannot be avoided by administrators, and it is not a mark of a dictatorial personality to think this way. An administrator may hire someone with whom he disagrees strongly simply because he wishes a message of variety for his students.

The administrator needs to decide whether he wishes to convey fact or attitude. A distinguished professor addressing a group of graduate teaching assistants planning to become university professors said, "Don't worry about what the syllabus says. Your main responsibility is to expose your students to a live, exciting topic, and personality. Teach what you find interesting and exciting; say, the work in your thesis. Facts and required materials students can get from books." Laudable as this is, many administrators might think this a fatal attitude in the first term of the three-term, multisection course taught by several instructors.

THE MESSAGE

Content, level, depth, and complexity are but a few of the attributes of the message that influence communication. More advanced topics are usually taught in a more abstract manner.

The message may vary in the depth of understanding sought and behavior desired of the receiver to show that understanding. One taxonomy (6) lists six levels of understanding:

1. Knowledge, or the ability to recall facts
2. Comprehension, or the ability to express the idea in different ways
3. Application, or the ability to use the idea in a new situation
4. Analysis, or the ability to break an idea into significant parts
5. Synthesis, or the ability to join the idea with others into a new message (Ability to explain the idea to others in a flexible way falls in this category. A rote explanation, coupled with inability to vary the explanation for different learners, may seem like a high level of understanding, but may be merely level one, even though the topic is subtle and advanced.)
6. Evaluation, or the ability to compare the topic with others and make judgments about relative value as determined by some criteria

Often individual differences among students are allowed for on a single topic by expecting the better students to achieve a higher level of understanding.

Logic, intuition, and telling (or assertion) may play differing roles in the message. The author once had the idea that most secondary and elementary teachers believe that logic is a fundamental part of a mathematics message. They believe that the use of logic makes the idea clearer and more convincing, that people believe mathematics only if it is logically developed with the content proved. The author proposed to test this idea by an analysis of the communication in several mathematics texts.

The basis for the test is that every author wishes to be believed. No author purposely misleads his readers, or hopes they will be so annoyed that they will rebel and adopt another attitude. Hence it was proposed to look at the textual material in short sections, sentence by sentence. For each sentence we ask, "Why should the student believe this?" or "On what basis would a student be expected to accept what is said in this sentence?"

In this preliminary study, seven books were chosen. The beginning exposition of derivative was analyzed in four college freshman texts: Griffin, Kline, Curtis, and Allendoerfer-Oakley. This was compared with the discussion of fractions in three college arithmetic books: Ward and Hardgrove, Mueller, and Wheeler.

There is a lot of judgment involved in trying to guess why a student should accept a particular sentence. Using the results of a similar analysis on several other books, it seemed reasonable to classify the reasons into six groups.

1. *Authoritative statement of fact.* The author makes an assertion such as a definition, a convention, or a fact. The ordinary student in this course would not already know this fact, and he would have no way of checking it. Mother tells him so, so he accepts it.

2. *Authoritative general statements.* Here the sentence is not a specific fact or definition, but is a general statement. Again this statement does not reflect the student's personal experience. For most students this is the first time they have seen the idea; they have no direct knowledge of its truth, but they accept it because the book says so.

3. *Road map.* Most authors tell the student what they are going to do before they do it. Also, many discussions need to be set up before they come to the interesting or logical part. Sentences in this category include instructions to the student ("Draw a two inch segment."), sentences that begin with "Consider" and "Let" ("Consider the odd numbers between ten and twenty. Let x and y be integers."), and rhetorical questions.

4. *Personal knowledge.* These are statements that recall previously learned knowledge, observations, or facts already known and accepted by the student. ("You know that π is about

$$\frac{22}{7}.$$

In chapter 2 we used π in the formula for the area of a circle.") Illustrations often refer to such personal observations (for example, the edge of a sheet of paper shows a line segment).

5. *Logical deductions.* These are statements that follow as some sort of logical deduction from other statements. These include conclusions, results of substitutions, identifying objects, applying definitions, and numerical examples.

6. *Analogy.* This includes forming a general statement from a few facts or observations, and using analogy and parallel construction to convince. Sentences using "like" and "as" often fall into this category.

The following table gives the percentage of the sentences that fell into these categories.

TABLE 1

Texts	Categories					
	1 Authority Facts	2 Authority General	3 Road Map	4 Personal Knowledge	5 Logic	6 Analogy
Griffin	7	7	15	11	49	11
Kline	32	11	15	18	16	8
Curtis	10	9	22	10	43	6
Allendoefer/ Oakley	9	16	25	11	34	5
Ward/ Hardgrove	44	20	10	8	14	4
Mueller	60	20	4	5	9	2
Wheeler	30	10	35	8	10	7

It seemed reasonable to group the four calculus books together, and the three arithmetic books together.

TABLE 2

Texts	Categories					
	1 Authority Facts	2 Authority General	3 Road Map	4 Personal Knowledge	5 Logic	6 Analogy
Calculus	15	11	19	12	35	8
Arithmetic	45	17	16	7	11	4

The first three categories represent statements made by the author and relatively blind acceptance by the reader. The second three categories require active thinking and observation by the reader. If we group these together, we get the following results.

TABLE 3

Texts	Categories	
	Author's Authority	Reader Participation
Calculus	45	55
Arithmetic	78	22

Anyone is free to draw his own conclusions. However, it appears that arithmetic authors are much more directive, leaving little for the student to do. This may lead to more learning at the recall level, with less development at deeper levels.

It is interesting that Griffin, first published in the twenties, is famous as an intuitive text and does have slightly more use of analogy than the others. But Griffin also has more logical steps. What does not show here is that more of Griffin's logical steps are substitution, so the reader is not forcibly aware that he is learning and using logic. In Curtis, the syllogism structure is much more obvious. One wonders if this sort of structure is part of the reason Griffin has been so successful in stimulating people to become mathematicians and scientists.

These figures are not highly reliable. Another person classifying the same material might easily classify any sentence a bit differently. Further, if more sentences were included from several sections of the texts, more reliable results would be obtained.

One is tempted to say that these figures suggest the calculus books are better written because they encourage more student participation. This may be true. But it also may be true that arithmetic and the students who take arithmetic require and accept more use of communication by telling. Further investigation is required. The author encourages readers to perform similar analyses on books they like and dislike. Perhaps this analysis will suggest some reasons for our attitudes.

CONCLUSION

Mathematics communication has many facets. In particular, no communication should be judged on the basis of the message alone, but also on the basis of the receiver who is to learn from the message, the sender who originated it, and the medium that carries the message. Much work needs to be done to identify the qualities and combinations of qualities of these components that make for better communication. This paper suggests a number of the factors to be considered and tested.

14 Linguistic Aspects of Mathematical Education

*Born in Brooklyn, New York, Leon A. Henkin ob-
tained his B.A. in mathematics and philosophy at
Columbia College, New York City, and received an
M.A. and a Ph.D. from Princeton University, in 1942
and 1947, respectively. After starting his career as a
mathematician at the Signal Corps Radar Laboratory
in Belman, N.J., and the Kellex Corporation in New
York City, he obtained his first professorial appoint-
ment at the University of Southern California in 1949.*

*Currently Dr. Henkin is a professor of mathematics
at the University of California, Berkeley, where he
went through the academic ranks in a most remarkable and distinguished manner. He was vice-chairman
and later acting chairman of the Department of
Mathematics at the University. Professor Henkin was
also elected Fellow of the American Association for
the Advancement of Science, Guggenheim Fellow and
Member of the Institute for Advanced Study, visiting
Fellow at Oxford, England, and president of the Association for Symbolic Logic.*

*While actively engaged in the teaching of mathe-
matics, he has constantly expressed his interest in the
mathematical education of our young school-attending
population as a participant in the Cambridge Conference on Teacher's Training (1966), author of several articles and films on mathematics education, and
the principal investigator for the Community Teaching Fellows Program in California.*

*Since Henkin is a strong believer in the hypothesis
that the teaching of new linguistic patterns is involved
in the teaching of mathematics, he discusses in his
article two significant and related problems with reference to the teaching of algebra: the use of symbols*

LEON A. HENKIN

and the use of quantifiers. In the study of algebra, says Henkin, a discussion of symbols and their manipulation, as opposed to their use as representing expressions about numbers, causes confusion. One such source of confusion is the use of a coefficient and an unknown in an equation where both are represented by letters. Another source of confusion is related to the explanation of processes that, in algebra, introduce extraneous roots, thus requiring checking procedures.

Linguistic problems also occur in connection with quantifiers and their use to form universal and existential sentences. There are two basic questions in this area: One is whether very young children can learn to use variables in formulating sentences, and the second is whether there is any point to their doing it. The first question, which lends itself to future experimentation, is reasonable, since children learn much of their complex natural language before the age of seven. A viable reason for the early introduction of such linguistic patterns is that it provides a flexible framework for expressing universal and existential propositions present in the curriculum at every stage of advancement.

To conclude, the author suggests some changes in school mathematics instruction, particularly in connection with linguistic problems. Such problems, he feels, should be the subject of experimentation in early childhood.

That mathematics uses a special language, or at least that it uses language in a special way, is completely obvious. The more radical viewpoint, that mathematical activity *is* simply the construction and application of special languages, has been advanced from two different perspectives: On the one hand, mathematics has been called "the language of science"; on the other hand, mathematical logicians have developed the concept of a formal language, supplied with a grammar and deductive rules, and have used this to give precision to the notion of a "mathematical theory."

Whatever philosophical view one adopts about the relation between mathematics and language, it is evident that the teaching of mathematics involves to some extent the teaching of new linguistic patterns. It seems worthwhile, therefore, to focus some attention on specific educational problems that arise from this involvement. We will consider two of these.

I

The traditional mathematics curriculum in the United States devotes the elementary grades (1–8) to arithmetic, and begins secondary material (grade 9) with the introduction of algebra. I still recall the explanation of my ninth-grade teacher that, whereas in arithmetic we study operations on numbers, in algebra we also study operations on letters!

The study of algebra usually begins by developing techniques for solving simple equations. In some modern revisions of the mathematics curriculum this study has been moved far forward, even to grade 1. We shall have something to say about this more rudimentary treatment of equations in the second section of our paper; here we wish to consider the traditional ninth-grade treatment of the subject.

What is an equation? Of course it is a linguistic object—a string of symbols consisting of an equality sign separating the two "sides" of the equation, which are terms generally containing numerals, letters, operation symbols, and parentheses. (Most often the sides of the equations considered are polynomials; while polynomials can be defined in contemporary mathematics as certain infinite sequences of ring elements, or as functions associating certain algebraic functions with each ring, the root, intuitive concept is that of a string of symbols having a certain form.)

The fact that at the very beginning of the study of algebra the teacher is led to talk about symbols and their manipulation, instead of simply using symbols to talk about numbers, leads to pedagogical difficulties and to confusion in the minds of most students. The difficulties arise because of the subtle requirements and sophisticated terminology needed to distinguish correctly and consistently between use and mention of given symbols within the same context. In practice, the teacher usually overlooks or ignores these difficulties, with the result that the student is forced to fall back on mechanically learned techniques because the conceptual framework is presented too obscurely for him to grasp. Let us consider two examples.

1. In the equation "$2x + 3 = 0$," the student is taught that x is the unknown and 2 is the coefficient. He sees a clear distinction: the unknown is a letter, the coefficient is a number or numeral (in traditional curricula these concepts are generally not distinguished). However, a little later the teacher is considering the equation $ax + b = 0$, and now the coefficient is said to be a, a letter.

If the student wonders why the letter a is the coefficient and x the unknown, he may conclude that it is because a is from the early part of the alphabet and x from the end. But then what about the equation "$2a + 3 = 0$?" If he decides that the coefficient is the symbol to the left of the unknown, he has to reckon with the equation $xa + b = 0$—and anyway, what about the commutative law of multiplication?

It is very puzzling, and of course there is no solution within the frame of reference generally supplied to the student. The unknowns are not, in general, determined by an equation, but have to be specified as an additional "given."

Shall we then speak not simply of equations, but of ordered pairs whose first component is an equation and whose second component is a set of symbols called unknowns? Monstrous!

It seems that instead of beginning by saying "Solve the equation $2x + 3 = 0$," the teacher should say "Find a number x such that $2x + 3 = 0$." That is, instead of *mentioning* the equation $2x + 3 = 0$ as an object of investigation, *use* it to pose a problem about numbers. Again, there is no need to talk about a symbol called the unknown if one says, "If a and b are rational numbers and $a \neq 0$, find a number x such that $ax + b = 0$."

Similarly, instead of saying "In the equation $2x + 3 = 0$, transpose the constant term to the right side to get $2x = -3$," we can simply say, "If x is a number such that $2x + 3 = 0$, then $2x = -3$." Instead of justifying this step in the computation by saying "We subtract 3 from both sides of the equation," we can do it by saying "Whenever $a = b$ we have also $a - 3 = b - 3$," or we may introduce terminology such as "the subtractive property of equality" for repeated use.

2. As a second example, consider the puzzling phenomenon of extraneous roots. By ignoring the singular case in the study of linear equations, the student is led to expect that each equation has one and only one solution. For some reason this fact is rarely formulated explicitly, and so the student is told that after solving an equation he should always check the solution by substituting for the unknown. When he comes to study quadratic equations, it is rather disconcerting to find that they may have two solutions (and that even when they have only one solution, he is expected to say "The two roots are the same"), but the checking process of substitution is certainly convincing.

However, when he comes to the study of surds and encounters the equation

$$\sqrt{y + 1} + \sqrt{2y + 1} = 2,$$

all of his previous experience is defeated. He solves the equation by successive operations of transposition, squaring both sides, expansion, and factoring, arriving at the solutions $y = 0, 24$. However, when he then goes to check these solutions by substitution, he finds that in fact 24 is *not* a root of the equation. On the basis of all his previous experience and understanding, the student has been led to believe that when a solution does not check, it is because he has made an error in the steps leading to the solution. Accordingly, he goes over the sequence of transpositions, squaring both sides, and so forth, that led to the solutions 0 and 24, but can find no error. I recall that the only explanation of this phenomenon that I received from my teacher was the statement, "In this type of equation, extraneous roots are introduced." Thus I learned that 24, which substitution shows is not a root of the given equation, is an extraneous root of it!

Instead of applying formal operations such as transposition and squaring-both-sides to solve a given equation, I would at first emphasize the application of universal laws (about numbers) to infer information about those numbers (if any) that satisfy the given equation. For example, this would lead us to assert "If y is any number such that

$$\sqrt{y+1} + \sqrt{2y+1} = 2,$$

then

$$y + 1 = (2 - \sqrt{2y+1})^2.$$

Eventually we would conclude "If y is any number such that

$$\sqrt{y+1} + \sqrt{2y+1} = 2,$$

then either $y = 0$ or $y = 24$." It would then be clear that we have nowhere asserted that 24—or 0, for that matter—is indeed a number y such that

$$\sqrt{y+1} + \sqrt{2y+1} = 2,$$

but only that no number *other than* 0 or 24 is such a number y. The substitution of these numbers into the equation is then seen to be not a process of checking a solution, but simply a further step in the search for a solution, after numbers other than 0 or 24 have been eliminated from consideration.

The suggestion given above that the formal mode of talking about symbols be replaced by language in which one talks about numbers is not meant to be a total prescription, but only a pedagogical device prescribed for the *beginning* of algebraic work in order to aid the student in forming a sound conceptual framework. After the student has learned to use equations to obtain and convey information about numbers, his attention can certainly be brought to bear on these tools, and he can then be led to talk *about* the equations. There is a natural motivation for this shift in viewpoint—namely, the observation that there is a common pattern of statements leading to the solution of problems of a certain kind (that is, problems about numbers that are formulated by means of equations) and the realization that the labor of writing down the sentences in such a pattern can be considerably shortened by following certain formal procedures involving operations on the equations. With this motivation and a background of working with equations as parts of sentences about numbers, the student is in an advantageous place for gaining a good understanding of the traditional theory of equations.

II

A second area where linguistic problems obtrude on questions of mathematics education is connected with what logicians call *quantifiers*. When we seek to embed an equation in a sentence about numbers, as recommended in section I above, we are led naturally to the use of quantifiers in forming universal and existential statements, so that their use is necessarily involved at the beginning of secondary mathematics. However, in the present section we would like to urge their introduction at the very beginning of mathematical education—that is, in grade 1.

In the first place, it seems to us that the discovery of regularities, facts that hold uniformly for all objects of some given domain, is of the very essence of mathematical activity, and since extremely simple examples of such regularity can be found, there is every reason to expose the beginning student to this type of activity. Perhaps no aspect of the traditional elementary mathematics curriculum is so stultifying and so misleading as to the true nature of mathematics as the constant emphasis on particular facts, such as $2 + 3 = 5$, to the almost complete exclusion of general statements, such as "The addition of 3 to any odd number yields an even number."

Needless to say, one would not begin by searching for universal truths in the set of all natural numbers, but would begin in domains with which beginning students are familiar—the set of integers from 1 to 10, say, or the set of students in the class. One could begin by introducing universal statements in such domains as abbreviations for long conjunctions, whose truth is established empirically by a separate examination of each individual in the domain.

When it comes to formulating a universal sentence to express the findings of such an empirical investigation, it is natural to employ the word *all*, together with a common noun to indicate the domain: "All numbers from 1 to 10 are either odd or can be obtained by adding 1 to an odd number," or "All students in the class are more than 38 inches tall." However, eventually the teacher will wish to guide the students to the realization that there is another method for establishing the truth of a universal statement—namely, by considering an arbitrary (but unspecified) individual of the domain, instead of by examining each specific individual. In this regard, mathematical practice suggests an alternative formulation of the proposition in question, specifically one in which variables are employed.

For example, the teacher may ask whether every student in the class has a teacher who is married to Mr. Brown. She may point out that one way to arrive at an answer is to begin by saying, "Let x be any student in this room." After suitable investigation, it may be possible to conclude, "x has a teacher who is married to Mr. Brown." Then the results of the investigation can be expressed by the sentence "For every student x in this room, x has a teacher who is married to Mr. Brown," which, of course, means the same as "All students in this room have a teacher who is married to Mr. Brown."

Is it possible to get first-grade students to learn to use variables in formulating universal (and existential) sentences? Is there any point to it?

As to the possibility, it seems to us that this can best be answered by experiment. To the best of our knowledge such efforts have not been seriously undertaken, either because they depart too radically from traditional practice, or perhaps because most first-grade teachers are not themselves familiar with these linguistic patterns. To encourage any would-be experimenter, we would point out that the very young ages are known to be the best ones for learning to use new linguistic patterns, and that the portions of natural languages that children succeed in learning before the age of 7, say, are much more complex and difficult than the small portions of mathematical language that we are here suggesting they master. Of course, the basic method of teaching the use of variables must *not* consist of formulating the logical formation or transformation rules for quantifiers; it should be the traditional method by which natural language is taught, as for example, by imitation and correction.

As to the point of getting first-grade students to use variables, it is simply that this is the most suitable age for acquiring new linguistic patterns, and the patterns in question will provide a flexible framework for expressing universal and existential propositions that should permeate the mathematical curriculum at every stage.

Although I have not heard of attempts to use variables for the formation of quantified statements at the elementary-school level, there has been some experimentation with the use of variables for the formulation of equational problems, such as "Find a number x such that $2 + x = 5$." The consensus of those who have attempted to introduce such problems in grade 1 mathematics is that students at that level do better if the variable is replaced by a box, so that the problem comes to be formulated as "Put a number in the box to make $2 + \square = 5$."

It may well be that insertion of a numeral into a blank space is innately simpler than substitution of the numeral for a letter. However, while the use of a box instead of a letter as a *placeholder* seems entirely appropriate, its use in place of letters for purposes of forming quantified statements would seem highly artificial, and the advantage of insertion over substitution would not be relevant in that context. For this reason, it seems to us worthwhile to introduce letters as variables into the linguistic patterns of first-grade mathematics, although the use of a box may be a valuable auxiliary device.

In any case, the introduction of box-type equations in grade 1 is of value because it represents the use of equations to talk about numbers, as we advocated in section I above. In general, there is very little talk about these equations in the new elementary curriculum, although the use of the term "open sentence" to describe the sentential contexts of these equations is a step in the wrong direction.

III

In sections I and II above, we have advocated certain changes in school mathematics instruction connected with what we consider to be linguistic problems essentially involved in mathematical education. Our advocacy arises from intuitive ideas suggested by limited observation. Obviously, such suggestions must be made the subject of experiment and testing before any substantial degree of confidence can be placed in them.

The devising of a detailed experimental program and the means for testing it against traditional linguistic patterns in the areas mentioned cannot be undertaken here. We point out, however, that such a program may serve to illuminate not only problems of mathematics education, but also more general questions involving the learning of language. The learning of one's mother tongue in the early years and a foreign language at a later period are phenomena of such vast complexity that detailed empirical investigation is exceedingly difficult. By concentrating on the introduction of limited linguistic patterns to be grafted onto the natural use of language in connection with precise mathematical concepts, we may be able to discern phenomena in the process of language learning that would otherwise escape us.

15 Remarks on the Teaching of Logic

Born in New York City in 1903, Marshall H. Stone completed all of his university education at Harvard University by 1926. In recognition of his extraordinary contributions to both mathematics and mathematics teaching, Professor Stone has received numerous honarary doctorates from leading universities all over the world. In the eyes of his peers, he is one of the most outstanding scholars. He has gained international renown as president of the International Committee on Mathematics Education (1961), the International Mathematics Union (1952-1954), and the International Commission on Mathematics Instruction (1959-1962), and he has received wide acclaim in the United States as the George D. Birkoff Professor of Mathematics at the University of Massachusetts. He is the recipient of the Andrew MacLeish Distinguished Service Award, and is an associate professor of the Guggenheim Memorial Foundation. Although his mathematical work is outstanding, it is as a teacher and as a mathematician concerned with modern mathematical education that he has made a most indelible mark.

For appreciation of some of the thoughts Professor Stone holds in this regard, some of his concerns with reference to the role, the placement, and the presentation of logic in modern mathematics education have been selected for discussion here. He believes that the present position of logic in the curriculum is the result of the apparent ability of students to learn the art of proofs without studying logic, and the minor, if not nonexistent, role that logic plays in insight, which is the essence of doing math and discovering new mathematics. However, as

MARSHALL H. STONE

*the curricular emphasis shifts to conceptual compre-
hension rather than technical ability, and as the
power of the axiomatic method as a tool for investigating human behavior is increasingly appreciated,
there is a growing trend toward a more systematic and
extensive treatment of logic for the sake of accuracy
and clarity. The increasing interest in computer-
science courses is still another motive for a greater
emphasis on logic. As great advances are being made
in understanding the relation of logic to the many
branches of math, the student of advanced mathematics needs a better background in logic.*

*The content of logic courses presents a most impor-
tant question—one that is very difficult to answer.
Obviously, only the most elementary logical topics
can be introduced in the school curriculum; some of
these can be taught as early as the fifth and sixth
grades, others not until the tenth or eleventh grades.
More advanced topics need to be reserved for college, and a complete treatment is suitable only for
graduate school.*

*However, the most difficult problems in teaching
logic in the schools are pedagogical and psychological.
Hence, in Stone's opinion, more studies are needed
to investigate the nature and development of the
mind's logical faculties in order to design properly
the timing and the order of the introduction of the
topics. Well-designed research programs in the psychology of logic and the application of the resulting
knowledge to educational programs would definitely
provide immense educational benefits.*

After some years of worldwide effort directed toward developing a modern mathematics curriculum, there are still many unanswered questions
and unsolved problems. One such subject, obviously of vital importance for
mathematics, is the place of logic in the curriculum. Despite my sustained
interest in the problems of mathematics education, I have run across very few
systematic treatments of this question. A more careful search than I have
ever made would undoubtedly extend the findings. Yet I doubt that even the
inclusion of casual remarks made in general discussions of mathematics
education would greatly lengthen the list. Clearly, the time has come when

the place of logic in the mathematics curriculum demands closer attention and more detailed discussion than it has yet received.

It is not that logic has been neglected in the numerous curricular proposals and modern programs put forward since the early forties. On the contrary, it is easy to verify that many of the new textbooks at both school and college levels devote considerable space to logical matters. Indeed, on comparing them with older books (say, those written between 1900 and 1940 or 1945), one sees that there is a new fashion of being explicit in discussing the nature and techniques of mathematical proof, which is quite different from the earlier practice of saying nothing whatsoever about logic in a school or college mathematics text. Nevertheless, it is apparent that no general agreement has yet been reached concerning the role to be assigned to logic in mathematics education or the ways of handling logic in the curriculum philosophically, scientifically, or pedagogically.

The present position of logic in the curriculum is the natural consequence of psychological facts and historical events. In the western world, mathematics and logic have been taught side by side for more than two thousand years; but in the formal scheme of education, logic has been placed with grammar, rhetoric, and philosophy rather than with mathematics. Teachers have not deemed it necessary or even useful to give explicit instruction in logic as part of their teaching of arithmetic, algebra, and geometry. Centuries of class-room experience have shown that gifted students as well as those who are just reasonably diligent can learn the art of mathematical proof through ob-servation and continued practice alone. It was therefore considered quite sufficient, for pedagogical purposes, to lead the student through many exam-ples of mathematical demonstration (particularly in geometry) and to assign him many exercises requiring proofs, without giving him in his mathemat-ics courses any explicit account of logic or proof-theory. For instruction in these matters, the student was expected to turn to his courses in grammar and philosophy. The disappearance from the schools of logic as a subject of instruction and its isolation at the college level in departments of philosophy had little effect on what was done in teaching mathematics until about twenty years ago, when new emphasis began to be put on precision and rigor in elementary mathematics. On psychological grounds, this could be justi-fied by the observation that, thought and reason being inseparable, especially in mathematical contexts, the attainment of scientific standards and stylis-tic norms in mathematics is more a matter of experience and continual exer-cise than it is of theoretical analysis or explication. Furthermore, mathe-maticians know that in working with mathematics, and especially in discover-ing new mathematics, logic generally plays a secondary role, because pene-tration into the unknown depends chiefly on spontaneous insights into conceptually meaningful mathematical patterns. In consequence, they rec-ognize that as teachers they must devote much more time and effort to giving their students an adequate knowledge of mathematical techniques and some conceptual grasp of mathematical patterns and structure than to teaching proof-theory or logic as such.

Nevertheless, all the signs presage a substantial change in these attitudes and a trend toward a much more systematic and extensive treatment of logic in the mathematics curriculum of the future. There are many reasons for such a trend, ranging from the pedagogical to the purely scientific. As we introduce more advanced and abstract mathematical topics into our school programs, and therefore place increased emphasis on conceptual comprehension and less on strictly technical mastery, we increase the need for accuracy of statement and clarity of demonstration. The natural response to this need—and the one that is being made in the current reform movement—is to teach certain aspects of logic as part of school mathematics. It can reasonably be maintained that the average student is often helped toward better understanding by explicit and fairly detailed logical analysis of the various techniques, procedures, and arguments he is studying. Evidence bearing on this point can almost certainly be drawn from experiments with some of the new programs in which this sort of analysis is found.

In traditional school mathematics, Euclidean geometry provided the sole explicit example of an axiomatic system, although its deep significance in this respect was, with rare exceptions, left vague and unexplained. Today, however, we are concerned about giving the secondary school student some idea of the axiomatic method and the related notion of a mathematical model by examples drawn from arithmetic, algebra, and physics, as well as from geometry. From a cultural and social point of view, further developments along this line seem likely to be encouraged as the power of the axiomatic method as a tool for investigating human behavior is better appreciated and more thoroughly exploited by social scientists. This is not to say that our schools should attempt to teach this side of the behavioral and social sciences in the near future. I wish merely to point out that if our schools are to offer a good preparation for university study in these fields, or even for intelligent participation in the socioeconomic decisions of the community and the nation, they will want to increase the attention given to the axiomatic method in their mathematics programs.

Still another motive for a greater emphasis on logic at the school level is the introduction of courses in which the rudiments of modern computer science are explained or used. Computer languages, flowcharting, programming, and simulation all have contacts with logic and model construction that can be developed in very fruitful ways by the high school mathematics teacher who has access to computer services.

Another reason for changing the teaching of logic (one that relates to college and postgraduate mathematics programs) is the great advance made during this century in our knowledge of logic and its technical ties with many branches of mathematics, particularly with algebra and topology. Not only do courses in logic need to be altered to reflect this progress, but the time seems to have come when the student of advanced mathematics needs to understand in a deeper way the axiomatics of set theory and some of the techniques to which we have just referred. Therefore, it appears very likely that university courses in logic, whether for undergraduates or graduates, will be offered a good deal more widely, with a considerable increase in their mathematical connections and content, and that they will also be offered more frequently than in the past by mathematics departments.

One of the most important questions we must ask about the emerging program of courses in logic is, "What should their content be?" In a sense, this question is fairly easy to answer simply by saying that the full program should provide the topics necessary for a good understanding of modern logic and its relation to modern mathematics. This answer would have to be spelled out, however, by giving a detailed list of topics to be covered and a detailed indication of their correlation with the mathematics sequence. In another sense, the question is difficult to answer, because it requires delicate decisions about the distribution of these topics in time and over the various levels. These decisions depend partly upon pedagogical considerations, but they also depend upon the sort of correlation that is envisaged with the mathematics curriculum.

As far as the school curriculum is concerned, it is evident that only quite elementary topics of logic can be taken up, but some of these can be taught even in elementary school, specifically in grades 5 or 6 (101), while others are thought by many experienced teachers to be unsuitable before grades 10 or 11 at the earliest. The symbolism and the language of logic can undoubtedly be introduced even in grade 6, as experiments have clearly shown (13), though the notions of "variable" and "quantifier" are difficult and should probably not be brought in until later. In the beginning it is enough to treat symbols and their manipulation as required in the logic of propositions, bringing out the bearing of what is taught upon mathematics and the analysis of everyday language (grammar and syntax). As soon as students have acquired sufficient experience with simple mathematical arguments (in arithmetic and algebra as well as in the introduction to geometry), their attention should be drawn to explicit formal statements of some of the most common patterns of logical inference and their combination in mathematical proofs. It seems to me that these patterns can advantageously be presented in the style of Gentzen as "rules of inference" and then, in many typical cases, be rephrased as formulas of a symbolic propositional, or first order predicate, calculus. There also seem to be advantages in emphasizing the roles of material implication, universal quantification, and negation as the primitive logical operations, as was originally done by Frege in his pioneer studies. By the time the student has done a substantial amount of axiomatic geometry, he should have become acquainted with the concept of a deductive system and should have learned something about axiomatics and the connection between symbolic logic and algebra (free groupoids, Hilbert algebras, Boolean algebras, and so on). How much can be done with these subjects at the high school level depends directly on how much algebra is offered in the curriculum. The greater part of this more advanced material should be reserved for grades 11 and 12, though it could possibly be started in grade 10. If variables and quantifiers have not been discussed before a high school study of calculus is begun, they should certainly be taught in conjunction with the theory of limits and other topics in analysis.

More sophisticated aspects of logic pose enough technical difficulties to exclude them from the school mathematics program for the present. However, some of them can be treated in college courses, possibly without complete detailed demonstrations of the more difficult results. There are many excellent modern texts upon which such courses can be based. The aim of college courses in logic should be to review and deepen the subject matter already offered in the schools, to give a thorough grounding in the essentials of modern logic, and to introduce major problems of logic as they are met in higher mathematics and in applications (for example, problems of definition, consistency, decision processes and associated algorithms, completeness and incompleteness, nonstandard analysis, non-Aristotelian logics, representation and modeling, axiomatic set theory, and so on). It is possible, without entering fully into the complicated technical details of these problems, to discuss them in a comprehensible and illuminating manner in an advanced course for undergraduates. However, anything like a complete treatment requires more preparation than is now possible at the college level and therefore has to be considered as belonging in the graduate school. While the professional mathematician (and to a lesser extent, the school or college teacher) certainly needs some orientation in the subtleties of logic, he hardly needs to delve into them in real depth. He can probably obtain what knowledge he does need from a good undergraduate course, if it is up to date, and a little supplementary reading on his own. Consequently, it can be maintained that a graduate department of mathematics is not yet under any obligation to offer really advanced courses in logic (unless the special interests of some of its members require it) but only to ensure that its students be enabled to supplement their undergraduate preparation, however weak, to the extent we have previously suggested. Of course, it should not be forgotten in teaching logic at either the college or the postgraduate level that the subject has its practical side in connection with computer science and the theory of electrical circuits. In certain circumstances, these applications should certainly be stressed, though there appears to be no reason why this should be done generally at these levels.

The most difficult problems in teaching logic as part of the school curriculum are the pedagogical and psychological ones. This is an area in which we need not only intensified discussion, but also much additional experimentation and theoretical analysis. It is in the early stages of the educational process that we are most seriously hampered by our comparative ignorance of the relevant basic psychological factors. If we knew more about the nature and the development of the mind's logical faculties, we could design the sequence and timing of specific topics from logic in the school curriculum with greatly increased confidence. At present, we find ourselves still at a stage where we lack essential fundamental knowledge and are therefore compelled to move ahead by trial and error, encouraged by the favorable results already obtained [for example, Suppes et al. (101)]. The psychological studies of Piaget and Inhelder, reported in their book *De la logique de l'enfant à la logique de l'adolescent,* provide a wealth of interesting experimental results accompanied by Piaget's theoretical analysis and interpretation. This fundamental work demands the attention of everyone interested in this challenging field, which is so open to future investigation.

The time appears to be ripe for pushing ahead with a well-designed research program calculated to probe in a substantially deeper manner the fundamental psychology of logic, along with a parallel program of exploitation aimed at the practical application of the new fruits of research to education. As these lines were being written, American astronauts set foot on the Moon, achieving the first major goal of a magnificently conceived, coordinated, and executed program of research and development. It is infinitely harder to find out what is going on in a small boy's head than it is to place a man on the Moon, but the former should prove to be far less costly, if only because the physical scale of the effort involved is of a much lower magnitude. There can be no question as to the immense educational benefits to be gained from a successful program of the kind proposed. They would more than amply repay a very substantial investment of time, effort, and money in the relatively near future. At the Royaumont Conference nearly ten years ago, I foresaw the need for highly organized research into the psychological foundations of mathematical education (96), and I made mention of it in my opening address. It seems to me now that the psychology of logic would be one of the most promising subjects of such research. I therefore wish to supplement what I then proposed by taking this opportunity to call for a special concentration of attention on the problems discussed in this paper.

Bibliography

1. Alder, H. L. "Partition Identities—from Euler to the Present." *The American Mathematical Monthly* 76 (August–September 1969), 733–46.

2. Alpert, Stoldwagon, and Becker. "Psychological Factors in Mathematics Education." *SMSG Newsletter* 15 (April 1963).

3. Arbib, M. A. "Memory Limitations of Stimulus-Response Models." *Psychological Review* 76 (1969), 507–10.

4. Bartlett, F. C. *Thinking: An Experimental and Social Study*. New York: Basic Books, 1958.

5. Biggs, J. B. *Anxiety, Motivation and Primary School Mathematics*. N.F.E.R., 1962.

6. Bloom, Benjamin S., ed. *Taxonomy of Educational Objectives*. New York: Longmans, Green, 1956.

7. Brownell, William A., and Moser, Harold E. *Meaningful Versus Mechanical Learning: A Study in Grade III Subtraction*. Research Studies in Education, no. 8. Durham, N.C.: Duke Univ. Press, 1949.

8. Bruner, Jerome S. *The Process of Education*. Cambridge: Harvard Univ. Press, 1960.

9. Bruner, Jerome S.; Goodnow, Jacqualine J.; and Austin, George A. *A Study of Thinking*. New York: Wiley, 1956.

10. Chomsky, N. *Aspects of the Theory of Syntax*. Cambridge: MIT Press, 1965.

11. ____. *Syntactic Structures*. The Hague: Mouton, 1957.

12. Chomsky, N., and Miller, G. A. "Introduction to the Formal Analysis of Natural Languages." In *Handbook of Mathematical Psychology*, II, edited by R. D. Luce, R. R. Bush, and E. Galanter, pp. 271–321. New York: Wiley, 1963.

13. Christiansen, Bent. "Logic and Analysis in School Programme," *UNESCO Mathematics Project for the Arab States* (Regional Seminar, Cairo, 1969), 114–43.

14. Church, A. "An Unsolvable Problem of Elementary Number Theory." *American Journal of Mathematics* 58 (1936), 345–63.

15. Corcoran, J. "Discourse Grammars and the Structure of Logical Reasoning." In *Mathematics and Structural Learning*, edited by J. M. Scandura. Englewood Cliffs, N.J.: Prentice-Hall, 1971.

16. Cronbach, L. J. "The Logic of Experiments on Discovery." In *Learning by Discovery*, edited by E. Keislar and L. M. Shulman, pp. 77–92. Chicago: Rand-McNally, 1966.

17. Davis, Robert B. *Explorations in Mathematics: A Text for Teachers*. Reading, Mass.: Addison-Wesley, 1966.

18. ____. "Goals for School Mathematics: The Madison Project View." *Journal of Research in Science Teaching* 2 (December 1964), 309–15.

19. ____. "How Do We Learn Mathematics?" *MIT Technology Review* 62 (1959), 28–30.

20. _____. "Mathematical Thought and the Nature of Learning: The Madison Project View." *Frontiers of Education*, pp. 79–83. Report of the Twenty-Seventh Educational Conference sponsored by the Educational Records Bureau. American Council on Education, Educational Records Bureau, 21 Audubon Ave., New York, New York.

21. _____. "Mathematics." Chapter 6 in *New Curriculum Developments*, edited by Glenys Unruh, pp. 46–56. ASCD.

22. _____. "Mathematics for Younger Children: The Present Status of the Madison Project." *New York State Mathematics Teachers Journal* 10 (April 1960), 75–79.

23. _____. "The Mathematics Revolution: Causes and Directions." Chapter 7 in *Frontiers of Secondary Education*. Syracuse, N.Y.: Syracuse Univ. Press, 1958.

✓ 24. _____. "Mathematics Teaching—with Special Reference to Epistemological Problems," *Journal of Research and Development in Education*, monograph 1 (Fall 1967).

25. _____. *A Modern Mathematics Program as It Pertains to the Interrelationship of Mathematical Content, Teaching Methods and Classroom Atmosphere* (The Madison Project). Report submitted to the Commissioner of Education, U.S. Department of Health, Education, and Welfare, 1967.

26. _____. "New Mathematics is Deeper than Mathematics." *Five Views of the "New Math,"* pp. 10–12. Washington: Council for Basic Education, April 1965.

27. Dawson, Alexander J. *The Implications of the Work of Popper, Polya, and Lakatos for a Model of Mathematics Instruction*. Unpublished doctoral dissertation. Edmonton, Alberta: Univ. of Alberta, May 1969.

28. Dienes, Z. P. *An Experimental Study of Mathematics Learning*. London: Hutchinson, 1964.

29. _____. *Building Up Mathematics*. 3d ed. London: Hutchinson, 1967.

30. _____. *The Learning of Group Structures by Young Children*. UNESCO Institute for Education, 1967.

31. _____. *Mathematics in the Primary School*. Melbourne, Australia: Macmillan, 1964.

32. _____. *Modern Mathematics for Young Children*. London: Educational Supply Assn., 1965.

33. _____. *The Power of Mathematics*. London: Hutchinson, 1964.

34. Dienes, Z. P., ed. *Mathematics in Primary Education*. UNESCO Institute for Education, ISGML, 1965.

35. Dienes, Z. P., and Golding, E. W. *First Years in Mathematics*. London: Educational Supply Assn., 1966.

36. Dienes, Z. P., and Jeeves, M. A. *Thinking in Structures*. London: Hutchinson, 1965.

37. *Educational Studies in Mathematics* 1 (1968), 3–246.

38. Freudenthal, Hans. "A Teachers Course Colloquium on Sets and Logic." *Educational Studies in Mathematics*, vol. 2, pp. 32–58. Dordrecht, Holland: D. Reidel, 1969.

39. _____. "The Role of Geometrical Intuition in Modern Mathematics." *ICSU Review*, vol. 6 (1964), 206–9. Amsterdam: Elsevier Publishing Co.

40. _____. "Trends in Modern Mathematics." *ICSU Review*, vol. 4 (1962), 54–61. Amsterdam: Elsevier Publishing Co.

41. _____. "Y avait-il une crise des fondements des mathématiques dans l'antiquité?" *Bulletin de la Societe Mathematique de Belgique* 18, 1966.

42. Gagné, R. M. "The Acquisition of Knowledge." *Psychological Review* 59 (1962), 355–65.

43. ____ . *The Conditions of Learning.* New York: Holt, Rinehart & Winston, 1965.

44. ____ . "Implications of Some Doctrines of Mathematics Teaching for Research in Human Learning." In *Psychological Problems and Research Methods in Mathematics Training,* edited by R. L. Feierabend and P. H. DeBois. St. Louis: Washington Univ. Press, 1959.

45. Gagné, R. M., and Bassler, O. C. "Study of Retention of Some Topics of Elementary Nonmetric Geometry." *Journal of Educational Psychology* 54 (1963), 123–31.

46. Gagné, R. M.; Mayor, J. R.; Garstens, H. L.; and Paradise, N. E. "Factors in Acquiring Knowledge of a Mathematical Task." *Psychological Monographs* 76, 7 (1962).

47. Gagné, R. M., and Rohwer, W. D., Jr. "Instructional Psychology." *Annual Review of Psychology* 20 (1969), 381–418.

48. Gagné, R. M., and staff, University of Maryland Mathematics Project. "Some Factors in Learning Non-metric Geometry." *Monographs of the Society for Research in Child Development* 30 (1965), 42–49.

49. Hadamard, Jacques S. *An Essay on the Psychology of Invention in the Mathematical Field.* Princeton, N. J.: Princeton Univ. Press, 1945.

50. Henkin, Leon A. *Retracing Elementary Mathematics.* New York: Macmillan, 1962.

51. Hilgard, Ernest R. *Theories of Learning.* New York: Appleton-Century-Crofts, 1956.

52. Hiz, H. "Methodological Aspects of the Theory of Syntax." *Journal of Philosophy* 64 (1967), 67–74.

53. Inhelder, Barbel, and Piaget, Jean. *De la logique de l'enfant à la logique de l'adolescent.* Paris: Presses Universitaires de France, 1955.

54. Kalish, D., and Montagne, R. *Logic: Techniques of Formal Reasoning.* New York: Harcourt, Brace & World, 1964.

55. Kuhn, Thomas. *The Structure of Scientific Revolutions.* Chicago: Univ. of Chicago Press, 1962.

56. Lakatos, Imre. "Proofs and Refutations." *British Journal for the Philosophy of Science* 14 (1963–64), pt. I, 1–25; pt. II, 120–76; pt. III, 221–64; pt. IV, 296–342.

57. Lamon, William. "Learning about Learning Mathematics." *Mensa Research Journal* 5 (December 1970).

58. ____ . "L'Exploration de la pensée mathématique et la valeur de la recherche clinique." *Le Courrier de la Recherche I.P.N.* Paris, 1970.

59. ____ . "Some Observations on Current Research in Mathematics Education." *Mensa Research Journal* 4 (June 1970).

60. ____ . "Teaching and Learning Group Structures in the Elementary School: An Experiment." *McGill Journal of Education* 5, 2 (Fall 1970).

61. ____ . "The Complexity in the Learning of Mathematics." *Journal for Research in Mathematics Education,* March 1971.

62. Millenson, J. R. "An Isomorphism between Stimulus-Response Notation and Information Processing Flow Diagrams." *The Psychological Record* 17 (1967), 305–19.

63. Miller, G. A. "The Magical Number Seven, Plus or Minus Two: Some Limits on Our Capacity for Processing Information." *Psychological Review* 63 (1956), 81–97.

64. Miller, G. A.; Galanter, E.; and Pribram, K. H. *Plans and the Structure of Behavior.* New York: Holt, Rinehard & Winston, 1960.

65. Nelson, R. J. *Introduction to Automata.* New York: Wiley, 1968.

66. Piaget, Jean; Inhelder, B.; and Szeminska, A. *The Child's Conception of Geometry.* New York: Basic Books, 1960.

67. Piaget, Jean. *The Child's Conception of Number.* New York: Humanities Press, 1964.

68. ———. *The Child's Conception of Space.* New York: Humanities Press, 1963.

69. ———. *Early Growth of Logic in the Child: Classification and Seriation.* New York: Harper & Row, 1964.

70. ———. "How Children Form Mathematical Concepts." *Scientific American* (November 1953), 79.

71. Polanyi, Michael. *Personal Knowledge.* Chicago: Univ. of Chicago Press, 1958.

72. Polya, Gyorgy. *Mathematics and Plausible Reasoning.* Princeton, N.J.: Princeton Univ. Press, 1956.

73. ———. *Mathematical Discovery,* vol. I. New York: Wiley, 1962.

74. Prawitz, D. *Natural Deduction: A Proof Theoretical Study.* Stockholm: Almquist and Wisdell, 1965.

75. Rogers, H. J. *Theory of Recursive Functions and Effective Computability.* New York: McGraw-Hill, 1967.

76. Rosenbloom, Paul. *Adventures in Mathematics.* Reading, Mass.: Addison-Wesley, 1958.

77. ———. *Modern Viewpoints in Curriculum.* New York: McGraw-Hill, 1963.

78. Rosenbloom, Paul, and Shuster, S. *Prelude to Analysis.* Englewood Cliffs, N.J.: Prentice-Hall, 1966.

79. Sanders, W. J. "The Use of Models in Mathematics Instruction." *The Arithmetic Teacher* 2 (March 1964), 157–65.

80. Scandura, J. M. "The Basic Unit in Meaningful Learning—Association or Principle?" *The School Review* 75 (1967), 329–41.

81. ———. "Deterministic Theorizing in Structural Learning: Three Levels of Empiricism," report 55, Mathematics Education Research Group, Structural Learning Series, Graduate School of Education, Univ. of Pennsylvania, 1970.

82. ———. "Learning Verbal and Symbolic Statements of Mathematical Rules." *Journal of Educational Psychology* 58 (1967), 356–64.

83. ———. *Mathematics and Structural Learning.* Englewood Cliffs, N.J.: Prentice-Hall, in press.

84. ———. *Mathematics: Concrete Behavioral Foundations.* New York: Harper & Row, 1971.

85. ———. "New Directions for Research and Theory on Rule Learning," I. "A Set-Function Language." *Acta Psychologica* 28 (1968), 301–21.

86. ———. "New Directions for Research and Theory on Rule Learning," II. "Empirical Research." *Acta Psychologica* 29 (1969), 101–33.

87. ———. "New Directions for Research and Theory on Rule Learning," III: "Analyses and Theoretical Direction." *Acta Psychologica* 29 (1969), 205–27.

88. ———. "Precision in Research on Mathematics Learning: The Emerging Field of Psycho-Mathematics." *Journal of Research in Science Teaching* 4 (1966), 253–74.

89. ———. "A Research Basis for Mathematics Education." *High School Journal* 53 (1970), 264–80.

90. ———. "The Role of Rules in Behavior: Toward an Operational Definition of What (Rule) Is Learned." *Psychological Review,* in press.

91. ———. "Theoretical Note: S–R Theory or Automata?" report 58, Mathematics Education Research Group, Structural Learning Series, Graduate School of Education, Univ. of Pennsylvania, 1970.

92. Scandura, J. M., ed. *Research in Mathematics Education*. Washington: National Council of Teachers of Mathematics, 1967.

93. Scandura, J. M., and Wells, J. N. "Advance Organizers in Learning Abstract Mathematics." *American Educational Research Journal* 4 (1967), 295–301.

94. Scandura, J. M.; Woodward, E.; and Lee, F. "Rule Generality and Consistency in Mathematics Learning." *American Educational Research Journal* 4 (1967), 303–19.

95. Scott, L. F. *Trends in Elementary School Mathematics* (Chicago: Rand-McNally, 1966).

96. Stone, Marshall H. "Reform in School Mathematics." In *New Thinking in School Mathematics*, pp. 14–29. Organization for European Economics Cooperation, 1961.

97. Suchman, J. Richard. "Inquiry Training in the Elementary School." *Science Teacher* 27 (November 1960), 42–43.

98. Suppes, Patrick. "Psychological Foundations of Mathematics," technical report 80, Institute for Mathematical Studies in the Social Sciences, Stanford Univ., 1965.

99. _____ . "Stimulus-Response Theory of Automata and Tote Hierarchies: A Reply to Arbib." *Psychological Review* 76 (1969), 511–14.

100. _____ . "Stimulus-Response Theory of Finite Automata." *Journal of Mathematical Psychology* 6 (1969), 327–55.

101. Suppes, Patrick, and Binford, Frederick. "Experimental Teaching of Mathematical Logic in the Elementary School." *The Mathematics Teacher* 12 (1965), 187–95.

102. Wilder, Raymond L. *Evolution of Mathematical Concepts*. New York: Wiley, 1968.

103. Williams, J.D. "Barriers to Mathematical Understanding." *Mathematics Teaching* 28 (Autumn 1964).

104. _____ . "Mathematics Reform in the Primary School." UNESCO, 1967.

105. _____ . *Research into Matters Relating to the Mathematical Learning of Children of Primary and Secondary Age*. National Foundation for Educational Research in England and Wales, 1965.

106. _____ . "Teaching Arithmetic by Concrete Analogy," I: "Miming Devices." *Educational Research* 3, 2 (February 1961).

107. _____ . "Teaching Arithmetic by Concrete Analogy," I: "Miming Devices (continued)." *Educational Research* 3, 3 (June 1961).

108. _____ . "Teaching Arithmetic by Concrete Analogy," II: "Structural Systems." *Educational Research* 4, 3 (June 1962).

109. _____ . "Teaching Arithmetic by Concrete Analogy" III: "Issues and Arguments." *Educational Research* 5, 2 (February 1963).

110. _____ . "The Teaching of Mathematics," VI: "Arithmetic and the Difficulties of Calculative Thinking." *Educational Research* 5, 3 (June 1963).

111. Willoughby, Stephen S. *Contemporary Teaching of Secondary School Mathematics*. New York: Wiley, 1967.

112. Wittrock, M. C. "The Learning by Discovery Hypothesis." In *Learning by Discovery*, edited by E. Keislar and L. M. Shulman. Chicago: Rand–McNally, 1966.

Index

Learning theory
  knowledge of, 71, 138, 165–66
  new interest in, 138
  requirement for research on,
    166–70
  research needed, 9, 67, 83, 165
Lectures, use of, 203–4
Leibniz, Gottfreid, 39, 104, 111
Lobachevsky, Nikolai, 39
Logic, 37, 42, 58, 134–36, 206
  classical, 43, 44, 46
  emphasis in curriculum, 22, 25,
    31, 87, 206, 220–25
  history of, 39
  mathematical, 44

Madison Project, 8, 81–83
Mathematical behavior, 142,
    149–51
Mathematics
  as an art, 86–87, 90
  as a science, 40, 41, 52,
    86–87, 89
  basis of, 51
  education
    basis, 86, 136, 165
    objectives, 18, 86–88, 140,
      168–69
  essence in learning, 88
  forces on evolution, 40
  history of, 12–13
    Babylonian, 37–38, 101–2
    Egyptian, 38
    Greek, 38–39, 42, 101–2
    Hindu, 104
    introduction of symbols, 103
    Sumerian, 37, 41
  nature of, 36, 62, 86, 212
    abstract, 66, 67, 100, 179
    ever-changing, 36
    hierarchical, 62
    rule-governed, 142
  pure versus applied, 41, 44–46
Meaning blindness, 185–87
Moore, E.H., 43
Multibase arithmetic blocks, 63

National Science Foundation, 48
Neugebauer, O., 38
New mathematics, 8, 12, 14, 16,
    18, 21–24, 48, 139
  effectiveness, 23–24
  goals, 4, 5
  origins, 12, 21
  results, 23

Newton, Isaac, 39, 104, 138, 197
Number neurosis, 183–85

Operational
  structure, 122–36
  thought, 54, 67, 122
Operations, 122
Operators, 53–54, 58, 67

Page, David, 8
Paradigms
  for learning mathematics, 72–83
  precision of, 73–74
Peano, Giuseppe, 42
Pedagogy. See Instructional theory
Piaget, Jean, 8, 9, 15, 26, 31, 65,
    89, 117, 180, 225
  developmental stages, 27
Pierce, B., 46
Polanyi, Michael, 75
Polya, George, 88
Preoperational
  stage, 67, 122, 124, 127
  thought, 54
Programmed learning, 63, 205
Psychological foundations of
    mathematics, 6–9, 65, 119,
    224–25
Psychology of cognitive functions,
    121

Quantifiers
  use in education, 215–17, 223

Relations in mathematics, 52–61
Research
  application to instruction, 173
  change in interest, 138
  history of, 138–40
  increase in, 165
  needed, 8–9, 67, 96
Retention
  conditions for, 172
Reversibility of thought, 122–27
Reynolds, Katie, 80
Rosenbloom, Paul, 82, 85
Russell, Bertrand, 42–44, 47
Rutherford, Sir Ernest, 140

Scandura, Joseph, 137, 171
Scott, Lloyd, 19
Sensory motor stage, 126
Set theory
  history of, 37, 40
  in new math, 7, 14–16, 25

Socrates, 17
Stevin, Simon, 103
Stimulus-response theory, 141–44
Stone, Marshall, 219
Stories, mathematical, 64
Structure, 59, 119–36
  algebraic, 112, 121, 129–32
  concrete embodiment of, 56–57,
    64
  emphasis on, 4–5, 22
  learning of, 24–26, 55–67
  of mathematics, 16, 22–26, 57,
    88, 141
  of order, 121, 126, 131
  relationships of, 126
  tests for knowledge of, 54–56
  topological, 121, 130–31
Students
  ability to discover, 5
  background in mathematics,
    199
  orientation in mathematics,
    201
Suppes, Patrick, 8, 65, 225

Symbolization, 6, 30, 31, 62
  history of, 39, 101–4
  introduction of, 103
  refinement of, 22
System
  family of, 148
  mathematical, 16, 61, 145
  properties of, 148

Texts, 201–3
Thompson, Gerald, 82
Topics
  selection of, 31, 66, 175
  sequence of, 22, 25–26, 31,
    57, 66–67, 174
Transfer of knowledge, 29, 56,
  161
Tutorials, 204

Vietus, 104

Wessel, Caspar, 110
Whitehead, A.N., 42–44
Wilder, Raymond, 35
Williams, John, 177